Calculus of Several Variables
An Introduction

In the editorial series of

I. M. SINGER

Massachusetts Institute of Technology

ROBERT T. SEELEY
Brandeis University

Calculus of Several Variables
An Introduction

SCOTT, FORESMAN AND COMPANY

Library of Congress Catalog Card No. 77-119872

Regional Offices of Scott, Foresman and Company are located in
Atlanta, Dallas, Glenview, Palo Alto, Oakland, N.J., and London, England.

Preface

This book is intended as the "several variables" part of a three- or four-semester calculus course. When he begins, the reader is expected to know the basic theory of functions of one variable, primarily the mean value theorem and the fundamental theorem of calculus. At the end of the book, he should be well prepared for most applications of partial differentiation and line and surface integrals, and for further study in linear algebra and calculus on manifolds.

We work toward an intuitive geometric understanding of vectors, gradients, line integrals, and surface integrals by stressing analytic calculations with a geometric or physical interpretation. Toward the end of Chapter 5 we suggest the unified mathematical framework embracing all these various concepts, laying the groundwork for the general "Stokes' theorem" given in more sophisticated approaches to this subject.

There are almost 400 problems, ranging from trivial exercises to substantial applications (for example, Frenet-Serret formulas, thermodynamics, the planimeter). Most of the difficult problems are broken down into small parts and provided with generous hints, so they need not be reserved for the very best students. There are many more of these problems than any class will have time to do as homework, and there will surely be some left over to serve as classroom examples.

The basic minimum for an introduction to functions of several variables is given in §1.1–1.4, 2.1, 3.1–3.4, 3.6, 4.1–4.3, 5.1, and 5.4. The rest of the material reaches out in various directions: linear algebra, differential geometry of curves, physics, extensions of the fundamental theorem of calculus, and differential forms. The use of these other sections depends, of course, on the time available.

Complete proofs are given for the theorems on differentiation. In integration, the basic result that $\int\int f\, dx\, dy = \int\int f\, dy\, dx$ is clearly formulated, but not proved; see §4.1 for the treatment of this point. Assuming this result, we continue giving complete proofs up to Gauss' theorem and differential forms; the presentation of these two topics is very informal but, we hope, suggestive.

The author gratefully acknowledges the support of Brandeis University, in the form of a sabbatical year, and the further support and hospitality of the Battelle Memorial Institute. He is indebted to S. Lukawecki, H. C. Wiser, and C. R. B. Wright for their useful suggestions, and to Nat Weintraub for his fine editorial work.

Contents

CHAPTER V: FUNCTIONS OF n VARIABLES

Chapter I

Vectors

This chapter provides the setting for the rest of the book. We assume as background a few geometric concepts (such as parallelism, orthogonality, and the Pythagorean theorem, and elementary trigonometry) and develop an abstract algebraic system, called the vector space R^3, in which these concepts have simple algebraic definitions.

§1.1 presents the properties that R^3 shares with the simpler two-dimensional space R^2; familiarity with R^2, though not required, would be useful in reading this section.

§1.2 introduces the cross product.

§1.3 applies vector space methods to analytic geometry.

§1.4 introduces R^n, carrying over the definitions and terminology from R^2 and R^3.

§1.5 introduces the rather abstract idea of *linear independence.* This section, though not essential to the rest of the book, is included partly as preparation for linear algebra (which many students will study sooner or later), and partly because it seems the best way to prove certain basic facts (for example, that **A**, **B**, and **C** form a basis if $\mathbf{A} \cdot (\mathbf{B} \times \mathbf{C}) \neq 0$). Such facts are used only rarely in the text, so it is possible to omit §1.5 and give intuitive geometric arguments on those few occasions when a reference to §1.5 is made.

We observe a strict separation of powers between "geometry" and "algebra"; geometry suggests and interprets many results, but definitions and proofs are based on elementary algebra. In keeping with this, we are not obliged to prove any statements about the geometric interpretations; they are given only to guide the intuition, not to provide proofs.

1.1 THE VECTOR SPACE R^3

When the Greeks studied solid geometry, they laid the foundations of a remarkably accurate mathematical model of the "physical space" in which stars, planets, rockets, baseballs, electrons, and so on all move about. Solid geometry is still the underlying model for a large part of natural science, but its study has been tremendously simplified by shifting from the purely geometric point of view taken by the Greeks to an algebraic one. From the modern (algebraic) point of view, we define the *vector space* R^3, and establish its various properties by elementary algebraic calculations. To relate the vector space to our intuitive understanding of "physical space" we introduce a coordinate system. Once this is done, all the algebraic results have a more or less obvious geometric meaning.

Definition 1.* The vector space R^3 consists of all ordered triples of real numbers (usually denoted $\mathbf{A} = (a_1,a_2,a_3)$, $\mathbf{B} = (b_1,b_2,b_3)$, etc.), together with the following algebraic operations:

$$\mathbf{A} + \mathbf{B} = (a_1 + b_1\,,\, a_2 + b_2\,,\, a_3 + b_3) \qquad \text{(addition)}$$

$$t\mathbf{A} = (ta_1,ta_2,ta_3), \quad t \text{ any real number} \qquad \text{(scalar multiplication)}$$

$$\mathbf{A}\cdot\mathbf{B} = a_1b_1 + a_2b_2 + a_3b_3 \qquad \text{(inner product, or dot product)}$$

The members of R^3 are called *points* or *vectors*. The vector (0,0,0) is denoted **0**. The *length* of a vector **A** is

$$|\mathbf{A}| = (\mathbf{A}\cdot\mathbf{A})^{1/2} = \sqrt{a_1^2 + a_2^2 + a_3^2}\,.$$

The numbers a_1, a_2, and a_3 are called *components* or *coordinates* of the vector (a_1,a_2,a_3).

From this definition follow many simple but useful identities, which for convenience we sum up in Theorem 1. You will not find it necessary to memorize all these, since they all reflect familiar properties of numbers.

---

* There is a slight discrepancy in notation and terminology between this definition and Chapter X of *Calculus of One Variable*, which distinguished between points and vectors, denoting points with parentheses (x_0,y_0) and vectors with brackets $[a,b]$. Here the distinction is dropped, and we feel free to think of an ordered triple (a,b,c) either as a point or as a vector. This dual point of view is explained in the discussion following Theorem 1.

Theorem 1. *Let* **A**, **B**, *and* **C** *be any members of* R^3, *and let* t *and* s *be any real numbers. Then*

(1)	$t(s\mathbf{A}) = (ts)\mathbf{A}$	(*associative laws*)
(2)	$(\mathbf{A} + \mathbf{B}) + \mathbf{C} = \mathbf{A} + (\mathbf{B} + \mathbf{C})$	
(3)	$t(\mathbf{A}\cdot\mathbf{B}) = (t\mathbf{A})\cdot\mathbf{B} = \mathbf{A}\cdot(t\mathbf{B})$	
(4)	$\mathbf{A} + \mathbf{B} = \mathbf{B} + \mathbf{A}$	(*commutative laws*)
(5)	$\mathbf{A}\cdot\mathbf{B} = \mathbf{B}\cdot\mathbf{A}$	
(6)	$(t + s)\mathbf{A} = t\mathbf{A} + s\mathbf{A}$	(*distributive laws*)
(7)	$t(\mathbf{A} + \mathbf{B}) = t\mathbf{A} + t\mathbf{B}$	
(8)	$(\mathbf{A} + \mathbf{B})\cdot\mathbf{C} = (\mathbf{A}\cdot\mathbf{C}) + (\mathbf{B}\cdot\mathbf{C})$	
(9)	$\mathbf{A}\cdot(\mathbf{B} + \mathbf{C}) = \mathbf{A}\cdot\mathbf{B} + \mathbf{A}\cdot\mathbf{C}$	
(10)	$1(\mathbf{A}) = \mathbf{A}, \quad 0\mathbf{A} = \mathbf{0}$	
(11)	$\mathbf{A} + \mathbf{0} = \mathbf{A}$	(*laws for the zero vector*)
(12)	$\lvert\mathbf{A}\rvert = 0 \Leftrightarrow \mathbf{A} = \mathbf{0}$	
(13)	$\lvert t\mathbf{A}\rvert = \lvert t\rvert(\lvert\mathbf{A}\rvert.)$	

Proof. Formula (1) follows directly from the commutativity of real numbers; since $a_1 + b_1 = b_1 + a_1$, etc., we have

$$\begin{aligned}\mathbf{A} + \mathbf{B} &= (a_1 + b_1, a_2 + b_2, a_3 + b_3)\\ &= (b_1 + a_1, b_2 + a_2, b_3 + a_3) = \mathbf{B} + \mathbf{A}.\end{aligned}$$

The proofs of (2)–(11) follow the same basic pattern; you compute each side, and observe that the corresponding components are equal. Finally, (12) and (13) follow from the formula for the length $|\mathbf{A}| = \sqrt{a_1^2 + a_2^2 + a_3^2}$. For example, to prove (12), observe that a sum of squares of real numbers $a_1^2 + a_2^2 + a_3^2$ is zero if and only if each term is zero.

In view of the associative law (2), we can let $\mathbf{A} + \mathbf{B} + \mathbf{C}$ stand for both $(\mathbf{A} + \mathbf{B}) + \mathbf{C}$ and $\mathbf{A} + (\mathbf{B} + \mathbf{C})$. More generally, we omit parentheses from any sum of three or more vectors; for example, we simplify $(\mathbf{A} + \mathbf{B}) + (\mathbf{C} + \mathbf{D})$ to $\mathbf{A} + \mathbf{B} + \mathbf{C} + \mathbf{D}$.

Any mathematical system in which formulas (1), (2), (4), (6), (7), (10), and (11) hold is called a *real vector space*. When all of formulas (1)–(13) hold, it is called a *vector space with inner product*. Thus, Theorem 1 states that R^3 *is a vector space with inner product.*

The geometric interpretation of R^3 is based on a rectangular coordinate system. Picture three mutually perpendicular lines intersecting at a given point 0 (the origin), as in Fig. 1. Call these lines the x axis, the y axis, and the z axis, and space the real numbers uniformly along each axis, with zero at the origin. With this picture, to every ordered triple

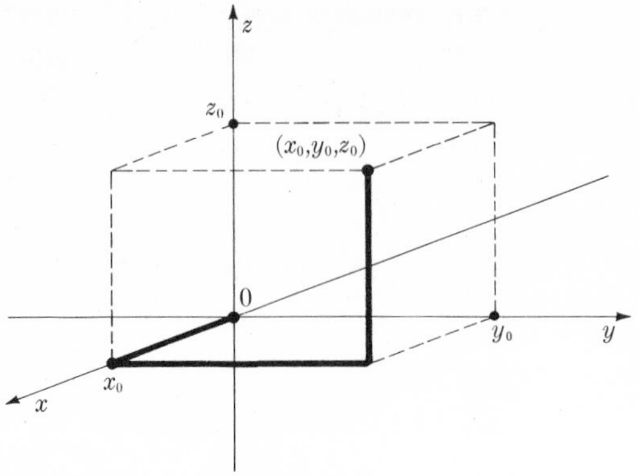

FIGURE 1.1

of real numbers (x_0, y_0, z_0) there corresponds a particular point in space, as shown in Fig. 1. The basic assumption underlying the applications of algebraic methods to concrete geometric and physical problems is that this correspondence is *reversible*; given the coordinate system, every ordered triple corresponds to a unique point in "physical space," and conversely every point corresponds to a unique ordered triple.

Since the members of R^3 are ordered triples, we can think of R^3 geometrically as the points in space. When we have this image in mind, we call the members of R^3 *points*, and generally label them $\mathbf{P} = (x, y, z)$, $\mathbf{P}_0 = (x_0, y_0, z_0)$, and so on. Figure 2 shows that the length $|\mathbf{P}_0|$ is the distance from the origin to the point representing $\mathbf{P}_0$.

$$\mathbf{P}_0 = (x_0, y_0, z_0)$$
$$r^2 = x_0{}^2 + y_0{}^2$$
$$|\mathbf{P}_0|^2 = r^2 + z_0{}^2 = x_0{}^2 + y_0{}^2 + z_0{}^2$$

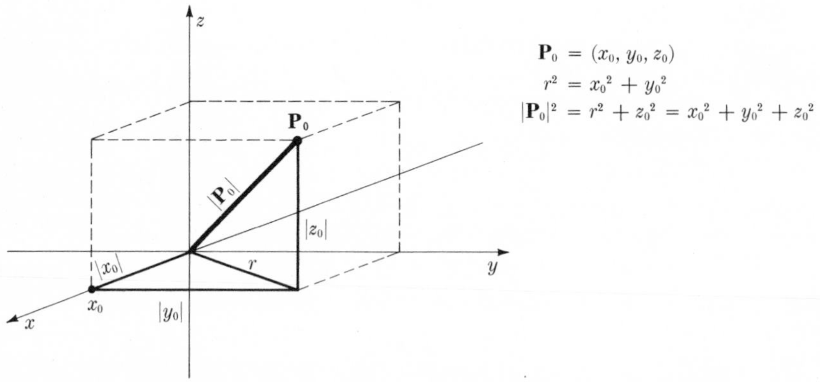

FIGURE 1.2

A second way to represent R^3 is by arrows. If $\mathbf{A} = (a_1,a_2,a_3)$ is any member of R^3, we represent it by an arrow from the origin, as in Fig. 3(a), or more generally by an arrow beginning at any point (x,y,z) and ending at the point $(x + a_1, y + a_2, z + a_3)$, as in Fig. 3(b). (You can think of $\mathbf{A}$ as giving a change in position from the initial point (x,y,z) to the terminal point $(x + a_1, y + a_2, z + a_3)$.) When we have this image in mind, we call the members of R^3 *vectors*. The arrow representing $\mathbf{A}$ can start at any point (and this turns out to be very helpful in visualizing the applications of vector theory), but no matter where it is drawn, it always has the same direction, and the length $|\mathbf{A}| = \sqrt{a_1^2 + a_2^2 + a_3^2}$. (We are overlooking the distortions of perspective entailed in drawing lines in three-space on two-dimensional paper.)

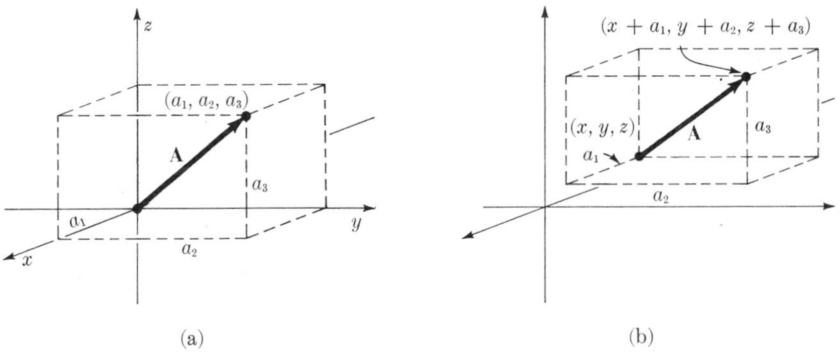

FIGURE 1.3

These two alternate interpretations (point in space, or arrow between two points in space) are closely related. When $\mathbf{A} = (a_1,a_2,a_3)$ is represented by an *arrow beginning at the origin*, as in Fig. 3(a), then the tip of the arrow coincides with the *point* representing (a_1,a_2,a_3). When in doubt as to which interpretation to use, use both, but let the arrow begin at the origin.

Addition has the effect of following one change of position, $\mathbf{A}$, by another, $\mathbf{B}$. Thus $\mathbf{A} + \mathbf{B}$ is represented by the third side of a triangle whose other two sides represent $\mathbf{A}$ and $\mathbf{B}$, as in Fig. 4. Combining this picture with the corresponding one for $\mathbf{B} + \mathbf{A}$ (as in Fig. 5), we find that the commutative law (1) expresses an "obvious fact": $\mathbf{A} + \mathbf{B}$ and $\mathbf{B} + \mathbf{A}$ are both represented by the same diagonal of the parallelogram in Fig. 5.

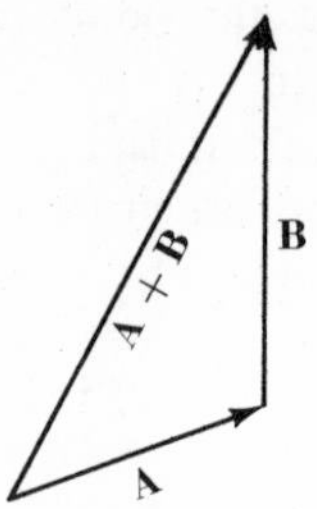

FIGURE 1.4

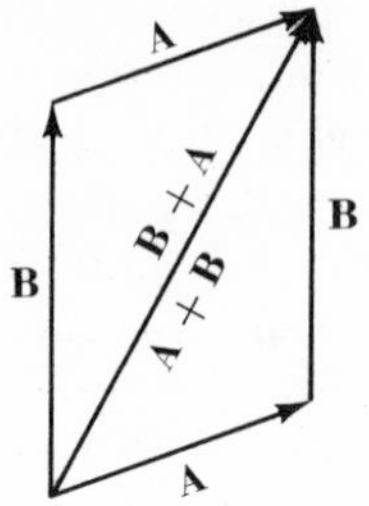

FIGURE 1.5

A familiar theorem of classical geometry states that

$$|\mathbf{A} + \mathbf{B}|^2 = |\mathbf{A}|^2 + |\mathbf{B}|^2 \tag{14}$$

if and only if the arrows representing **A** and **B** in Fig. 4 are orthogonal; thus it would be natural to define the vectors themselves to be orthogonal when equation (14) holds. However, this equation can be reduced to a much simpler form if we expand $|\mathbf{A} + \mathbf{B}|^2$ as a dot product:

$$\begin{aligned} |\mathbf{A} + \mathbf{B}|^2 &= (\mathbf{A} + \mathbf{B}) \cdot (\mathbf{A} + \mathbf{B}) && \text{(by Definition 1)} \\ &= (\mathbf{A} \cdot (\mathbf{A} + \mathbf{B})) + (\mathbf{B} \cdot (\mathbf{A} + \mathbf{B})) && \text{(by (8))} \\ &= (\mathbf{A} \cdot \mathbf{A} + \mathbf{A} \cdot \mathbf{B}) + (\mathbf{B} \cdot \mathbf{A} + \mathbf{B} \cdot \mathbf{B}) && \text{(by (9))} \\ &= |\mathbf{A}|^2 + 2(\mathbf{A} \cdot \mathbf{B}) + |\mathbf{B}|^2 && \text{(by (2) and (5).)} \end{aligned}$$

Hence $|\mathbf{A} + \mathbf{B}|^2 = |\mathbf{A}|^2 + |\mathbf{B}|^2$ if and only if $\mathbf{A} \cdot \mathbf{B} = 0$. This motivates

Definition 2. **A** and **B** are called *orthogonal* if and only if $\mathbf{A} \cdot \mathbf{B} = 0$.

Turning next to the *scalar product* $t\mathbf{A}$ of a real number t and a vector **A**, we find that if $t > 0$, then $t\mathbf{A}$ is a change of position in the same direction as **A** but t times as far, while if $t < 0$, then $t\mathbf{A}$ is in the opposite direction from **A** but $|t|$ times as far (Fig. 6). In any case, the vector $t\mathbf{A}$ appears to be *parallel* to **A**; this motivates

Definition 3. Two vectors are *parallel* if and only if one is a scalar multiple of the other. In other words, **A** and **B** are parallel if and only if either $\mathbf{A} = t\mathbf{B}$ for some real t or $\mathbf{B} = t\mathbf{A}$ for some real t.

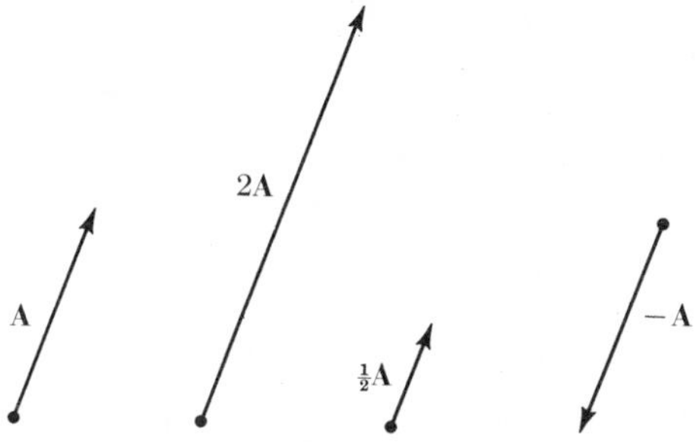

FIGURE 1.6

Combining addition and scalar multiplication leads to interesting results. Given two vectors **A** and **B**, with $\mathbf{B} \neq \mathbf{0}$, look at the vectors of the form

$$\mathbf{A} + t\mathbf{B}, \tag{15}$$

where t varies over all real numbers. With $t = 0$ we get **A**; with $t = 1$ we get $\mathbf{A} + \mathbf{B}$; with $t = -1$ we get $\mathbf{A} + (-1)\mathbf{B}$, which is usually written simply $\mathbf{A} - \mathbf{B}$ and called the *difference* of **A** and **B**. In general, as t varies over the real numbers, the vectors (15) generate a *line* as sketched in Fig. 7, called the line through **A** in the direction **B**. (It must be assumed that $\mathbf{B} \neq \mathbf{0}$, for otherwise (15) gives only the point **A**, not a whole line.) Visualize the line as consisting of all the points that represent $\mathbf{A} + t\mathbf{B}$ for various t or, equivalently, as the tips of the arrows representing $\mathbf{A} + t\mathbf{B}$, when the arrows begin at the origin.

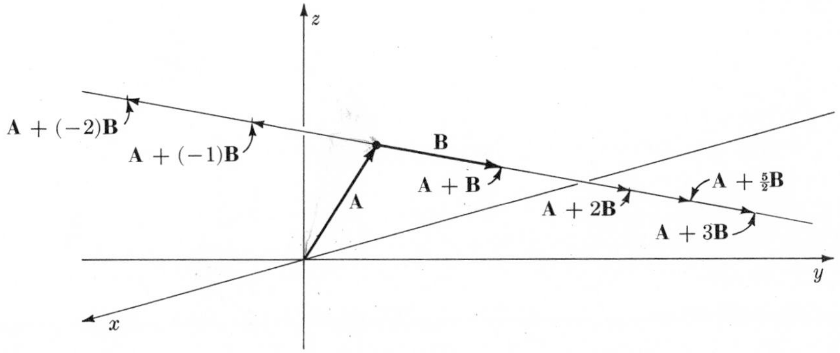

FIGURE 1.7

Figure 7 shows the difference $\mathbf{A} - \mathbf{B}$ as the sum of the vectors $\mathbf{A}$ and $(-1)\mathbf{B}$. Figure 8 shows another useful representation; when $\mathbf{A}$ and $\mathbf{B}$ are drawn from a common initial point, then $\mathbf{A} - \mathbf{B}$ is represented by an arrow from the tip of $\mathbf{B}$ to the tip of $\mathbf{A}$. The resulting triangle illustrates the identity

$$\mathbf{B} + (\mathbf{A} - \mathbf{B}) = \mathbf{A}.$$

Returning to the line given by (15), we can collect an unexpected dividend by computing the distance from the origin to the line. By definition, this distance is the minimum of $|\mathbf{A} + t\mathbf{B}|$ as t varies over all real numbers. To find the minimum, expand $|\mathbf{A} + t\mathbf{B}|^2$ as a dot product (just like the calculation preceding Definition 2):

$$|\mathbf{A} + t\mathbf{B}|^2 = \mathbf{A}\cdot\mathbf{A} + 2t(\mathbf{A}\cdot\mathbf{B}) + t^2\mathbf{B}\cdot\mathbf{B}. \tag{16}$$

On the right in (16) is a quadratic in t (since $|\mathbf{B}| \neq 0$), and its minimum is easily found to occur at $t = -\mathbf{A}\cdot\mathbf{B}/\mathbf{B}\cdot\mathbf{B}$. Putting this value of t in each side of (16), we find the square of the distance from the line to the origin to be

$$\begin{aligned} \left|\mathbf{A} - \frac{\mathbf{A}\cdot\mathbf{B}}{\mathbf{B}\cdot\mathbf{B}}\mathbf{B}\right|^2 &= \mathbf{A}\cdot\mathbf{A} - 2\frac{(\mathbf{A}\cdot\mathbf{B})^2}{\mathbf{B}\cdot\mathbf{B}} + \frac{(\mathbf{A}\cdot\mathbf{B})^2}{\mathbf{B}\cdot\mathbf{B}} \\ &= |\mathbf{A}|^2 - \frac{(\mathbf{A}\cdot\mathbf{B})^2}{|\mathbf{B}|^2} \\ &= \frac{1}{|\mathbf{B}|^2}\left(|\mathbf{A}|^2|\mathbf{B}|^2 - (\mathbf{A}\cdot\mathbf{B})^2\right). \end{aligned} \tag{17}$$

Since the number in (17) is a square, it cannot be negative; hence $(\mathbf{A}\cdot\mathbf{B})^2 \leq |\mathbf{A}|^2\cdot|\mathbf{B}|^2$. Taking square roots, we collect our dividend, the *Schwarz inequality*:

$$|(\mathbf{A}\cdot\mathbf{B})| \leq |\mathbf{A}|\cdot|\mathbf{B}|. \tag{18}$$

This derivation assumed $\mathbf{B} \neq \mathbf{0}$, but (18) is obviously true when $\mathbf{B} = \mathbf{0}$ as well, since both sides reduce to zero in that case.

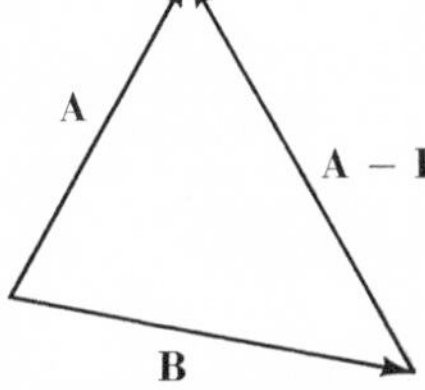

FIGURE 1.8

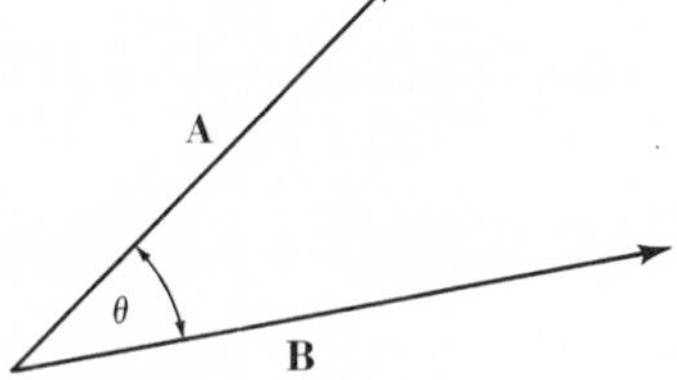

FIGURE 1.9

The Schwarz inequality implies, in turn, the *triangle inequality*:

$$|\mathbf{A} + \mathbf{B}| \leq |\mathbf{A}| + |\mathbf{B}|. \tag{19}$$

The proof of (19) is straightforward; from (16) we have already found that

$$|\mathbf{A} + \mathbf{B}|^2 = |\mathbf{A}|^2 + 2(\mathbf{A}\cdot\mathbf{B}) + |\mathbf{B}|^2; \tag{20}$$

hence

$$\begin{aligned} |\mathbf{A} + \mathbf{B}|^2 &\leq |\mathbf{A}|^2 + 2|(\mathbf{A}\cdot\mathbf{B})| + |\mathbf{B}|^2 \\ &\leq |\mathbf{A}|^2 + 2|\mathbf{A}|\cdot|\mathbf{B}| + |\mathbf{B}|^2 \qquad \text{(by (18))} \\ &= (|\mathbf{A}| + |\mathbf{B}|)^2, \end{aligned}$$

and the triangle inequality (19) follows by taking square roots. Figure 4 interprets this inequality as a familiar principle of Euclidean geometry, namely, any side of a triangle is less than or equal to the sum of the other two sides. (Hence the name "triangle inequality.")

The geometric interpretation of the dot product is based on the Schwarz inequality. When $\mathbf{A} \neq \mathbf{0}$ and $\mathbf{B} \neq \mathbf{0}$, we can rewrite (18) as

$$-1 \leq \frac{\mathbf{A}\cdot\mathbf{B}}{|\mathbf{A}|\cdot|\mathbf{B}|} \leq 1.$$

Hence $\arccos\left(\dfrac{\mathbf{A}\cdot\mathbf{B}}{|\mathbf{A}|\cdot|\mathbf{B}|}\right)$ is defined; namely, it is the number θ such that $0 \leq \theta \leq \pi$ and

$$\cos\theta = \frac{\mathbf{A}\cdot\mathbf{B}}{|\mathbf{A}|\cdot|\mathbf{B}|}. \tag{21}$$

This is called the *angle between* **A** *and* **B** (see Fig. 9). Notice that (21) is consistent with the definition of orthogonal vectors, since for $0 \leq \theta \leq \pi$

$$\theta = \frac{\pi}{2} \quad \Leftrightarrow \quad \cos\theta = 0 \quad \Leftrightarrow \quad \mathbf{A}\cdot\mathbf{B} = 0.$$

It is also consistent with the definition of parallel vectors, and with the law of cosines, as shown in the problems below. When (21) is multiplied out, it gives

$$\mathbf{A}\cdot\mathbf{B} = |\mathbf{A}|\cdot|\mathbf{B}|\cos\theta,$$

which is the geometric interpretation we were looking for: the dot product of two vectors is the product of the lengths times the cosine of the angle between the vectors.

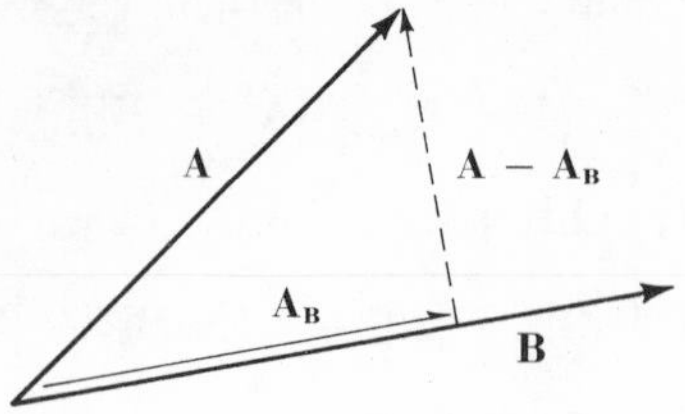

FIGURE 1.10

Figure 10 illustrates *orthogonal projection*, which is the main geometric use of the dot product. The orthogonal projection $\mathbf{A_B}$ of $\mathbf{A}$ on a nonzero vector $\mathbf{B}$ is characterized by two properties:

(i) $\mathbf{A_B}$ is parallel to $\mathbf{B}$

(ii) $\mathbf{A} - \mathbf{A_B}$ is orthogonal to $\mathbf{B}$.

Condition (i) implies $\mathbf{A_B} = t\mathbf{B}$ for some t, and combining this with condition (ii) gives

$$0 = (\mathbf{A} - \mathbf{A_B})\cdot\mathbf{B} = (\mathbf{A} - t\mathbf{B})\cdot\mathbf{B} = \mathbf{A}\cdot\mathbf{B} - t(\mathbf{B}\cdot\mathbf{B}).$$

Hence $t = \mathbf{A}\cdot\mathbf{B}/\mathbf{B}\cdot\mathbf{B}$, and the projection is

$$\mathbf{A_B} = \frac{\mathbf{A}\cdot\mathbf{B}}{\mathbf{B}\cdot\mathbf{B}}\mathbf{B}. \tag{22}$$

When $\mathbf{B}$ happens to be a unit vector, i.e. when $|\mathbf{B}| = 1$, the projection formula simplifies to

$$\mathbf{A_B} = (\mathbf{A}\cdot\mathbf{B})\mathbf{B} \qquad (\mathbf{B} \text{ a unit vector}).$$

For example, the projection of $\mathbf{A} = (a_1,a_2,a_3)$ on the unit vector $\mathbf{E}_1 = (1, 0, 0)$ is

$$(\mathbf{A}\cdot\mathbf{E}_1)\mathbf{E}_1 = a_1(1,0,0) = (a_1,0,0).$$

Similarly, the projections on $\mathbf{E}_2 = (0,1,0)$ and $\mathbf{E}_3 = (0,0,1)$ are

$$(\mathbf{A}\cdot\mathbf{E}_2)\mathbf{E}_2 = (0,a_2,0), \qquad (\mathbf{A}\cdot\mathbf{E}_3)\mathbf{E}_3 = (0,0,a_3).$$

From this you can see immediately that $\mathbf{A}$ equals the sum of its projections on $\mathbf{E}_1$, $\mathbf{E}_2$, and $\mathbf{E}_3$ (see Fig. 11):

$$\mathbf{A} = (\mathbf{A}\cdot\mathbf{E}_1)\mathbf{E}_1 + (\mathbf{A}\cdot\mathbf{E}_2)\mathbf{E}_2 + (\mathbf{A}\cdot\mathbf{E}_3)\mathbf{E}_3\,.$$

Toward the end of this chapter we will be able to show that this same formula holds when $\mathbf{E}_1$, $\mathbf{E}_2$, and $\mathbf{E}_3$ are replaced by any three unit vectors $\mathbf{U}_1$, $\mathbf{U}_2$, $\mathbf{U}_3$ which are orthogonal to each other.

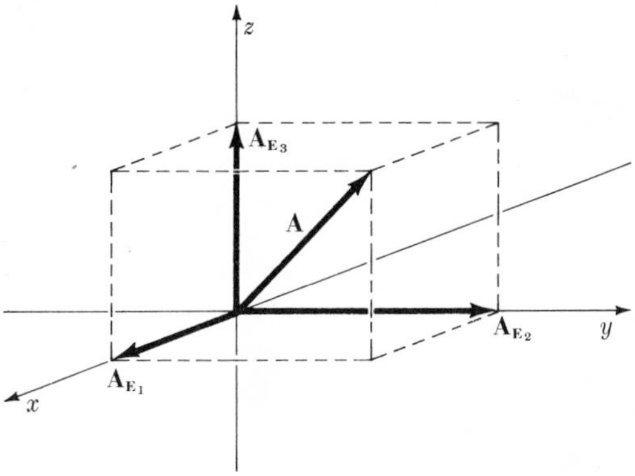

FIGURE 1.11

PROBLEMS

1. Represent the following vectors as arrows starting at the origin **0**.
   (a) (0,1,3) (b) (−1,2,5) (c) (−1,−3,−4)
   (d) (1,−5,3) (e) (1,−3,−5) (f) (1,3,−5)

2. Represent the vectors in Problem 1 as arrows starting at the point (1,1,1).

3. Let $\mathbf{A} = (0,1,5)$, $\mathbf{B} = (-\sqrt{14},5,1)$.
   (a) Find $|\mathbf{A}|$ and $|\mathbf{B}|$.
   (b) Find $\mathbf{A}\cdot\mathbf{B}$.
   (c) Find the angle between **A** and **B**.

4. (a) Find the angle between the vectors in Problem 1(a) and (b).
   (b) Find the angle between the vectors in Problem 1(e) and (f).

5. Which of the following vectors are parallel to (1,1,−1)?
   (a) (2,2,−2) (b) (2,−2,2) (c) (−2,2,2)
   (d) (1,2,−2) (e) $(-\frac{1}{2},-\frac{1}{2},\frac{1}{2})$ (f) $(\pi,\pi,-\pi)$

6. (a) Find *all* vectors that are orthogonal to $\mathbf{E}_1 = (1,0,0)$.
   (b) Find *all* vectors that are orthogonal both to $\mathbf{E}_1$ and to $\mathbf{E}_2 = (0,1,0)$.
   (c) Find *all* vectors that are orthogonal to $\mathbf{E}_1$, to $\mathbf{E}_2$, and to $\mathbf{E}_3 = (0,0,1)$. (There is exactly one.)

7. (a) Find a nonzero vector orthogonal to (1,2,−1). (There are many.)
   (b) Find a nonzero vector orthogonal to (1,2,−1) and to (−1,0,3). (There are still quite a few.)

8. Let

$$\mathbf{U}_1 = \left(\frac{1}{\sqrt{3}}, \frac{1}{\sqrt{3}}, \frac{-1}{\sqrt{3}}\right), \quad \mathbf{U}_2 = \left(\frac{1}{\sqrt{6}}, \frac{1}{\sqrt{6}}, \frac{2}{\sqrt{6}}\right), \quad \mathbf{U}_3 = \left(\frac{1}{\sqrt{2}}, \frac{-1}{\sqrt{2}}, 0\right).$$

(a) Show that each of $\mathbf{U}_1$, $\mathbf{U}_2$, $\mathbf{U}_3$ is orthogonal to the other two, and that each is a unit vector.
(b) Find the projection of $\mathbf{E}_1 = (1,0,0)$ on each of $\mathbf{U}_1$, $\mathbf{U}_2$, $\mathbf{U}_3$.
(c) Find the projection of the general vector $\mathbf{A} = (a_1,a_2,a_3)$ on $\mathbf{U}_1$, $\mathbf{U}_2$, $\mathbf{U}_3$.
(d) Prove that $\mathbf{A} = (\mathbf{A}\cdot\mathbf{U}_1)\mathbf{U}_1 + (\mathbf{A}\cdot\mathbf{U}_2)\mathbf{U}_2 + (\mathbf{A}\cdot\mathbf{U}_3)\mathbf{U}_3$. (This is a tedious calculation. Later on, we will develop an easier but more sophisticated way to prove such formulas.)

9. (a) Prove that $|\mathbf{A} - \mathbf{B}|^2 = |\mathbf{A}|^2 + |\mathbf{B}|^2 - 2(\mathbf{A}\cdot\mathbf{B})$.
(b) Referring to Figs. 8 and 9, show that the formula in part (a) is the *law of cosines*: $c^2 = a^2 + b^2 - 2ab\cos\theta$.

10. Suppose that $\mathbf{A}$ and $\mathbf{B}$ are orthogonal, and let θ be the angle between $\mathbf{A}$ and $\mathbf{A} + \mathbf{B}$. Prove (algebraically) that $|\mathbf{A}| = |\mathbf{A} + \mathbf{B}|\cos\theta$ and $|\mathbf{B}| = |\mathbf{A} + \mathbf{B}|\sin\theta$. Draw a sketch relating these formulas to the definitions of the sine and the cosine of an angle in a right triangle.

11. Prove the *parallelogram law*: $|\mathbf{A} + \mathbf{B}|^2 + |\mathbf{A} - \mathbf{B}|^2 = 2|\mathbf{A}|^2 + 2|\mathbf{B}|^2$. Draw a figure showing why this is called the parallelogram law. (Hint: Fig. 5 above shows $\mathbf{A} + \mathbf{B}$ as the diagonal of a parallelogram. What is the other diagonal?)

12. Suppose that $t\mathbf{A} = \mathbf{0}$. Prove that either $t = 0$ or $\mathbf{A} = \mathbf{0}$.

13. Suppose that $\mathbf{A}$ and $\mathbf{B}$ are parallel, and that $\mathbf{B} \neq \mathbf{0}$. Prove that $\mathbf{A} = t\mathbf{B}$ for some real t. (Hint: Parallelism means *either* $\mathbf{A} = t\mathbf{B}$ or $\mathbf{B} = s\mathbf{A}$. In the first case, there is nothing to prove; in the second case, use the previous problem.)

14. Suppose that $\mathbf{B} \neq \mathbf{0}$. Prove that a vector $\mathbf{A}$ is parallel to $\mathbf{B}$ if and only if $\mathbf{A}$ equals $\mathbf{A}_\mathbf{B}$, its projection on $\mathbf{B}$. (Hint: In proving $\mathbf{A} = \mathbf{A}_\mathbf{B}$, use formula (22) and the previous problem.)

15. Suppose that $\mathbf{A}$ and $\mathbf{B}$ are both nonzero. Prove that $\mathbf{A}$ and $\mathbf{B}$ are parallel if and only if the angle θ between them is 0 or π. (Hint: In proving the "if" part, show that $|\mathbf{A} - \mathbf{A}_\mathbf{B}|^2 = \mathbf{0}$ when $|\cos\theta| = 1$.)

16. (a) Obtain a formula for the distance d from a point $\mathbf{P}_0$ to the line with parametric formula $\mathbf{A} + t\mathbf{B}$. (When $\mathbf{P}_0 = \mathbf{0}$, your formula should reduce to the expression in the text for the distance from the line to the origin.)

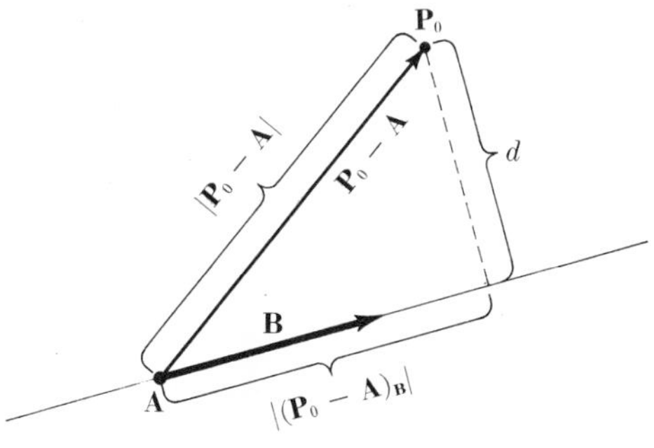

FIGURE 1.12 $d^2 = |\mathbf{P}_0 - \mathbf{A}|^2 - |(\mathbf{P}_0 - \mathbf{A})_{\mathbf{B}}|^2$

(b) Show that your formula for the distance d can be described in terms of orthogonal projection as $d^2 = |\mathbf{P}_0 - \mathbf{A}|^2 - |(\mathbf{P}_0 - \mathbf{A})_{\mathbf{B}}|^2$. (This is an easy geometric way to remember the formula; see Fig. 12.)

17. Prove at least some of the following formulas in the text above: (2), (3), (4), (5), (6), (7), (8), (9), (10), (11), (13).

1.2 THE CROSS PRODUCT

Many geometric constructions in R^3 reduce ultimately to the same algebraic problem: Given two nonparallel vectors **A** and **B**, find a nonzero vector **C** which is orthogonal to both **A** and **B**. (See Fig. 13.) This problem has a standard solution called the *cross product* of **A** and **B**, denoted **A** × **B**.

Definition 2. If $\mathbf{A} = (a_1,a_2,a_3)$ and $\mathbf{B} = (b_1,b_2,b_3)$, then the *cross product* of **A** and **B** is defined by the formula

$$\mathbf{A} \times \mathbf{B} = (a_2b_3 - a_3b_2\,,\ a_3b_1 - a_1b_3\,,\ a_1b_2 - a_2b_1). \qquad (1)$$

The rest of this section develops the algebraic properties and geometric meaning of the strange expression (1).

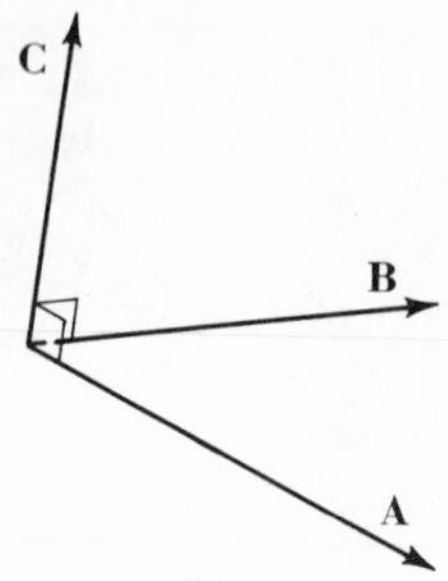

FIGURE 1.13

Theorem 2. $\mathbf{A} \times \mathbf{B}$ *is orthogonal to both* **A** *and* **B**. *Further,*

$$\mathbf{A} \times \mathbf{B} = -(\mathbf{B} \times \mathbf{A}) \tag{2}$$

$$\mathbf{A} \times \mathbf{A} = \mathbf{0} \tag{3}$$

$$(t\mathbf{A}) \times \mathbf{B} = t(\mathbf{A} \times \mathbf{B}) = \mathbf{A} \times (t\mathbf{B}) \tag{4}$$

$$|\mathbf{A} \times \mathbf{B}|^2 = |\mathbf{A}|^2 \cdot |\mathbf{B}|^2 - (\mathbf{A} \cdot \mathbf{B})^2 \tag{5}$$

$$\mathbf{A} \cdot (\mathbf{B} \times \mathbf{C}) = \mathbf{B} \cdot (\mathbf{C} \times \mathbf{A}) = \mathbf{C} \cdot (\mathbf{A} \times \mathbf{B}) \tag{6}$$

$$(\mathbf{A} + \mathbf{B}) \times \mathbf{C} = (\mathbf{A} \times \mathbf{C}) + (\mathbf{B} \times \mathbf{C}) \tag{7}$$

$$\mathbf{A} \times (\mathbf{B} + \mathbf{C}) = (\mathbf{A} \times \mathbf{B}) + (\mathbf{A} \times \mathbf{C}). \tag{8}$$

Proof. We begin with formulas (2)–(8). Interchanging **A** and **B** in Definition 2 produces

$$\mathbf{B} \times \mathbf{A} = (b_2a_3 - b_3a_2\,,\, b_3a_1 - b_1a_3\,,\, b_1a_2 - b_2a_1)\,;$$

comparing this to the expression (1) for $\mathbf{A} \times \mathbf{B}$, you can see that $\mathbf{B} \times \mathbf{A} = -(\mathbf{A} \times \mathbf{B})$, so (2) is proved. Formula (3) can be seen immediately by setting $\mathbf{B} = \mathbf{A}$ in (1). Formula (4) is an easy calculation which is left to you. Formulas (5)–(8) are not quite so easy, but they can be proved simply by expanding both sides; this, too, is left to you (Problem 5).

Finally, we prove that $\mathbf{A} \times \mathbf{B}$ is orthogonal to **A**. Setting $\mathbf{C} = \mathbf{A}$ in (6) yields

$$\mathbf{A} \cdot (\mathbf{A} \times \mathbf{B}) = \mathbf{B} \cdot (\mathbf{A} \times \mathbf{A});$$

since $\mathbf{A} \times \mathbf{A} = \mathbf{0}$, we find that

$$\mathbf{A} \cdot (\mathbf{A} \times \mathbf{B}) = \mathbf{B} \cdot \mathbf{0} = 0,$$

which says precisely that $\mathbf{A} \times \mathbf{B}$ is orthogonal to **A**. Similarly, $\mathbf{A} \times \mathbf{B}$ is orthogonal to **B**, and Theorem 2 is proved.

Notice that we have distributive laws (7) and (8) and an associative law (4), all of which resemble the usual "laws of algebra." But formula (2) is *not* the usual commutative law; generally, $\mathbf{A} \times \mathbf{B} \neq \mathbf{B} \times \mathbf{A}$ unless the product is $\mathbf{0}$. Moreover, the associative "law" $\mathbf{A} \times (\mathbf{B} \times \mathbf{C}) = (\mathbf{A} \times \mathbf{B}) \times \mathbf{C}$ is *not* valid. (See Problem 7 below.)

Formula (5) gives

$$\begin{aligned} |\mathbf{A} \times \mathbf{B}|^2 &= |\mathbf{A}|^2 \cdot |\mathbf{B}|^2 - |\mathbf{A}|^2 \cdot |\mathbf{B}|^2 \cos^2 \theta \\ &= |\mathbf{A}|^2 \cdot |\mathbf{B}|^2 (1 - \cos^2 \theta); \end{aligned}$$

hence

$$|\mathbf{A} \times \mathbf{B}| = |\mathbf{A}| \cdot |\mathbf{B}| \sin \theta, \tag{9}$$

where θ is the angle between $\mathbf{A}$ and $\mathbf{B}$. (Since $0 \leq \theta \leq \pi$, we have $\sin \theta \geq 0$; hence $\sqrt{1 - \cos^2 \theta}$ equals $\sin \theta$, not $-\sin \theta$.) Geometrically, (9) says that the length of $\mathbf{A} \times \mathbf{B}$ is the area of the parallelogram spanned by $\mathbf{A}$ and $\mathbf{B}$ (Fig. 14).

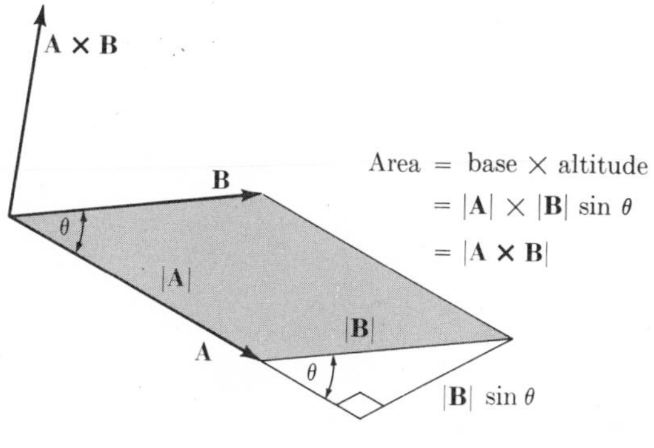

FIGURE 1.14

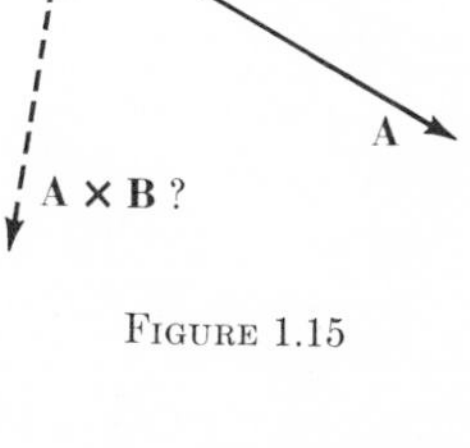

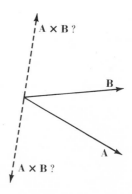

FIGURE 1.15

Now we know that the cross product $\mathbf{A} \times \mathbf{B}$ is perpendicular to both $\mathbf{A}$ and $\mathbf{B}$, and we know its length $|\mathbf{A} \times \mathbf{B}|$. Intuitively, this leaves only two possibilities for $\mathbf{A} \times \mathbf{B}$, as suggested in Fig. 15. Which arrow represents $\mathbf{A} \times \mathbf{B}$ can be determined by a convenient "rule of thumb," whose exact nature depends on the labeling of the coordinate axes.

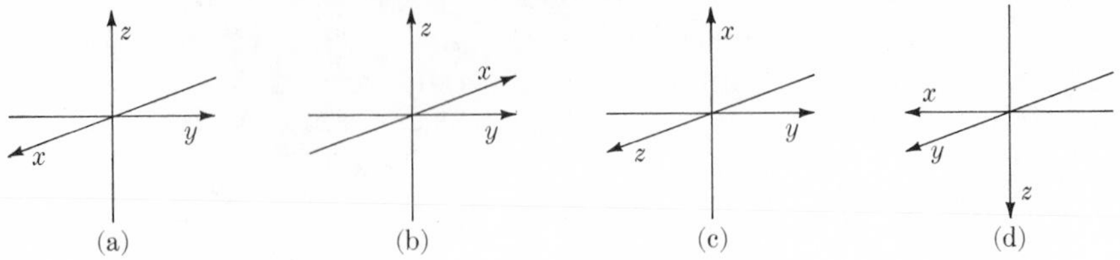

FIGURE 1.16

There are many ways to label the axes (see Fig. 16), but they fall into two main types called *right-hand* and *left-hand.* To tell which type you have, sketch the three basic unit vectors

$$\mathbf{E}_1 = (1,0,0), \qquad \mathbf{E}_2 = (0,1,0), \qquad \mathbf{E}_3 = (0,0,1),$$

which point respectively in the positive direction along the first, second, and third axes (i.e. the x, y, and z axes). Figure 17(a) shows $\mathbf{E}_1$, $\mathbf{E}_2$, and $\mathbf{E}_3$ in what is called a *right-hand* coordinate system. The mysterious hand in the figure explains this name; if you hold the third unit vector $\mathbf{E}_3 = (0,0,1)$ with your *right* hand, fingers pointing from $\mathbf{E}_1$ to $\mathbf{E}_2$, then the thumb points in the same direction as $\mathbf{E}_3$. A *left-hand* system works the same way, but (naturally) with the left hand (see Fig. 17(b)).

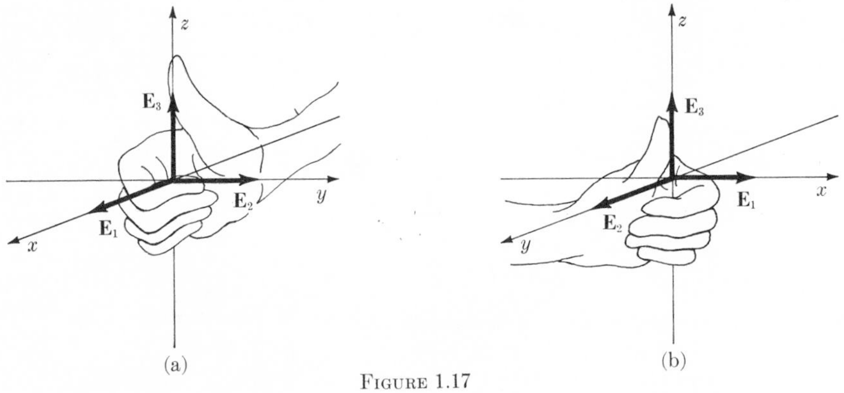

FIGURE 1.17

The rule for visualizing the cross product is that the three vectors **A**, **B**, and $\mathbf{A} \times \mathbf{B}$ are oriented like the three vectors $\mathbf{E}_1$, $\mathbf{E}_2$, $\mathbf{E}_3$. Specifically: In a right-hand coordinate system the cross product is directed so that *if you hold* $\mathbf{A} \times \mathbf{B}$ *with the right hand, with the fingers pointing from* **A** *toward* **B**, *then the thumb points in the direction of* $\mathbf{A} \times \mathbf{B}$ (see Fig. 18). In a left-hand coordinate system, the same method works if you use the left hand.

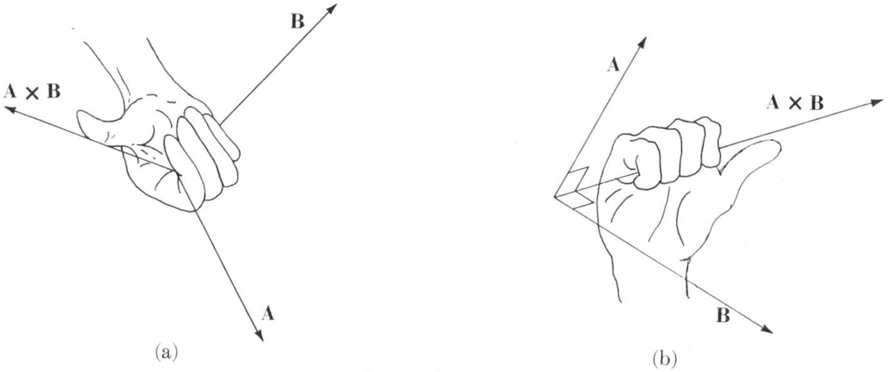

FIGURE 1.18

Please do not expect a mathematical proof of the "right-hand rule." It is just an experimental fact that when we think of vectors as arrows, the cross product works out this way.

Since $|\mathbf{B} \times \mathbf{C}|$ is the area of the parallelogram spanned by **B** and **C**, it follows that $|\mathbf{A} \cdot (\mathbf{B} \times \mathbf{C})|$ is the volume of the parallelepiped spanned by **A**, **B**, and **C**; for, as Fig. 19 shows,

$$\begin{aligned} \mathbf{A} \cdot (\mathbf{B} \times \mathbf{C}) &= |\mathbf{A}| \cdot |\mathbf{B} \times \mathbf{C}| \cos \varphi \\ &= (|\mathbf{B} \times \mathbf{C}|)(|\mathbf{A}| \cos \varphi) \\ &= \pm (\text{area of base}) \cdot (\text{altitude}). \end{aligned}$$

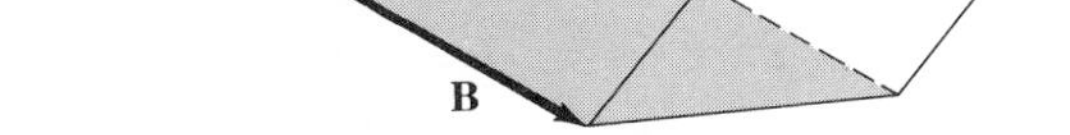

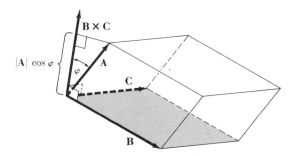

FIGURE 1.19 $|\mathbf{A} \cdot (\mathbf{B} \times \mathbf{C})|$ = area of parallelepiped

We have shown how to visualize everything about the cross product except the complicated formula (1) that defines it. This is easy to remember as a 3 × 3 determinant

$$\mathbf{A} \times \mathbf{B} = \begin{vmatrix} \mathbf{E}_1 & \mathbf{E}_2 & \mathbf{E}_3 \\ a_1 & a_2 & a_3 \\ b_1 & b_2 & b_3 \end{vmatrix}.$$

In the first row are the basic unit vectors

$$\mathbf{E}_1 = (1,0,0), \qquad \mathbf{E}_2 = (0,1,0), \qquad \mathbf{E}_3 = (0,0,1),$$

and in the second and third rows are the components of **A** and **B** respectively. Expanding by minors of the first row gives

$$\mathbf{A} \times \mathbf{B} = \begin{vmatrix} a_2 & a_3 \\ b_2 & b_3 \end{vmatrix} \mathbf{E}_1 - \begin{vmatrix} a_1 & a_3 \\ b_1 & b_3 \end{vmatrix} \mathbf{E}_2 + \begin{vmatrix} a_1 & a_2 \\ b_1 & b_2 \end{vmatrix} \mathbf{E}_3 ,$$

which reduces to (1).

In case you are not familiar with determinants, we can easily fill in the necessary background. A 2×2 determinant assigns numbers to square arrays of four numbers. If the square array is

$$\begin{matrix} a & b \\ c & d \end{matrix}$$

then the determinant is

$$\begin{vmatrix} a & b \\ c & d \end{vmatrix} = ad - bc,$$

that is, the product of the entries a and d on one diagonal minus the product of the entries b and c on the other diagonal. For example,

$$\begin{vmatrix} 0 & 1 \\ 1 & 0 \end{vmatrix} = -1, \qquad \begin{vmatrix} 1 & 0 \\ 0 & 1 \end{vmatrix} = 1, \qquad \begin{vmatrix} 1 & 2 \\ 3 & 4 \end{vmatrix} = -2, \qquad \begin{vmatrix} -1 & 5 \\ 0 & 2 \end{vmatrix} = -2.$$

Using 2×2 determinants, the cross product (1) is written

$$\mathbf{A} \times \mathbf{B} = \left(\begin{vmatrix} a_2 & a_3 \\ b_2 & b_3 \end{vmatrix}, -\begin{vmatrix} a_1 & a_3 \\ b_1 & b_3 \end{vmatrix}, \begin{vmatrix} a_1 & a_2 \\ b_1 & b_2 \end{vmatrix} \right).$$

To remember this expression, write the components of **A** and **B** in two rows,

$$\begin{matrix} a_1 & a_2 & a_3 \\ b_1 & b_2 & b_3 \end{matrix} . \tag{10}$$

Then the components of $\mathbf{A} \times \mathbf{B}$ are obtained as follows:

First component: Disregard the *first* column in (10), and take the determinant of the remaining entries:

$$\begin{matrix} \cancel{a_1} \\ \cancel{b_1} \end{matrix} \begin{vmatrix} a_2 & a_3 \\ b_2 & b_3 \end{vmatrix}$$

Second component: Disregard the *second* column in (10), and take *minus* the determinant of the remaining entries:

$$-\begin{vmatrix} a_1 & \cancel{a_2} & a_3 \\ b_1 & \cancel{b_2} & b_3 \end{vmatrix}$$

Third component: Disregard the *third* column in (10), and take the determinant of the remaining entries:

$$\begin{vmatrix} a_1 & a_2 \\ b_1 & b_2 \end{vmatrix}\!\!\not{\begin{matrix} a_3 \\ b_3 \end{matrix}}$$

For example, if $\mathbf{A} = (1,2,3)$ and $\mathbf{B} = (4,5,6)$, write the components in two rows,

$$\begin{matrix} 1 & 2 & 3 \\ \\ 4 & 5 & 6 \end{matrix}$$

and following the prescription above, find

$$\begin{aligned} \mathbf{A} \times \mathbf{B} &= \left(\begin{vmatrix} 2 & 3 \\ 5 & 6 \end{vmatrix}, -\begin{vmatrix} 1 & 3 \\ 4 & 6 \end{vmatrix}, \begin{vmatrix} 1 & 2 \\ 4 & 5 \end{vmatrix} \right) \\ &= ((12 - 15), -(6 - 12), (5 - 8)) \\ &= (-3, 6, -3). \end{aligned}$$

As a check, you can verify that $(-3, 6, -3)$ is orthogonal to both $\mathbf{A}$ and $\mathbf{B}$.

This method provides a useful expansion of the "triple product" $\mathbf{A}\cdot(\mathbf{B} \times \mathbf{C})$. We have

$$\mathbf{B} \times \mathbf{C} = \left(\begin{vmatrix} b_2 & b_3 \\ c_2 & c_3 \end{vmatrix}, -\begin{vmatrix} b_1 & b_3 \\ c_1 & c_3 \end{vmatrix}, \begin{vmatrix} b_1 & b_2 \\ c_1 & c_2 \end{vmatrix} \right);$$

hence

$$\mathbf{A}\cdot(\mathbf{B} \times \mathbf{C}) = a_1\begin{vmatrix} b_2 & b_3 \\ c_2 & c_3 \end{vmatrix} - a_2\begin{vmatrix} b_1 & b_3 \\ c_1 & c_3 \end{vmatrix} + a_3\begin{vmatrix} b_1 & b_2 \\ c_1 & c_2 \end{vmatrix}.$$

The expression on the right-hand side is exactly the definition of the 3×3 *determinant*

$$\begin{vmatrix} a_1 & a_2 & a_3 \\ b_1 & b_2 & b_3 \\ c_1 & c_2 & c_3 \end{vmatrix} = a_1\begin{vmatrix} b_2 & b_3 \\ c_2 & c_3 \end{vmatrix} - a_2\begin{vmatrix} b_1 & b_3 \\ c_1 & c_3 \end{vmatrix} + a_3\begin{vmatrix} b_1 & b_2 \\ c_1 & c_2 \end{vmatrix}.$$

Hence the formulas in Theorem 2 can be used to deduce some of the properties of 3×3 determinants. (See Problem 10 below.)

Example 1. Find $(0,-2,-1) \times (-1,-1,1)$. *Solution.* From the array

$$\begin{matrix} 0 & -2 & -1 \\ \\ -1 & -1 & 1 \end{matrix}$$

we obtain the cross product

$$(-2\cdot1 - (-1)\cdot(-1),\quad -1\cdot(-1) - 0\cdot1,\quad 0\cdot(-1) - (-2)(-1))$$
$$= (-3,1,-2).$$

Example 2. Show that $\mathbf{P}_1 = (1,2,3)$, $\mathbf{P}_2 = (1,0,2)$, $\mathbf{P}_3 = (0,-1,3)$ and $\mathbf{P}_4 = (0,1,4)$ form the four vertices of a parallelogram, and find its area. *Solution.* The four points are the vertices of a parallelogram, since (Fig. 20) $\mathbf{P}_2 - \mathbf{P}_1 = \mathbf{P}_3 - \mathbf{P}_4 = (0,-2,-1)$. To compute the area, notice that $\mathbf{P}_2 - \mathbf{P}_1$ and $\mathbf{P}_4 - \mathbf{P}_1$ form two adjacent sides of the parallelogram. Thus, referring to Fig. 20, the area of the parallelogram is

$$\begin{aligned}|(\mathbf{P}_2 - \mathbf{P}_1) \times (\mathbf{P}_4 - \mathbf{P}_1)| &= |(0,-2,-1) \times (-1,-1,1)| \\ &= |(-3,1,-2)| = \sqrt{14}\,.\end{aligned}$$

Example 3. Compute the area of the triangle with vertices $\mathbf{P}_1 = (1,5,2)$, $\mathbf{P}_2 = (-1,3,0)$ and $\mathbf{P}_3 = (0,1,4)$. *Solution.* This is half the area of the parallelogram spanned by arrows representing $\mathbf{P}_2 - \mathbf{P}_1$ and $\mathbf{P}_3 - \mathbf{P}_1$, so the area is

$$\begin{aligned}\tfrac{1}{2}|(\mathbf{P}_2 - \mathbf{P}_1) \times (\mathbf{P}_3 - \mathbf{P}_1)| &= \tfrac{1}{2}|(-2,-2,-2) \times (-1,-4,2)| \\ &= \tfrac{1}{2}|(-12,6,6)| = 3|(-2,1,1)| = 3\sqrt{6}\,.\end{aligned}$$

You can check this result by interchanging the vertices; you will find, for instance, that

$$\tfrac{1}{2}|(\mathbf{P}_1 - \mathbf{P}_3) \times (\mathbf{P}_2 - \mathbf{P}_3)| = \tfrac{1}{2}|(-12,6,6)| = 3\sqrt{6}\,.$$

PROBLEMS

The first four problems are routine calculations with the cross product. Problems 5–8 ask you to prove some general formulas for the cross product. Problem 9 proves that $\mathbf{A} \times \mathbf{B} = \mathbf{0}$ if and only if $\mathbf{A}$ and $\mathbf{B}$ are parallel. Problems 10 and 11 concern trigonometry; 12 and 13 concern Cramer's rule and determinants.

1. (a) Check algebraically that

$$\mathbf{E}_1 \times \mathbf{E}_2 = \mathbf{E}_3\,, \qquad \mathbf{E}_2 \times \mathbf{E}_3 = \mathbf{E}_1\,, \qquad \mathbf{E}_3 \times \mathbf{E}_1 = \mathbf{E}_2\,.$$

(b) Find $\mathbf{E}_1 \times \mathbf{E}_3$.

(c) Sketch a right-hand coordinate system, and check the products in (a) and (b) visually by the right-hand rule.

2. In the following cases, compute $\mathbf{A} \times \mathbf{B}$ and $(\mathbf{A} \times \mathbf{B}) \cdot \mathbf{C}$.

(a) $\mathbf{A} = (1,2,0)$, $\mathbf{B} = (-3,1,0)$, $\mathbf{C} = (4,9,-3)$.
(Here $(\mathbf{A} \times \mathbf{B}) \cdot \mathbf{C} = -21$.)

(b) $\mathbf{A} = (-3,1,-2)$, $\mathbf{B} = (2,0,4)$, $\mathbf{C} = (1,1,1)$.
(Here $(\mathbf{A} \times \mathbf{B}) \cdot \mathbf{C} = 10$.)

3. (a) Find the area of the parallelogram whose vertices are at the points $\mathbf{P}_1 = (0,0,0)$, $\mathbf{P}_2 = (1,1,1)$, $\mathbf{P}_3 = (2,0,0)$, and $\mathbf{P}_4 = (1,-1,-1)$. (Notice that $\mathbf{P}_3 = \mathbf{P}_2 + \mathbf{P}_4$; hence this parallelogram is spanned by arrows representing $\mathbf{P}_2 = (1,1,1)$ and $\mathbf{P}_4 = (1,-1,-1)$.)

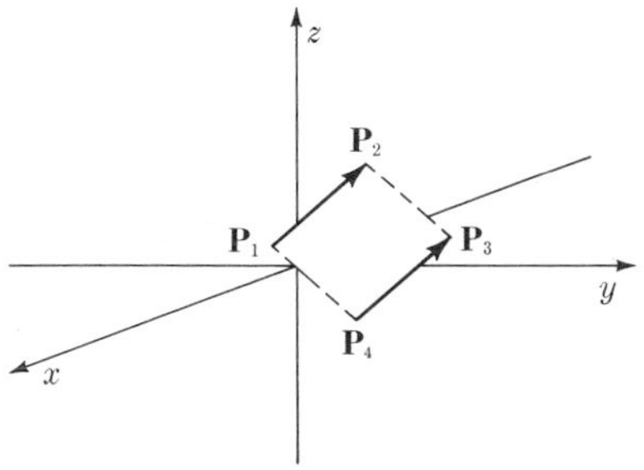

FIGURE 1.20

(b) Find the area of the triangle with vertices (0,0,0), (1,1,1), and (1,−1,−1).

4. Four points $\mathbf{P}_1$, $\mathbf{P}_2$, $\mathbf{P}_3$, $\mathbf{P}_4$, taken in order, form the vertices of a parallelogram if and only if $\mathbf{P}_2 - \mathbf{P}_1 = \mathbf{P}_3 - \mathbf{P}_4$ (see Fig. 20). Prove that $\mathbf{P}_1 = (1,1,1)$, $\mathbf{P}_2 = (1,2,2)$, $\mathbf{P}_3 = (2,3,2)$, and $\mathbf{P}_4 = (2,2,1)$ are the vertices of a parallelogram, and compute its area. (Hint: The vectors $\mathbf{P}_2 - \mathbf{P}_1$, $\mathbf{P}_3 - \mathbf{P}_2$, $\mathbf{P}_4 - \mathbf{P}_3$, $\mathbf{P}_1 - \mathbf{P}_4$ correspond to the sides of the parallelogram, as in Fig. 20.)

5. In Theorem 2 prove:
(a) Formula (4)
(b) Formula (5)
(c) Formula (6)
(d) Formula (7)
(e) Formula (8) (Hint: Instead of expanding both sides, you can use (2) and (7).)

6. Prove the following equalities, noticing particularly those with minus signs. (None of the proofs require expansion; they should be based on formulas (2)–(8), plus properties of the inner product.)
(a) $(\mathbf{A} \times \mathbf{B})\cdot\mathbf{C} = \mathbf{C}\cdot(\mathbf{A} \times \mathbf{B})$
(b) $(\mathbf{A} \times \mathbf{B})\cdot\mathbf{C} = \mathbf{A}\cdot(\mathbf{B} \times \mathbf{C})$
(c) $(\mathbf{A} \times \mathbf{B})\cdot\mathbf{C} = -(\mathbf{A} \times \mathbf{C})\cdot\mathbf{B}$
(d) $(\mathbf{A} \times \mathbf{B})\cdot\mathbf{C} = -\mathbf{A}\cdot(\mathbf{C} \times \mathbf{B})$

7. Prove that $\mathbf{E}_1 \times (\mathbf{E}_1 \times \mathbf{E}_2) \neq (\mathbf{E}_1 \times \mathbf{E}_1) \times \mathbf{E}_2$.

8. (a) Prove the *Lagrange identity:*

$$(\mathbf{A} \times \mathbf{B})\cdot(\mathbf{C} \times \mathbf{D}) = (\mathbf{A}\cdot\mathbf{C})(\mathbf{B}\cdot\mathbf{D}) - (\mathbf{A}\cdot\mathbf{D})(\mathbf{B}\cdot\mathbf{C}).$$

(b) Deduce the formula for $|\mathbf{A} \times \mathbf{B}|^2$ from part (a).

9. (a) Prove that if $\mathbf{A}$ and $\mathbf{B}$ are parallel, then $\mathbf{A} \times \mathbf{B} = \mathbf{0}$.
(b) Suppose that $\mathbf{B} \neq \mathbf{0}$. Prove that if $\mathbf{A} \times \mathbf{B} = \mathbf{0}$, then $\mathbf{A} = t\mathbf{B}$ for some constant t.
(c) Prove that $\mathbf{A} \times \mathbf{B} = \mathbf{0}$ if and only if $\mathbf{A}$ and $\mathbf{B}$ are parallel.

10. (a) Prove that $\mathbf{A} \times (\mathbf{A} + \mathbf{B}) = \mathbf{A} \times \mathbf{B}$.
(b) Prove the *law of sines:*

$$\frac{|\mathbf{A}|}{\sin \alpha} = \frac{|\mathbf{B}|}{\sin \beta} = \frac{|\mathbf{C}|}{\sin \gamma}.$$

(See Fig. 21; use formula (9) to compute $\sin \alpha$, etc.)

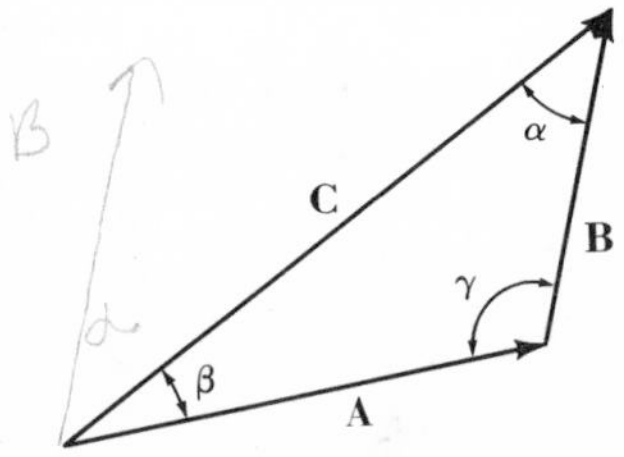

FIGURE 1.21 $\mathbf{C} = \mathbf{A} + \mathbf{B}$

11. Let $\mathbf{A}$ and $\mathbf{B}$ be any vectors in R^3, and let α, β, and γ be the angles indicated in Fig. 21. Prove that $\cos(\alpha + \beta + \gamma) = -1$. (Hint: Prove that $\cos(\alpha + \beta) = -\cos \gamma$ and $\sin(\alpha + \beta) = \sin \gamma$. Use the addition formula for $\cos(\alpha + \beta)$, etc., and formulas (9) and (5) above.)

12. This problem deduces half of *Cramer's rule* for three simultaneous linear equations. Given $a_1, b_1, c_1, d_1, a_2, \ldots, d_3$, the system of equations

$$\begin{aligned} ra_1 + sb_1 + tc_1 &= d_1 \\ ra_2 + sb_2 + tc_2 &= d_2 \\ ra_3 + sb_3 + tc_3 &= d_3 \end{aligned} \tag{11}$$

can be written as a single vector equation:

$$r\mathbf{A} + s\mathbf{B} + t\mathbf{C} = \mathbf{D}. \tag{12}$$

(a) Take the inner product of both sides of (12) with $\mathbf{B} \times \mathbf{C}$, and show that

$$r(\mathbf{A} \cdot (\mathbf{B} \times \mathbf{C})) = \mathbf{D} \cdot (\mathbf{B} \times \mathbf{C}).$$

(b) Show that

$$s(\mathbf{B}\cdot(\mathbf{A}\times\mathbf{C})) = \mathbf{D}\cdot(\mathbf{A}\times\mathbf{C})$$

and

$$t(\mathbf{C}\cdot(\mathbf{A}\times\mathbf{B})) = \mathbf{D}\cdot(\mathbf{A}\times\mathbf{B}).$$

(c) Deduce that if $\mathbf{A}\cdot(\mathbf{B}\times\mathbf{C}) \neq 0$, then the only possible solution of (11) for r, s, and t is

$$r = \frac{\mathbf{D}\cdot(\mathbf{B}\times\mathbf{C})}{\mathbf{A}\cdot(\mathbf{B}\times\mathbf{C})}$$

$$s = \frac{\mathbf{A}\cdot(\mathbf{D}\times\mathbf{C})}{\mathbf{A}\cdot(\mathbf{B}\times\mathbf{C})}$$

$$t = \frac{\mathbf{A}\cdot(\mathbf{B}\times\mathbf{D})}{\mathbf{A}\cdot(\mathbf{B}\times\mathbf{C})}.$$

(In this problem you have *not* proved that these values of r, s, and t actually solve the equation (11); that is the other half of Cramer's rule. Its proof is outlined in §1.5, Problem 21.)

13. Let D stand for the determinant

$$D = \begin{vmatrix} a_1 & a_2 & a_3 \\ b_1 & b_2 & b_3 \\ c_1 & c_2 & c_3 \end{vmatrix} = \mathbf{A}\cdot(\mathbf{B}\times\mathbf{C}).$$

Use Theorem 2 to prove the following:

(a) $\begin{vmatrix} b_1 & b_2 & b_3 \\ c_1 & c_2 & c_3 \\ a_1 & a_2 & a_3 \end{vmatrix} = D$

(b) $\begin{vmatrix} b_1 & b_2 & b_3 \\ a_1 & a_2 & a_3 \\ c_1 & c_2 & c_3 \end{vmatrix} = -D$

(c) $\begin{vmatrix} a_1 & a_2 & a_3 \\ b_1+ta_1 & b_2+ta_2 & b_3+ta_3 \\ c_1 & c_2 & c_3 \end{vmatrix} = D$

(d) $\begin{vmatrix} a_1+tc_1 & a_2+tc_2 & a_3+tc_3 \\ b_1 & b_2 & b_3 \\ c_1 & c_2 & c_3 \end{vmatrix} = D$

1.3 SPHERES, PLANES, AND LINES

We are ready to define the elementary geometric figures in R^3.

The *sphere of radius r with center at a given point* $\mathbf{P}_0$ is the set of all points $\mathbf{P}$ such that $|\mathbf{P} - \mathbf{P}_0| = r$ (Fig. 22). This set is denoted

$$\{\mathbf{P}: |\mathbf{P} - \mathbf{P}_0| = r\}$$

or equivalently

$$\{(x,y,z): (x - x_0)^2 + (y - y_0)^2 + (z - z_0)^2 = r^2\}.$$

The *closed ball* of radius r about $\mathbf{P}_0$ is the set

$$\{\mathbf{P}: |\mathbf{P} - \mathbf{P}_0| \leq r\},$$

and the set

$$\{\mathbf{P}: |\mathbf{P} - \mathbf{P}_0| < r\}$$

is the *open ball* of radius r about $\mathbf{P}_0$. A closed ball (like a closed interval) contains all its boundary points, and an open ball contains none of them.

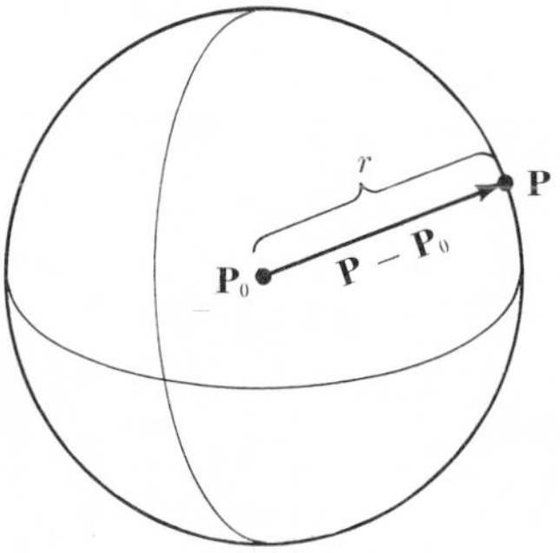

FIGURE 1.22

A *plane* is by definition any set of the form

$$\{\mathbf{P}: \mathbf{N}\cdot\mathbf{P} = d\} \tag{1}$$

where $\mathbf{N}$ is a given nonzero vector and d is a given number. If $\mathbf{N} = (a,b,c)$, then the condition $\mathbf{N}\cdot\mathbf{P} = d$ takes the form

$$ax + by + cz = d; \tag{2}$$

this is the *equation* of the plane (1). For example,

$\{(x,y,z): x = 0\}$ is the yz plane (Fig. 23)

$\{(x,y,z): x = 1\}$ is a plane parallel to the yz plane (Fig. 24)

$\{(x,y,z): z = 0\}$ is the xy plane (Fig. 25)

$\{(x,y,z): y = z\}$ is a plane containing the x axis and bisecting the y and z axes. (Fig. 26)

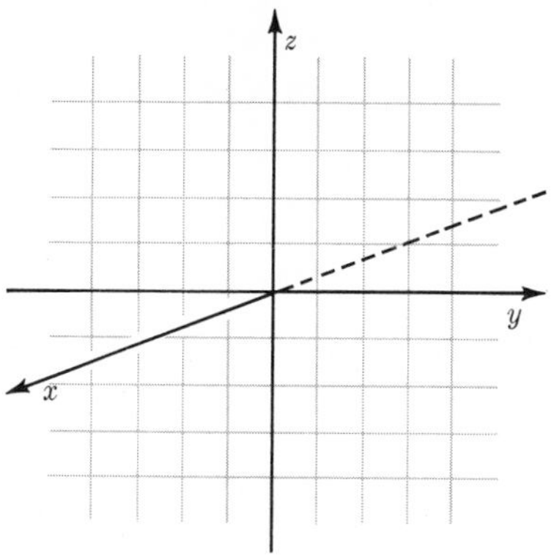

FIGURE 1.23

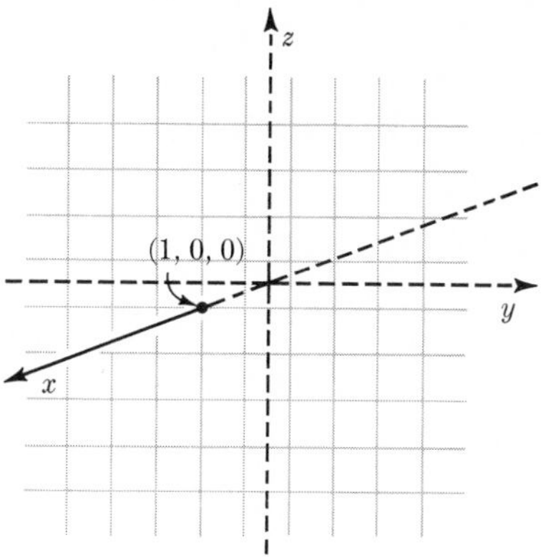

FIGURE 1.24

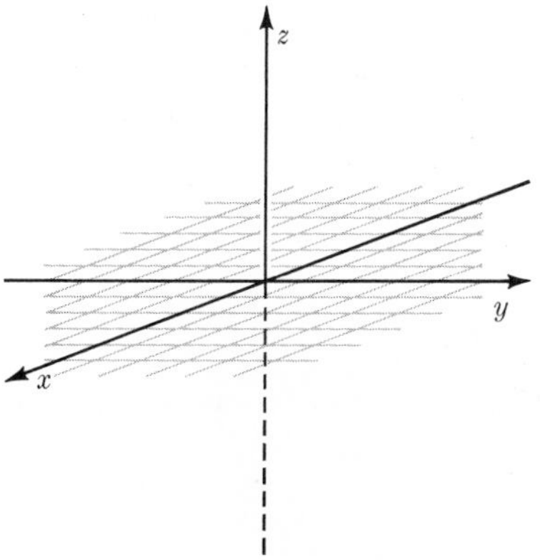

FIGURE 1.25

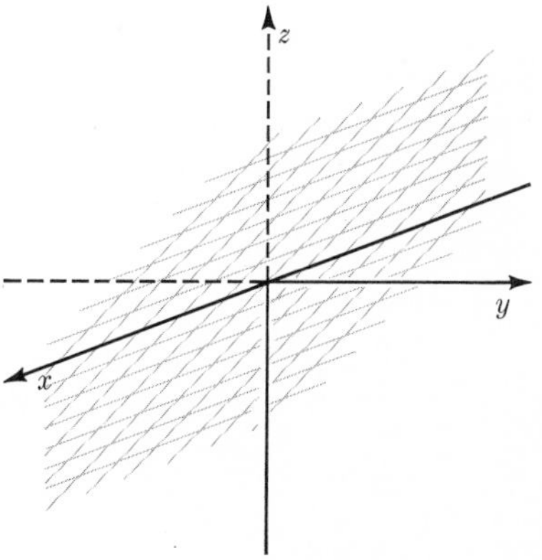

FIGURE 1.26

Let $\mathbf{P}_0$ be any point on the plane (1). Then $\mathbf{N}\cdot\mathbf{P}_0 = d$, so the equation $\mathbf{N}\cdot\mathbf{P} = d$ can be written

$$\mathbf{N}\cdot\mathbf{P} = \mathbf{N}\cdot\mathbf{P}_0$$

or

$$\mathbf{N}\cdot(\mathbf{P} - \mathbf{P}_0) = 0. \tag{3}$$

Thus the plane consists of all points $\mathbf{P}$ such that $\mathbf{P} - \mathbf{P}_0$ is orthogonal to $\mathbf{N}$ (see Fig. 27). The vector $\mathbf{N}$ is called a *normal vector* to the plane. Equation (3) is an algebraic version of a traditional Euclidean characterization: the set of all lines through a given point $\mathbf{P}_0$ and orthogonal to a given line through $\mathbf{P}_0$ is a plane.

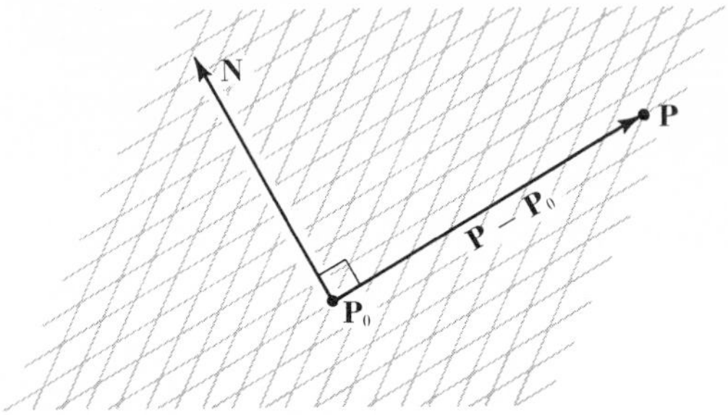

FIGURE 1.27

Lines were introduced in §1.1; by definition, a line is any set of the form

$$\{\mathbf{P}: \mathbf{P} = \mathbf{A} + t\mathbf{B} \text{ for some real number } t\}, \tag{4}$$

line thru A, direction B.

where $\mathbf{B}$ is assumed to be nonzero. The equation $\mathbf{P} = \mathbf{A} + t\mathbf{B}$ is called a *parametric equation of the line,* with t as parameter. You can think of t as time, and imagine the line as traced by a point moving with constant speed and direction; at time $t = 0$ the point is at $\mathbf{A}$, at $t = 1$ it is at $\mathbf{A} + \mathbf{B}$, at $t = -1$ it was at $\mathbf{A} - \mathbf{B}$, and so on. (See Fig. 28.)

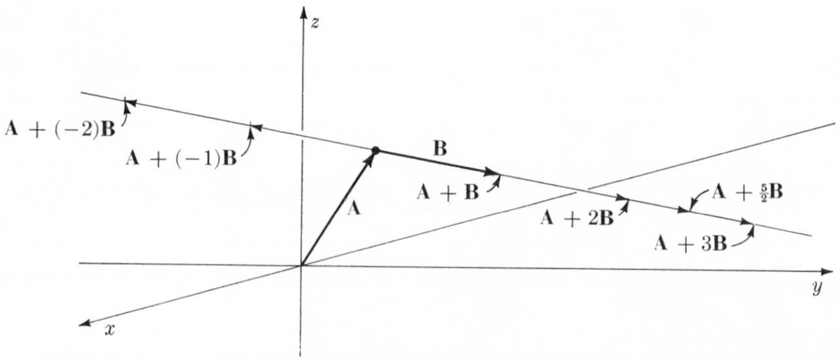

FIGURE 1.28

Given any two distinct points $\mathbf{P}_1$ and $\mathbf{P}_2$, there is a line

$$\{\mathbf{P}: \mathbf{P} = \mathbf{P}_1 + t(\mathbf{P}_2 - \mathbf{P}_1) \text{ for some } t\}$$

which contains both $\mathbf{P}_1$ (set $t = 0$) and $\mathbf{P}_2$ (set $t = 1$). (See Fig. 29.) The points obtained with $0 \leq t \leq 1$ form the *line segment* from $\mathbf{P}_1$ to $\mathbf{P}_2$; the *midpoint* of the segment, obtained with $t = \frac{1}{2}$, is the point

$$\mathbf{M} = \mathbf{P}_1 + \tfrac{1}{2}(\mathbf{P}_2 - \mathbf{P}_1) = \tfrac{1}{2}(\mathbf{P}_1 + \mathbf{P}_2).$$

The term "midpoint" is justified since $|\mathbf{P}_1 - \mathbf{M}| = |\mathbf{P}_2 - \mathbf{M}|$, as you can easily check.

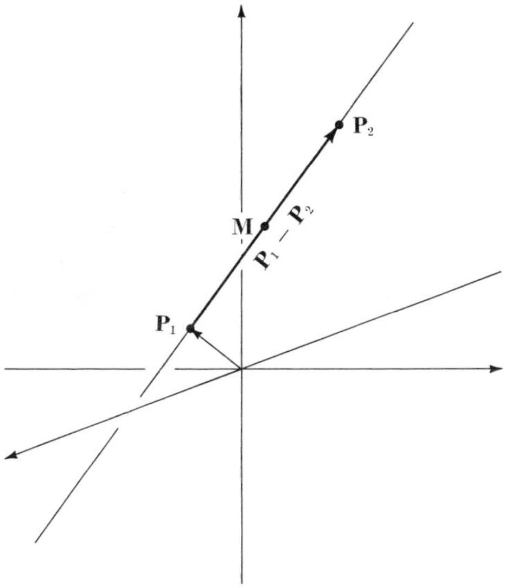

FIGURE 1.29

Now that we have defined spheres, planes, and lines, we could prove algebraically all the classical axioms and theorems of Euclidean solid geometry, but that would be a long and somewhat irrelevant detour. The main objective is to understand the translation of geometric statements into vector language and vice versa, and to be familiar with algebraically based proofs. This is the point of the following examples and problems.

Example 1. The y axis is defined as the set $\{(x,y,z): x = 0 \text{ and } z = 0\}$. Prove that the plane $\{(x,y,z): x + 3z = 0\}$ contains the y axis. ***Solution.*** If (x,y,z) is any point on the y axis, then $x = 0$ and $z = 0$; hence $x + 3z = 0$, and (x,y,z) is in the given plane.

Example 2. Do the following two lines intersect?

$$\{\mathbf{P}: \mathbf{P} = (0,1,-1) + t(-3,4,5)\} \quad \text{and} \quad \{\mathbf{Q}: \mathbf{Q} = (0,-1,1) + t(4,3,2)\}.$$

Solution. The lines might intersect in a point **R** even though **P** and **Q** do not "arrive at **R** at the same time," so we have to use different parameters t and s for the two lines. The question is, are there numbers t and s such that

$$(0,1,-1) + t(-3,4,5) = (0,-1,1) + s(4,3,2)\ ?$$

This vector equation is equivalent to the three simultaneous equations obtained by equating components:

$$\begin{aligned} 0 - 3t &= 0 + 4s \\ 1 + 4t &= -1 + 3s \\ -1 + 5t &= 1 + 2s. \end{aligned} \tag{5}$$

The first equation says that $s = -3t/4$, and then the second gives $1 + 4t = -1 - 9t/4$, or $t = -8/25$. Thus, if the equations (5) have any solution at all, it must be $t = -8/25$ and $s = -3t/4 = 6/25$. But these values do *not* satisfy the third equation, so there is no solution. Hence the lines do not intersect.

Example 3. Find the equation of a plane through the three points $\mathbf{P}_0 = (0,0,0)$, $\mathbf{P}_1 = (1,1,1)$, $\mathbf{P}_2 = (-1,1,1)$.

First Method. We use the definition of a plane as the set with equation $ax + by + cz = d$. The constants a, b, c, d must be chosen so that the three given points lie on the plane: thus

$$\begin{aligned} a\cdot 0 + b\cdot 0 + c\cdot 0 &= d \qquad (\mathbf{P}_0 \text{ is on the plane}) \\ a + b + c &= d \qquad (\mathbf{P}_1 \text{ is on the plane}) \\ a\cdot(-1) + b + c &= d \qquad (\mathbf{P}_2 \text{ is on the plane}). \end{aligned}$$

These are three homogeneous equations in four unknowns, so they have lots of solutions. One solution is $a = 0$, $b = 1$, $c = -1$, $d = 0$; hence

$$\{(x,y,z): y - z = 0\} \tag{6}$$

is a plane containing $\mathbf{P}_0$, $\mathbf{P}_1$, and $\mathbf{P}_2$.

Second Method. We use equation (3). A point $\mathbf{P}_0$ is already given, so we only have to find a normal **N**. Since $\mathbf{P}_1 - \mathbf{P}_0$ and $\mathbf{P}_2 - \mathbf{P}_0$ should both be perpendicular to **N**, we take **N** to be their cross product:

$$\mathbf{N} = (\mathbf{P}_1 - \mathbf{P}_0) \times (\mathbf{P}_2 - \mathbf{P}_0) = (1,1,1) \times (-1,1,1) = (0,-2,2).$$

Thus the desired plane has the equation $\mathbf{N}\cdot(\mathbf{P} - \mathbf{P}_0) = 0$, which with $\mathbf{N} = (0,-2,2)$, $\mathbf{P} = (x,y,z)$, $\mathbf{P}_0 = (0,0,0)$ reduces to $-2y + 2z = 0$. This is not exactly the same as the equation we found in (6), $y - z - 0$; but the two equations have the same solutions, so they define the same plane. It is sketched in Fig. 26.

Example 4. The line $\{\mathbf{P}: \mathbf{P} = \mathbf{A} + t\mathbf{B}\}$ is called *orthogonal* to the plane $\{\mathbf{P}: \mathbf{P}\cdot\mathbf{N} = d\}$ if and only if **B** and **N** are parallel. Find a line passing through $(-1,3,2)$ and orthogonal to the plane with equation

$$x + 2y - z = 5. \tag{7}$$

Solution. The normal to the plane can be read off from the coefficients of x, y, and z in equation (7); it is $\mathbf{N} = (1,2-1)$. Hence the desired line is

$$\{\mathbf{P}: \mathbf{P} = (-1,3,2) + t(1,2,-1)\}.$$

PROBLEMS

The first twelve problems give plenty of routine practice with lines and planes. The remaining eleven problems illustrate the vector approach to solid geometry: tangents to a sphere, distance from a point to a plane, a line as the intersection of two planes, two points determine a line, direction cosines, triangles, tetrahedra, cones.

1. Find parametric equations of lines through the following pairs of points, and find the midpoint of the segment between each pair.
(a) $(-5,-6,8)$ and $(1,3,7)$
(b) $(2,4,6)$ and $(1,2,3)$
(c) $(1,3,10)$ and $(-3,6,-2)$
(d) $(10,3,1)$ and $(6,-2,-3)$

2. For each of the following equations, find a normal vector to the corresponding plane, and find any point $\mathbf{P}_0$ on the plane.
(a) $x + y + z = 1$
(b) $2x + 3y - z = 2$
(c) $(x - 2) + 3(y - 5) - 4(z + 1) = 0$

3. Find an equation of a plane through the three given points $\mathbf{P}_0$, $\mathbf{P}_1$, $\mathbf{P}_2$.
(a) $\mathbf{P}_0 = (1,0,0)$, $\mathbf{P}_1 = (0,1,0)$, $\mathbf{P}_2 = (0,0,1)$
(b) $\mathbf{P}_0 = (1,0,0)$, $\mathbf{P}_1 = (-1,0,0)$, $\mathbf{P}_2 = (0,1,0)$
(c) $\mathbf{P}_0 = (0,1,0)$, $\mathbf{P}_1 = (0,2,0)$, $\mathbf{P}_2 = (0,0,-1)$

4. (a) Prove (algebraically) that the plane in Problem 3(b) contains the x axis, the set $\{(x,y,z) : y = 0 \text{ and } z = 0\}$. Sketch the three points in 3(b), and sketch the plane.
(b) Prove (algebraically) that the plane in Problem 3(c) contains the y axis. Sketch the three points in 3(c), and sketch the plane.
(c) Prove that the plane in Problem 3(a) does not contain the origin.

5. (a) Prove that the x axis is a line, by finding parametric equations for it.
(b) Do the same for the y axis and z axis.

6. Find a point of intersection of the following two lines:

$$\{\mathbf{P}: \mathbf{P} = (1,-5,2) + t(-3,4,0)\} \quad \text{and} \quad \{\mathbf{P}: \mathbf{P} = (3,-13,1) + t(4,0,1)\}.$$

7. Prove that the line $\{\mathbf{P}: \mathbf{P} = (1,3,-1) + t(0,3,5)\}$ lies entirely in the plane $\{(x,y,z): 2x - 5y + 3z = -16\}$.

8. Suppose that $\mathbf{P}_1$ and $\mathbf{P}_2$ lie on the plane $\{\mathbf{P}: \mathbf{P}\cdot\mathbf{N} = d\}$. Prove that every point of the line $\{\mathbf{P}: \mathbf{P} = \mathbf{P}_1 + t(\mathbf{P}_2 - \mathbf{P}_1)\}$ lies in the given plane.

9. (a) The two lines $\{\mathbf{P}: \mathbf{P} = (-2,4,6) + t(1,2,3)\}$ and $\{\mathbf{P}: \mathbf{P} = (-2,4,6) + t(3,2,1)\}$ intersect in the point $\mathbf{P}_0 = (-2,4,6)$. Find the equation of a plane containing the two lines. (Since you have $\mathbf{P}_0$, all you need is the normal $\mathbf{N}$.)

(b) Suppose that $\mathbf{B}$ and $\mathbf{C}$ are nonzero and not parallel. Prove that there is a plane containing the two lines $\{\mathbf{P}: \mathbf{P} = \mathbf{A} + t\mathbf{B}\}$ and $\{\mathbf{P}: \mathbf{P} = \mathbf{A} + t\mathbf{C}\}$.

10. Find all points of intersection of the given line and the given plane.

(a) $\{\mathbf{P}: \mathbf{P} = t(1,-3,6)\}$ and $\{\mathbf{P}: x + 3y + z = 2\}$

(b) $\{\mathbf{P}: \mathbf{P} = (1,-3,6) + t(1,0,0)\}$ and $\{\mathbf{P}: z = 6\}$

(c) $\{\mathbf{P}: \mathbf{P} = (1,-3,6) + t(1,0,0)\}$ and $\{\mathbf{P}: z = 0\}$

11. (a) Prove that if $\mathbf{B}\cdot\mathbf{N} \neq 0$, then the line $\{\mathbf{P}: \mathbf{P} = \mathbf{A} + t\mathbf{B}\}$ intersects the plane $\{\mathbf{P}: (\mathbf{P} - \mathbf{P}_0)\cdot\mathbf{N} = 0\}$ in exactly one point. (See Problem 10(a).)

(b) Prove that if $\mathbf{B}\cdot\mathbf{N} = 0$ and $\mathbf{A}$ is on the plane $\{\mathbf{P}: (\mathbf{P} - \mathbf{P}_0)\cdot\mathbf{N} = 0\}$, then the entire line $\{\mathbf{P}: \mathbf{P} = \mathbf{A} + t\mathbf{B}\}$ lies in the plane. (See Problem 10(b).)

(c) Prove that if $\mathbf{B}\cdot\mathbf{N} = 0$ and $\mathbf{A}$ is *not* on the plane

$$\{\mathbf{P}: (\mathbf{P} - \mathbf{P}_0)\cdot\mathbf{N} = 0\},$$

then the line $\{\mathbf{P}: \mathbf{P} = \mathbf{A} + t\mathbf{B}\}$ does not intersect the plane in any point. (See Problem 10(c).)

(d) Draw sketches illustrating parts (a), (b), and (c). (The line is called *parallel* to the plane when $\mathbf{B}\cdot\mathbf{N} = 0$. You have proved a *theorem*: A line L and a plane Π intersect in a single point if and only if they are not parallel.)

12. The line $\{\mathbf{P}: \mathbf{P} = \mathbf{A} + t\mathbf{B}\}$ is called *normal* to the plane

$$\{\mathbf{P}: (\mathbf{P} - \mathbf{P}_0)\cdot\mathbf{N} = 0\}$$

if and only if $\mathbf{B}$ is parallel to $\mathbf{N}$.

(a) Find a line through the point $\mathbf{P}_1 = (-5,2,1)$ and normal to the plane $\{(x,y,z): x = y\}$.

(b) Find the intersection $\mathbf{P}_2$ of the line and plane in part (a).

(c) Show that $|\mathbf{P}_2 - \mathbf{P}_1| = (\mathbf{P}_1 - \mathbf{P}_0)_{\mathbf{N}}$, where $\mathbf{P}_0 = \mathbf{0}$.

(d) Sketch the plane, $\mathbf{N}$, $\mathbf{P}_0$, $\mathbf{P}_1$, and $\mathbf{P}_2$.

13. (a) Find a line through a given point $\mathbf{P}_1 = (x_1,y_1,z_1)$ and normal to the plane $\{(x,y,z): ax + by + cz = d\}$.

(b) Find the point $\mathbf{P}_0$ in which the line and plane in part (a) intersect.

(c) Prove that if $\mathbf{P}$ is any point on the plane in part (a), and $\mathbf{P}_0$ is the point found in (b), then $\mathbf{P}_1 - \mathbf{P}_0$ is orthogonal to $\mathbf{P} - \mathbf{P}_0$. Sketch this situation.

(d) Continuing part (c), prove that if $\mathbf{P}$ is any point on the plane, then $|\mathbf{P}_1 - \mathbf{P}|^2 \geq |\mathbf{P}_1 - \mathbf{P}_0|^2$. (Hint: Use the Pythagorean theorem.)

(e) Part (d) shows that $|\mathbf{P}_1 - \mathbf{P}_0|$ is the distance from the point $\mathbf{P}_1$ to the plane $\{(x,y,z): ax + by + cz = d\}$. Show that this distance is

$$\frac{|ax_1 + by_1 + cz_1 - d|}{\sqrt{a^2 + b^2 + c^2}}.$$

14. Let $\mathbf{P}_0$ be a point on the sphere $\{\mathbf{P}: |\mathbf{P}| = r\}$. Prove that the line $\{\mathbf{P}: \mathbf{P} = \mathbf{P}_0 + t\mathbf{B}\}$ intersects the sphere in two distinct points unless $\mathbf{B} \cdot \mathbf{P}_0 = 0$.

15. (a) Suppose that $\mathbf{P}_0$ lies on the sphere

$$\{\mathbf{P}: |\mathbf{P}| = r\}. \tag{8}$$

Prove that the plane $\{\mathbf{P}: (\mathbf{P} - \mathbf{P}_0) \cdot \mathbf{P}_0 = 0\}$ intersects the sphere *only* at $\mathbf{P}_0$. (Hint: Assuming $\mathbf{P}$ is on the plane, you can compute $|\mathbf{P}|$ by setting $\mathbf{P} = \mathbf{P}_0 + (\mathbf{P} - \mathbf{P}_0)$ and using the Pythagorean theorem.)

(b) Suppose that $\mathbf{P}_0$ lies on the sphere (8), and

$$\{\mathbf{P}: (\mathbf{P} - \mathbf{P}_0) \cdot \mathbf{N} = 0\} \tag{9}$$

is a plane through $\mathbf{P}_0$. Prove that there is a point $\mathbf{P}_1$ which lies on the sphere (8), on the plane (9), and on the line

$$\{\mathbf{P}: \mathbf{P} = -\mathbf{P}_0 + t\mathbf{N}\}. \qquad \text{(See Fig. 30.)}$$

(c) In part (b), prove that $\mathbf{P}_1 = \mathbf{P}_0$ if and only if $\mathbf{N}$ is parallel to $\mathbf{P}_0$.

(d) Conclude that the plane (9) intersects the sphere (8) in more than one point, unless $\mathbf{P}_0$ is normal to the plane (9). (When $\mathbf{P}_0$ is normal to it, the plane is called *tangent* to the sphere.)

16. Let $\mathbf{A} = (1,8,2)$ and $\mathbf{B} = (-3,1,1)$.

(a) Write out the equation $\mathbf{P} = \mathbf{A} + t\mathbf{B}$ by components, setting $\mathbf{P} = (x,y,z)$.

(b) Show that

$$\mathbf{P} = \mathbf{A} + t\mathbf{B} \quad \text{for some } t$$

if and only if

$$x = 7 - 3z \qquad \text{and} \qquad y = 6 + z.$$

(Hint: Eliminate t from the equation in part (a). Part (b) proves that the line $\{\mathbf{P}: \mathbf{P} = \mathbf{A} + t\mathbf{B}\}$ is the intersection of two planes.)

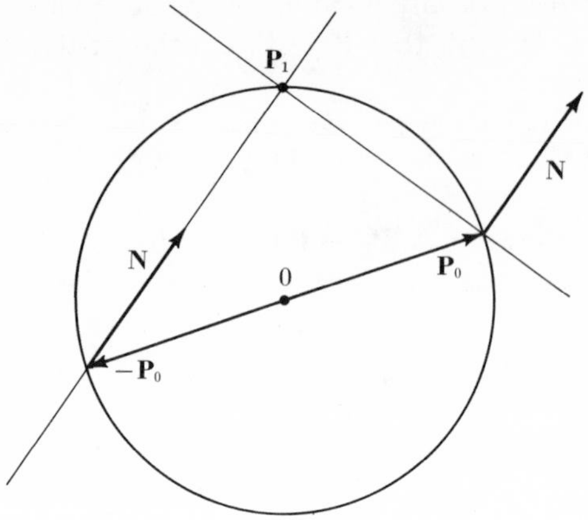

FIGURE 1.30

17. Prove that every line is the intersection of two planes. (See the previous problem.)

18. Given two distinct points $\mathbf{P}_1$ and $\mathbf{P}_2$, prove that the set

$$\{\mathbf{P}: |\mathbf{P} - \mathbf{P}_1| = |\mathbf{P} - \mathbf{P}_2|\}$$

is a plane containing $\frac{1}{2}(\mathbf{P}_1 + \mathbf{P}_2)$, with normal $\mathbf{P}_2 - \mathbf{P}_1$. Draw an appropriate sketch.

19. The *direction cosines* of the line $\{\mathbf{P}: \mathbf{P} = \mathbf{A} + t\mathbf{B}\}$ are the cosines of the angles between $\mathbf{B}$ and the three basic unit vectors $\mathbf{E}_1$, $\mathbf{E}_2$, $\mathbf{E}_3$, as shown in Fig. 31.

(a) Show that

$$\cos\alpha = \frac{b_1}{|\mathbf{B}|}, \qquad \cos\beta = \frac{b_2}{|\mathbf{B}|}, \qquad \cos\gamma = \frac{b_3}{|\mathbf{B}|}.$$

(b) Show that if $\mathbf{P}_1 = (x_1,y_1,z_1)$ and $\mathbf{P}_2 = (x_2,y_2,z_2)$ are any two points on the line $\{\mathbf{P}: \mathbf{P} = \mathbf{A} + t\mathbf{B}\}$, then the direction cosines are either

$$\cos\alpha = \frac{x_1 - x_2}{|\mathbf{P}_1 - \mathbf{P}_2|}, \qquad \cos\beta = \frac{y_1 - y_2}{|\mathbf{P}_1 - \mathbf{P}_2|}, \qquad \cos\gamma = \frac{z_1 - z_2}{|\mathbf{P}_1 - \mathbf{P}_2|},$$

or

$$\cos\alpha = \frac{x_2 - x_1}{|\mathbf{P}_2 - \mathbf{P}_1|}, \qquad \cos\beta = \frac{y_2 - y_1}{|\mathbf{P}_2 - \mathbf{P}_1|}, \qquad \cos\gamma = \frac{z_2 - z_1}{|\mathbf{P}_2 - \mathbf{P}_1|}.$$

(c) Find direction cosines of a line through the points $(-8,3,5)$ and $(6,1,0)$.

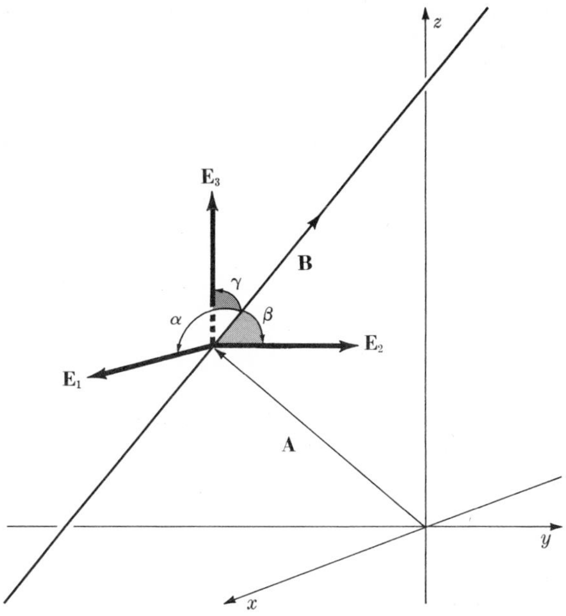

FIGURE 1.31

20. The *triangle* with three given vertices $\mathbf{P}_1$, $\mathbf{P}_2$, and $\mathbf{P}_3$ is the set

$$\{\mathbf{P}: \mathbf{P} = t_1\mathbf{P}_1 + t_2\mathbf{P}_2 + t_3\mathbf{P}_3,\ t_j \geq 0,\ \sum_{j=1}^{3} t_j = 1\}. \tag{10}$$

For example, taking $t_1 = 1$, $t_2 = 0$, $t_3 = 0$, we find that $1\cdot\mathbf{P}_1 + 0\cdot\mathbf{P}_2 + 0\cdot\mathbf{P}_3 = \mathbf{P}_1$ is in the triangle. Taking $t_1 = t_2 = t_3 = \frac{1}{3}$, we obtain the *barycenter* $\mathbf{C}$ of the triangle:

$$\mathbf{C} = \tfrac{1}{3}\mathbf{P}_1 + \tfrac{1}{3}\mathbf{P}_2 + \tfrac{1}{3}\mathbf{P}_3.$$

(See Fig. 32.)

(a) Prove that the vertex $\mathbf{P}_2$ is in the triangle (10); i.e. find nonnegative numbers t_1, t_2, t_3 such that $\sum_{j=1}^{3} t_j = 1$ and

$$\mathbf{P}_2 = t_1\mathbf{P}_1 + t_2\mathbf{P}_2 + t_3\mathbf{P}_3.$$

(b) Show that $\mathbf{P}_3$ is in the triangle; show also that the midpoint of the segment from $\mathbf{P}_1$ to $\mathbf{P}_2$ is in the triangle.

(c) Let $\mathbf{M}_3$ denote the midpoint found in part (b). Prove that the segment from $\mathbf{P}_3$ to $\mathbf{M}_3$ lies in the triangle. (This segment is called a *median* of the triangle.)

(d) Prove that the median in part (c) contains the barycenter $\mathbf{C}$.
(e) Prove that all three medians of the triangle interesect at $\mathbf{C}$.

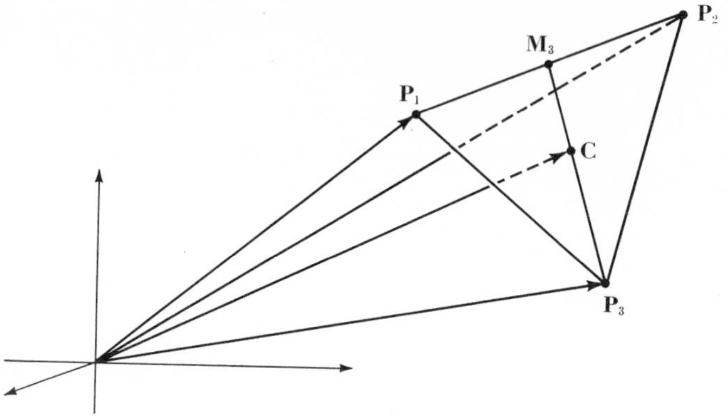

FIGURE 1.32

21. Four points $\mathbf{P}_1$, $\mathbf{P}_2$, $\mathbf{P}_3$, $\mathbf{P}_4$ determine a *tetrahedron*

$$T = \{\mathbf{P}\colon \mathbf{P} = \sum_1^4 t_j\mathbf{P}_j\,,\ t_j \geq 0,\ \sum_1^4 t_j = 1\},$$

a polygonal solid with four triangular faces and the four vertices $\mathbf{P}_1$, $\mathbf{P}_2$, $\mathbf{P}_3$, $\mathbf{P}_4$. The *barycenter* of the tetrahedron is the point

$$\mathbf{C} = \sum_1^4 \tfrac{1}{4}\mathbf{P}_j\,.$$

(a) Prove that T contains the triangle with vertices $\mathbf{P}_1$, $\mathbf{P}_2$, $\mathbf{P}_3$. (See the previous problem.)
(b) Prove that $\mathbf{P}$ contains the segment from $\mathbf{P}_4$ to the barycenter of the triangle in part (a). (This segment is a *median* of the tetrahedron.)
(c) Prove that the barycenter $\mathbf{C}$ lies on the median in part (b).
(d) Prove that the barycenter $\mathbf{C}$ lies on the intersection of all four medians of T.
(e) Prove that if $\mathbf{Q}_1$ and $\mathbf{Q}_2$ are any two points in T, then T contains the entire segment between $\mathbf{Q}_1$ and $\mathbf{Q}_2$.

22. This problem proves that "two points determine a line" by showing that if $\mathbf{A} + t\mathbf{B}$ is any line containing the two distinct points $\mathbf{P}_1$ and $\mathbf{P}_2$, then

$$\{\mathbf{P}\colon \mathbf{P} = \mathbf{A} + t\mathbf{B} \text{ for some } t\} \tag{11}$$

is exactly the same set as

$$\{\mathbf{P}: \mathbf{P} = \mathbf{P}_1 + s(\mathbf{P}_2 - \mathbf{P}_1)\} \text{ for some } s\}. \tag{12}$$

(a) Suppose that $\mathbf{P}_1$ and $\mathbf{P}_2$ lie on the line (11). Prove that there are two *distinct* numbers t_1 and t_2 such that $\mathbf{P}_1 = \mathbf{A} + t_1\mathbf{B}$ and $\mathbf{P}_2 = \mathbf{A} + t_2\mathbf{B}$.

(b) Prove that

$$\mathbf{B} = \frac{1}{t_2 - t_1}(\mathbf{P}_2 - \mathbf{P}_1) \quad \text{and} \quad \mathbf{A} = \mathbf{P}_1 - \frac{t_1}{t_2 - t_1}(\mathbf{P}_2 - \mathbf{P}_1).$$

(c) Prove that

$$\mathbf{A} + t\mathbf{B} = \mathbf{P}_1 + \frac{t - t_1}{t_2 - t_1}(\mathbf{P}_2 - \mathbf{P}_1),$$

and conclude that every point on the line (11) lies on the line (12).

(d) Prove, conversely, that every point on (12) lies on (11).

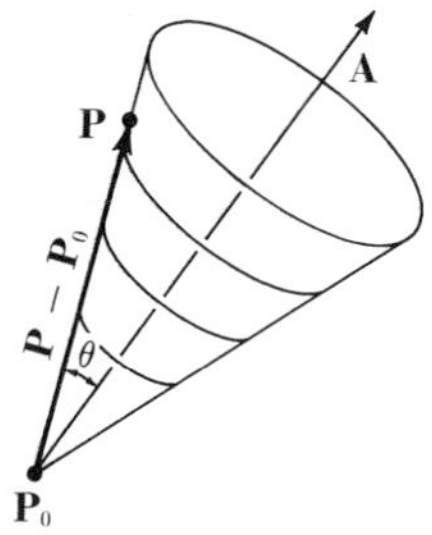

FIGURE 1.33

23. Given a point $\mathbf{P}_0$, a vector $\mathbf{A}$, and a number θ, the equation

$$(\mathbf{P} - \mathbf{P}_0)\cdot\mathbf{A} = |\mathbf{A}| \cos\theta\, |\mathbf{P} - \mathbf{P}_0|$$

defines a *single cone* with *vertex* $\mathbf{P}_0$, *axial direction* $\mathbf{A}$, and *angle* θ. (See Fig. 33.) The equation

$$|(\mathbf{P} - \mathbf{P}_0)\cdot\mathbf{A}| = |\mathbf{A}|\, |\cos\theta|\, |\mathbf{P} - \mathbf{P}_0|$$

defines the corresponding *double cone.*

(a) Prove that if $\theta = \pi/2$, the "cone" is actually a plane.

(b) Prove that if $\theta = 0$, the "double cone" is actually the line $\{\mathbf{P}: \mathbf{P} = \mathbf{P}_0 + t\mathbf{A}\}$.

(c) Let $\mathbf{P}_0 = (0,0,2)$, $\mathbf{A} = (0,1,-1)$, $\theta = \pi/4$, and find the intersection of the corresponding cone with the xy plane. (This is a familiar parabola.)

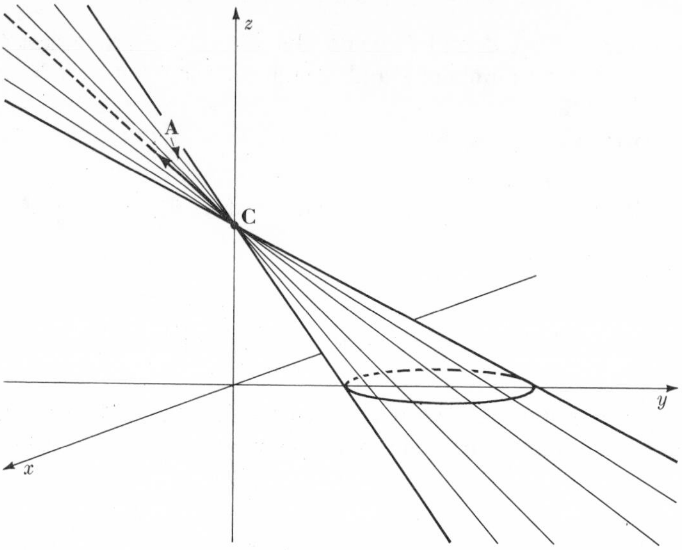

FIGURE 1.34

(d) Let $\mathbf{P}_0 = (0,0,2)$, $\mathbf{A} = (0,-1,1)$, and θ be arbitrary; find the intersection of the resulting double cone with the xy plane. (For $\theta < \pi/4$, this is an ellipse

$$\frac{x^2}{a^2} + \frac{(y - y_0)^2}{b^2} = 1,$$

and for $\theta > \pi/4$, it is a hyperbola

$$-\frac{x^2}{a^2} + \frac{(y - y_0)^2}{b^2} = 1.$$

See Fig. 34.)

(e) Prove that every double cone is defined by a quadratic equation

$$ax^2 + bxy + cxz + dy^2 + eyz + fz^2 + gx + hy + iz + j = 0.$$

(However, not all quadratic equations define cones; for example, a sphere is defined by a quadratic equation, but a sphere is not a cone. From part (e) it follows that the intersection of any double cone with the xy plane is determined by the equation $z = 0$ and a quadratic in x and y,

$$ax^2 + bxy + dy^2 + gx + hy + j = 0.)$$

1.4 THE VECTOR SPACE R^n

R^3 is surely the most interesting vector space because it reflects faithfully the three-dimensional space around us. But vector analysis neither starts nor stops there; we need the plane R^2, the four-dimensional space R^4, and in fact we need R^n for every positive integer n.

Fortunately, almost everything can be done in R^n just as in R^3. A point, or vector, is an ordered n-tuple of real numbers, $\mathbf{A} = (a_1, \ldots, a_n)$, $\mathbf{X} = (x_1, \ldots, x_n)$, etc. *Addition* is defined by

$$\mathbf{A} + \mathbf{B} = (a_1 + b_1, a_2 + b_2, \ldots, a_n + b_n),$$

subtraction by

$$\mathbf{A} - \mathbf{B} = (a_1 - b_1, \ldots, a_n - b_n),$$

scalar multiplication by

$$t\mathbf{A} = (ta_1, ta_2, \ldots, ta_n),$$

the *inner product* by

$$\mathbf{A}\cdot\mathbf{B} = a_1b_1 + \cdots + a_nb_n = \sum_1^n a_jb_j,$$

and the *length* by

$$|\mathbf{A}| = (\mathbf{A}\cdot\mathbf{A})^{1/2} = \left(\sum_1^n a_j^2\right)^{1/2}.$$

The *zero vector* is $(0, 0, \ldots, 0)$, denoted $\mathbf{0}$.

The facts about R^3 established in §1.1 hold equally well for R^n. The proofs are exactly the same as before; we merely list the most important results for reference.

Theorem 4. *Let* $\mathbf{A}$, $\mathbf{B}$, *and* $\mathbf{C}$ *be any vectors in* R^n, *and let* t *and* s *be any real numbers. Then*

$$t(s\mathbf{A}) = (ts)\mathbf{A} \tag{1}$$

$$(\mathbf{A} + \mathbf{B}) + \mathbf{C} = \mathbf{A} + (\mathbf{B} + \mathbf{C}) \tag{2}$$

$$t(\mathbf{A}\cdot\mathbf{B}) = (t\mathbf{A})\cdot\mathbf{B} = \mathbf{A}\cdot(t\mathbf{B}) \tag{3}$$

$$\mathbf{A} + \mathbf{B} = \mathbf{B} + \mathbf{A} \tag{4}$$

$$\mathbf{A}\cdot\mathbf{B} = \mathbf{B}\cdot\mathbf{A} \tag{5}$$

$$(\mathbf{A} + \mathbf{B})\cdot\mathbf{C} = \mathbf{A}\cdot\mathbf{C} + \mathbf{B}\cdot\mathbf{C} \tag{6}$$

$$\mathbf{A} + \mathbf{0} = \mathbf{A} \tag{7}$$

$$1\mathbf{A} = \mathbf{A} \tag{8}$$

$$|\mathbf{A}| = 0 \Leftrightarrow \mathbf{A} = \mathbf{0} \tag{9}$$

$$|t\mathbf{A}| = |t|\cdot|\mathbf{A}| \tag{10}$$

$$|\mathbf{A}\cdot\mathbf{B}| \le |\mathbf{A}|\cdot|\mathbf{B}| \tag{11}$$

$$|\mathbf{A} + \mathbf{B}| \le |\mathbf{A}| + |\mathbf{B}|. \tag{12}$$

Notice - No cross product

The Schwarz inequality (11) shows that $\mathbf{A}\cdot\mathbf{B}/|\mathbf{A}|\cdot|\mathbf{B}|$ lies between -1 and 1, so we can define the angle between $\mathbf{A}$ and $\mathbf{B}$ by

$$\cos\theta = \frac{\mathbf{A}\cdot\mathbf{B}}{|\mathbf{A}|\cdot|\mathbf{B}|};$$

hence

$$\mathbf{A}\cdot\mathbf{B} = |\mathbf{A}|\cdot|\mathbf{B}|\cos\theta. \tag{13}$$

$\mathbf{A}$ and $\mathbf{B}$ are *orthogonal* if $\mathbf{A}\cdot\mathbf{B} = 0$, and *parallel* if one vector is a scalar multiple of the other.

We visualize vectors in R^2 as arrows or points in the plane, and vectors in R^3 as arrows or points in three-space, but beginning with R^4 there is no such concrete geometric image. We either forget about visualization, or cheat a little and continue to imagine n-dimensional vectors as if they were in R^2 or R^3. The terminology used for R^n reflects this. For example, the set $\{\mathbf{X}: |\mathbf{X} - \mathbf{A}| < r\}$ is called the *open ball* (or open disk) *of radius r with center* $\mathbf{A}$, and its boundary $\{\mathbf{X}: |\mathbf{X} - \mathbf{A}| = r\}$ is called the *sphere* of radius r with center $\mathbf{A}$. (In R^2, such a "sphere" is really a circle.)

A *line* in R^n is any set of the form

$$\{\mathbf{X}: \mathbf{X} = \mathbf{A} + t\mathbf{B} \text{ for some } t\}$$

where $\mathbf{A}$ and $\mathbf{B}$ are fixed vectors in R^n and $\mathbf{B} \neq \mathbf{0}$.

Any set of the form $\{\mathbf{X}: \mathbf{X}\cdot\mathbf{N} = d\}$, where $\mathbf{N}$ is a given nonzero vector and d is a given constant, is called a *hyperplane*. In R^2 a hyperplane is a line, and in R^3 it is an ordinary plane. In general, we think of a hyperplane in R^n as something that looks like R^{n-1}. For example, in R^4 the set of all vectors $(x,y,z,0)$ is a hyperplane, since it is obtained by taking $N = (0,0,0,1)$ and $d = 0$ in the definition $\{\mathbf{X}: \mathbf{X}\cdot\mathbf{N} = d\}$; this set looks very much like R^3, i.e., like the set of all vectors (x,y,z).

The cross product has been defined only in R^3, where it solved the problem of finding a nonzero vector orthogonal to two given (nonparallel) vectors. The corresponding problem in R^n is to find a nonzero vector orthogonal to $n - 1$ given vectors $\mathbf{A}_1, \ldots, \mathbf{A}_{n-1}$. It is not necessary to have an explicit solution like the cross product, but it *is* important to know that the problem can always be solved.

Theorem 5. *Given any k vectors $\mathbf{A}_1, \ldots, \mathbf{A}_k$ in R^n, $k < n$, there is a nonzero vector $\mathbf{X}$ orthogonal to each of $\mathbf{A}_1, \ldots, \mathbf{A}_k$.*

To prove the theorem, we rephrase the result in terms of simultaneous linear equations. Denote the components of the jth given vector $\mathbf{A}_j$ by $a_{j1}, \ldots, a_{jn}$. Then the required orthogonality conditions

$$\begin{aligned} \mathbf{A}_1\cdot\mathbf{X} &= 0, \\ \vdots \quad & \quad \vdots \\ \mathbf{A}_k\cdot\mathbf{X} &= 0 \end{aligned}$$

are equivalent to the system of k simultaneous linear homogeneous equations

$$\begin{aligned} a_{11}x_1 + \cdots + a_{1n}x_n &= 0 \\ \vdots \qquad\qquad \vdots \quad &\quad \vdots \\ a_{k1}x_1 + \cdots + a_{kn}x_n &= 0. \end{aligned}$$

Thus Theorem 5 is equivalent to the following basic result:

Theorem 6. *Any system of k simultaneous linear homogeneous equations in n unknowns $x_1, \ldots, x_n$, with $k < n$, has a nonzero solution.*

Proof. We use induction on k, the number of equations.

(i) When $k = 1$, we are solving a single equation

$$a_{11}x_1 + a_{12}x_2 + \cdots + a_{1n}x_n = 0 \tag{14}$$

with $n > 1$. If $a_{11} = 0$, there is a nonzero solution $x_1 = 1, x_2 = 0, \ldots, x_n = 0$. If $a_{11} \neq 0$, we can set $x_2 = 1, x_3 = 0, \ldots, x_n = 0$, and $x_1 = -a_{12}/a_{11}$.

(ii) Suppose that Theorem 6 is true for systems of $k - 1$ equations in m unknowns whenever $m > k - 1$. We then want to prove it for an arbitrary system of k equations in n unknowns

$$a_{11}x_1 + \cdots + a_{1n}x_n = 0 \tag{15_1}$$

$$a_{21}x_1 + \cdots + a_{2n}x_n = 0 \tag{15_2}$$

$$\vdots$$

$$a_{k1}x_1 + \cdots + a_{kn}x_n = 0, \tag{15_k}$$

where $n > k$. If the coefficients $a_{11}, \ldots, a_{k1}$ in the first column are all zero, we obtain a nonzero solution of (15) simply by setting

$$x_1 = 1, x_2 = 0, \ldots, x_n = 0.$$

Suppose, then, that one of the coefficients in the first column is different from zero. By relabeling the equations, we can assume that a_{11} is different from zero. Now eliminate x_1 from the last $k - 1$ equations in (15) by subtracting appropriate multiples of the first equation, obtaining

$$\left(a_{22} - \frac{a_{21}a_{12}}{a_{11}}\right)x_2 + \cdots + \left(a_{2n} - \frac{a_{21}a_{1n}}{a_{11}}\right)x_n = 0 \tag{16_2}$$

$$\vdots$$

$$\left(a_{k2} - \frac{a_{k1}a_{12}}{a_{11}}\right)x_2 + \cdots + \left(a_{kn} - \frac{a_{k1}a_{1n}}{a_{11}}\right)x_n = 0. \tag{16_k}$$

This is a set of $k - 1$ simultaneous linear homogeneous equations in the $n - 1$ unknowns $x_2, \ldots, x_n$, and $n - 1 > k - 1$. Since we are supposing Theorem 6 to be true for systems of $k - 1$ equations, the system (16) has a nonzero solution. Let $x_2, \ldots, x_n$ stand for this solution, and set

$$x_1 = -\frac{1}{a_{11}}(a_{12}x_2 + \cdots + a_{1n}x_n). \tag{17}$$

Then $(x_1, \ldots, x_n)$ obviously satisfies equation (15_1), and together (16) and (17) show that the other equations in (15) are satisfied too. For example, (15_2) follows from (16_2) and (17), since

$$\begin{aligned} a_{21}x_1 &+ a_{22}x_2 + \cdots + a_{2n}x_n \\ &= -\frac{a_{21}}{a_{11}}(a_{12}x_2 + \cdots + a_{1n}x_n) + a_{22}x_2 + \cdots + a_{2n}x_n \quad \text{(by (17))} \\ &= \left(a_{22} - \frac{a_{21}a_{12}}{a_{11}}\right)x_2 + \cdots + \left(a_{2n} - \frac{a_{21}a_{1n}}{a_{11}}\right)x_n = 0. \quad \text{(by } (16_2)) \end{aligned}$$

Example 1. Find a nonzero vector **X** orthogonal to $(-1,2)$. *Solution.* Following the first step in the proof of Theorem 6, we find $\mathbf{X} = (2,1)$.

Example 2. Find a nonzero vector **X** orthogonal to (1,2,3,4), (2,3,4,5), and (3,4,5,6). *Solution.* If $\mathbf{X} = (x_1, \ldots, x_4)$, we have to solve

$$x_1 + 2x_2 + 3x_3 + 4x_4 = 0 \tag{18_1}$$

$$2x_1 + 3x_2 + 4x_3 + 5x_4 = 0 \tag{18_2}$$

$$3x_1 + 4x_2 + 5x_3 + 6x_4 = 0. \tag{18_3}$$

Eliminating x_1 from the last two equations (as in the proof of Theorem 6), we get

$$-x_2 - 2x_3 - 3x_4 = 0 \tag{19_1}$$

$$-2x_2 - 4x_3 - 6x_4 = 0. \tag{19_2}$$

These two equations are obviously equivalent; a nonzero solution is found by taking $x_2 = 1$, $x_3 = -\frac{1}{2}$, $x_4 = 0$. Returning to (18_1), we find $x_1 = -2x_2 - 3x_3 - 4x_4 = -\frac{1}{2}$. Thus $\mathbf{X} = (-\frac{1}{2},1,-\frac{1}{2},0)$ is orthogonal to the given vectors. So is $-2\mathbf{X} = (1,-2,1,0)$.

PROBLEMS

1. Find the angle between the given pair of vectors.

(a) (1,0,0,0) and (0,1,1,3)
(b) (1,1,1,1) and (1,−1,1,1)
(c) (1,1,1,1) and (1,−1,−1,1)
(d) (4,3,2,1) and (8,6,4,2)
(e) (4,3,2,1) and (−8,−6,−4,−2)
(f) (2,−3,4,6,1) and (1,3,1,0,−3)

2. Find the intersection of the line and the hyperplane with the given equations. (The intersection may be a single point, or the whole line, or it may be empty.)

(a) $\mathbf{X} = (1,3) + t(-2,-1)$; $\mathbf{X}\cdot(1,2) = 4$
(b) $\mathbf{X} = (0,3,8,-1) + t(2,-1,3,0)$; $\mathbf{X}\cdot(1,3,2,0) = 1$
(c) $\mathbf{X} = t(3,5)$; $\mathbf{X}\cdot(5,-3) = 0$
(d) $\mathbf{X} = t(3,5)$; $\mathbf{X}\cdot(5,-3) = 1$
(e) $\mathbf{X} = t(3,5,7,2)$; $\mathbf{X}\cdot(2,4,-2,1) = 0$
(f) $\mathbf{X} = t(3,5,7,2)$; $\mathbf{X}\cdot(2,4,-2,1) = 5$

3. Find the points of intersection of the given line and the given sphere.

(a) $\mathbf{X} = (1,3) + t(-2,-1)$; $|\mathbf{X} - (1,3)| = 2$
(b) $\mathbf{X} = (1,3) + t(-2,-1)$; $|\mathbf{X}| = r$
(c) $\mathbf{X} = (0,3,8,-1) + t(2,-1,3,0)$; $|\mathbf{X}| = r$

4. (a) In Problem 3(b), choose r so that there is exactly one point of intersection. (This gives the distance from the line to the origin.)
(b) In Problem 3(c), choose r so that there is exactly one point of intersection.

5. Prove Theorem 4. (This problem has twelve parts. For hints, you can refer to the proofs in §1.1.)

6. Prove that $|\mathbf{A}| \le \sum_1^n |a_j|$

(a) by squaring both sides; or
(b) by writing

$$\mathbf{A} = (a_1,0,\ldots,0) + (0,a_2,0,\ldots,0) + \cdots + (0,\ldots,0,a_n)$$

and applying the triangle inequality.

7. Prove that $-|\mathbf{A} - \mathbf{B}| \le |\mathbf{A}| - |\mathbf{B}| \le |\mathbf{A} - \mathbf{B}|$. (Hint: To get the first inequality, notice that $|\mathbf{B}| = |\mathbf{A} + (\mathbf{B} - \mathbf{A})| \le |\mathbf{A}| + |\mathbf{B} - \mathbf{A}|$.)

8. In each case, find a nonzero vector orthogonal to the given set of vectors $\mathbf{A}_1, \ldots, \mathbf{A}_k$.

(a) $\mathbf{A}_1 = (2,-5)$
(b) $\mathbf{A}_1 = (2,3,4)$, $\mathbf{A}_2 = (-1,3,-4)$
(c) $\mathbf{A}_1 = (1,2,3)$, $\mathbf{A}_2 = (-2,-4,-6)$
(d) $\mathbf{A}_1 = (1,2,3,4)$, $\mathbf{A}_2 = (2,3,4,5)$, $\mathbf{A}_3 = (3,4,5,0)$

9. (a) Although Theorem 5 does not guarantee that there is one, try to find a nonzero vector in R^3 that is orthogonal to $\mathbf{A}_1 = (1,0,-1)$, $\mathbf{A}_2 = (0,1,3)$, and $\mathbf{A}_3 = (1,1,2)$.
(b) Prove that $\mathbf{A}_1$, $\mathbf{A}_2$, and $\mathbf{A}_3$ lie on a common plane through the origin.

10. Suppose that $\mathbf{A}_1, \ldots, \mathbf{A}_k$ are any vectors in R^n, where $k > n$. Prove that there are numbers $t_1, \ldots, t_k$, not all zero, such that

$$t_1\mathbf{A}_1 + \cdots + t_k\mathbf{A}_k = 0.$$

(Hint: Write out this relation as a system of simultaneous linear equations.)

1.5 LINEAR DEPENDENCE AND BASES

To avoid misunderstandings, we advise you that this final section is a little more subtle than the rest of the chapter, and does not form part of the main line of development of the text. The material is included in spite of these considerations because it solves many problems that are inaccessible by less subtle methods, for example the existence of a partial fractions decomposition for every rational function (see the problems below); and because it provides a brief introduction to the important subject of linear algebra.

A sum $t_1\mathbf{A}_1 + \cdots + t_k\mathbf{A}_k$, where the t_j are numbers and the $\mathbf{A}_j$ are vectors, is called a *linear combination* of $\mathbf{A}_1, \ldots, \mathbf{A}_k$. For example, $(5,-1)$ is a linear combination of $(1,1)$ and $(1,-1)$, since

$$(5,-1) = 2(1,1) + 3(1,-1).$$

Given any vectors $\mathbf{A}_1, \ldots, \mathbf{A}_k$ $(k \geq 1)$, we can write the zero vector in a rather simple-minded way as a linear combination

$$\mathbf{0} = 0 \cdot \mathbf{A}_1 + \cdots + 0 \cdot \mathbf{A}_k.$$

If there is any other way to write $\mathbf{0}$ as a linear combination of these vectors, they are called *linearly dependent.* Precisely:

Definition 3. A set of vectors $\mathbf{A}_1, \ldots, \mathbf{A}_k$ is called *linearly dependent* if and only if there are numbers $t_1, \ldots, t_k$, not all zero, such that

$$t_1\mathbf{A}_1 + t_2\mathbf{A}_2 + \cdots + t_k\mathbf{A}_k = \mathbf{0}. \tag{1}$$

This imposing definition has a rather simple geometric meaning, which shows up when we examine the cases $k = 1, 2, 3$.

A single vector $\mathbf{A}_1$ *forms a linearly dependent set if and only if* $\mathbf{A}_1 = \mathbf{0}$.

Proof. $t_1\mathbf{A}_1 = \mathbf{0}$ for some $t_1 \neq 0$ if and only if $\mathbf{A}_1 = \mathbf{0}$.

Two vectors $\mathbf{A}_1$ *and* $\mathbf{A}_2$ *form a linearly dependent set if and only if they are parallel* (see Fig. 35).

Proof. Suppose that $\mathbf{A}_1$ and $\mathbf{A}_2$ are linearly dependent, i.e.

$$t_1\mathbf{A}_1 + t_2\mathbf{A}_2 = \mathbf{0},$$

where t_1 and t_2 are not both zero. If $t_1 \neq 0$, then $\mathbf{A}_1 = -\frac{t_2}{t_1}\mathbf{A}_2$, and if $t_2 \neq 0$, then $\mathbf{A}_2 = -\frac{t_1}{t_2}\mathbf{A}_1$; in either case, the vectors are parallel.

Conversely, if $\mathbf{A}$ and $\mathbf{B}$ are parallel, then either $\mathbf{A} = t\mathbf{B}$ or $\mathbf{B} = t\mathbf{A}$. In the first case, $1\cdot\mathbf{A} + (-t)\mathbf{B} = \mathbf{0}$; in the second case, $t\mathbf{A} + (-1)\mathbf{B} = \mathbf{0}$; in either case, the pair is linearly dependent.

Three vectors $\mathbf{A}_1$, $\mathbf{A}_2$, $\mathbf{A}_3$ *in* R^3 *form a linearly dependent set if and only if they lie on a common plane through the origin* (see Fig. 36).

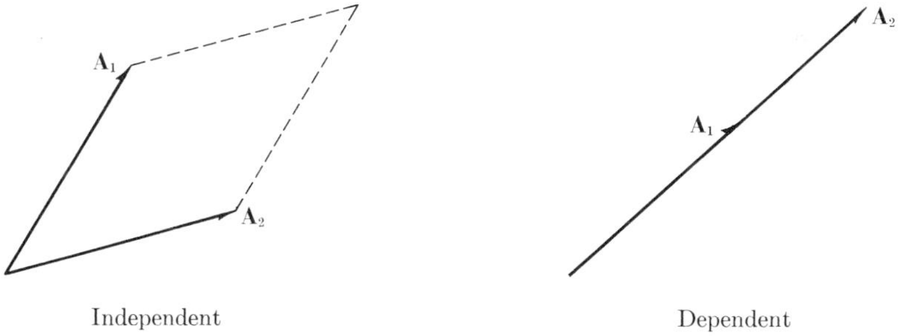

FIGURE 1.35

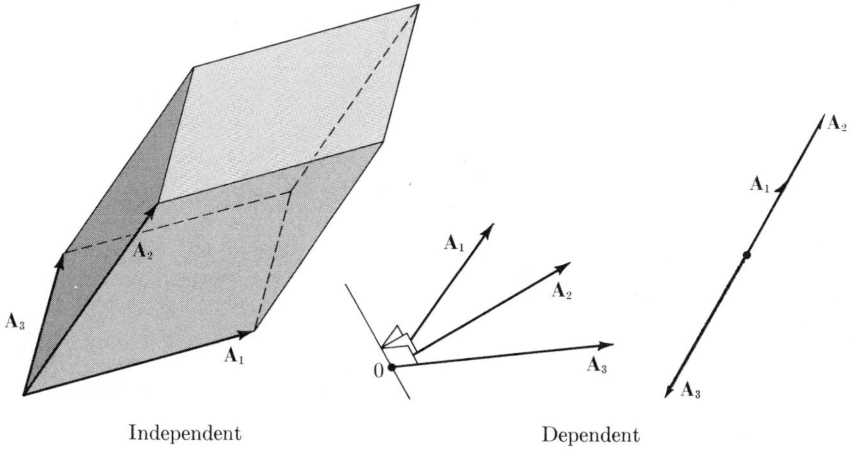

FIGURE 1.36

Proof. If $\mathbf{A}_1$, $\mathbf{A}_2$, $\mathbf{A}_3$ are linearly dependent, then

$$t_1\mathbf{A}_1 + t_2\mathbf{A}_2 + t_3\mathbf{A}_3 = \mathbf{0},$$

where at least one of the t_j is not zero, say $t_3 \neq 0$. By Theorem 5, there is a nonzero vector $\mathbf{N}$ orthogonal to both $\mathbf{A}_1$ and $\mathbf{A}_2$, so these two vectors lie on the plane through the origin

$$\{\mathbf{P}: \mathbf{P}\cdot\mathbf{N} = 0\}. \tag{2}$$

Since $t_3 \neq 0$, we have

$$\mathbf{A}_3 = -\frac{t_1}{t_3}\mathbf{A}_1 - \frac{t_2}{t_3}\mathbf{A}_2,$$

so

$$\mathbf{A}_3\cdot\mathbf{N} = -\frac{t_1}{t_3}\mathbf{A}_1\cdot\mathbf{N} - \frac{t_2}{t_3}\mathbf{A}_2\cdot\mathbf{N} = 0;$$

hence $\mathbf{A}_1$, $\mathbf{A}_2$, $\mathbf{A}_3$ all lie on the plane (2). The converse implication (that three vectors coplanar with the origin form a linearly dependent set) is Problem 6 below.

These three cases show that linear dependence is a sort of degeneracy. A pair of vectors generally spans a parallelogram, but when the pair is linearly dependent, the parallelogram degenerates to a line segment (see Fig. 35) or even to a single point (when both vectors are zero). Three vectors generally span a parallelepiped, but when the three are linearly dependent, the parallelepiped degenerates to a plane figure.

A nondegenerate set, i.e. a set that is not linearly dependent, is called *linearly independent.* Thus $\mathbf{A}_1, \ldots, \mathbf{A}_k$ is a linearly independent set if no relation (1) exists except the trivial one with $t_1 = 0, \ldots, t_k = 0$. In other words, $\mathbf{A}_1, \ldots, \mathbf{A}_k$ *is a linearly independent set if and only if*

$$t_1\mathbf{A}_1 + \cdots + t_k\mathbf{A}_k = \mathbf{0} \quad\Rightarrow\quad t_1 = t_2 = \cdots = t_k = 0.$$

It can be rather tedious to determine whether a given set of vectors in R^n is linearly dependent or not, especially when $n > 3$; but two important cases can be decided at a glance. The first is the case where $\mathbf{A}_1, \ldots, \mathbf{A}_k$ are mutually orthogonal, i.e. where $\mathbf{A}_j\cdot\mathbf{A}_m = 0$ for $m \neq j$.

Theorem 7. *If $\mathbf{A}_1, \ldots, \mathbf{A}_k$ are all nonzero and mutually orthogonal, then they are linearly independent.*

Proof. Suppose that

$$t_1\mathbf{A}_1 + \cdots + t_k\mathbf{A}_k = \mathbf{0}.$$

Taking the inner product of each side with $\mathbf{A}_j$, we get

$$t_1\mathbf{A}_1\cdot\mathbf{A}_j + \cdots + t_j\mathbf{A}_j\cdot\mathbf{A}_j + \cdots + t_k\mathbf{A}_k\cdot\mathbf{A}_j = \mathbf{0}\cdot\mathbf{A}_j = 0. \tag{3}$$

Since $\mathbf{A}_m \cdot \mathbf{A}_j = 0$ for $m \neq j$, equation (3) reduces to

$$t_j \mathbf{A}_j \cdot \mathbf{A}_j = 0.$$

Since $\mathbf{A}_j \cdot \mathbf{A}_j = |\mathbf{A}_j|^2 \neq 0$, it follows that $t_j = 0$. Thus $t_1\mathbf{A}_1 + \cdots + t_k\mathbf{A}_k = \mathbf{0}$ implies $t_j = 0$ for every j. *Q.E.D.*

The second important case arises when there are "more vectors than dimensions"; in this case the set is always *linearly dependent.*

Theorem 8. *Let $\mathbf{A}_1, \ldots, \mathbf{A}_k$ be vectors in R^n. If $k > n$, then the set of vectors is linearly dependent. (If $k \leq n$, the set may or may not be linearly dependent.)*

Proof. We have to find $t_1, \ldots, t_k$, not all zero, such that

$$t_1\mathbf{A}_1 + \cdots + t_k\mathbf{A}_k = \mathbf{0}. \tag{4}$$

If we denote $\mathbf{A}_j$ by $(a_{j1}, \ldots, a_{jn})$ and write out (4) by components, we get

$$\begin{aligned} t_1a_{11} + \cdots + t_ka_{k1} &= 0 \\ t_1a_{12} + \cdots + t_ka_{k2} &= 0 \\ \vdots \qquad \qquad \vdots \quad &\ \ \vdots \\ t_1a_{1n} + \cdots + t_ka_{kn} &= 0. \end{aligned}$$

This is a set of n simultaneous linear homogeneous equations in k unknowns, with $k > n$. By Theorem 6, there is a nonzero solution, and the proof is complete.

The most important consequence of Theorem 8 is

Theorem 9. *If $\mathbf{A}_1, \ldots, \mathbf{A}_n$ is a linearly independent set of vectors in R^n, then every vector $\mathbf{X}$ in R^n can be written in one and only one way as a linear combination of $\mathbf{A}_1, \ldots, \mathbf{A}_n$,*

$$\mathbf{X} = t_1\mathbf{A}_1 + \cdots + t_n\mathbf{A}_n .$$

Proof. By Theorem 8, the set of $n + 1$ vectors $\mathbf{X}, \mathbf{A}_1, \ldots, \mathbf{A}_n$ is linearly dependent; hence there is a linear combination

$$t_0\mathbf{X} + t_1\mathbf{A}_1 + \cdots + t_n\mathbf{A}_n = \mathbf{0}, \tag{5}$$

with at least one of the t_j different from zero. It follows that $t_0 \neq 0$; for if $t_0 = 0$, then $t_1, \ldots, t_n$ are not all zero, and $t_1\mathbf{A}_1 + \cdots + t_n\mathbf{A}_n = \mathbf{0}$, contradicting the assumption that $\mathbf{A}_1, \ldots, \mathbf{A}_n$ are linearly independent. Since $t_0 \neq 0$, we can solve (5) and obtain $\mathbf{X}$ as the linear combination

$$\mathbf{X} = \left(-\frac{t_1}{t_0}\right)\mathbf{A}_1 + \cdots + \left(-\frac{t_n}{t_0}\right)\mathbf{A}_n .$$

It remains to prove that there is *only one* such combination giving $\mathbf{X}$. Suppose that

$$\mathbf{X} = t_1\mathbf{A}_1 + \cdots + t_n\mathbf{A}_n\,, \tag{6}$$

and also

$$\mathbf{X} = s_1\mathbf{A}_1 + \cdots + s_n\mathbf{A}_n\,. \tag{7}$$

Subtracting (7) from (6), we obtain

$$\mathbf{0} = (t_1 - s_1)\mathbf{A}_1 + \cdots + (t_n - s_n)\mathbf{A}_n\,. \tag{8}$$

Since $\mathbf{A}_1, \ldots, \mathbf{A}_n$ are linearly independent, equation (8) implies that $t_1 - s_1 = 0, \ldots, t_n - s_n = 0$; hence the representations (6) and (7) are identical, and the proof is complete.

Any linearly independent set of vectors whose linear combinations produce the whole space is called a *basis*; in this language, Theorem 9 says that *in R^n any linearly independent set of n vectors forms a basis.* This fundamental result is the reason for having introduced the concept of linear independence.

According to Theorem 9, any pair of nonparallel vectors $\mathbf{A}$, $\mathbf{B}$ in R^2 forms a basis, so every vector $\mathbf{P}$ can be written uniquely as a linear combination $\mathbf{P} = s\mathbf{A} + t\mathbf{B}$, as suggested in Fig. 37.

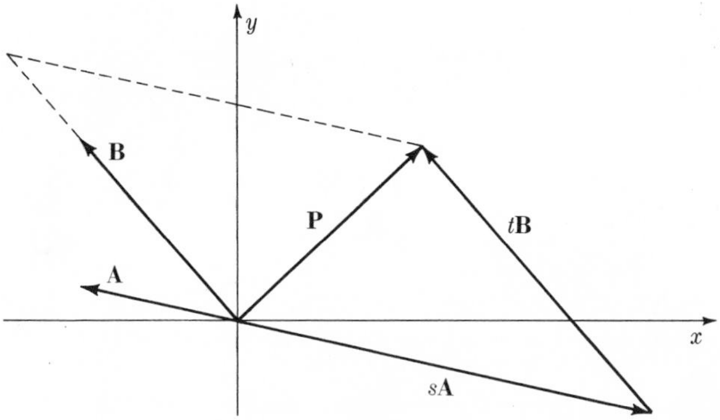

FIGURE 1.37

In R^n the unit vectors

$$\mathbf{E}_1 = (1,0,\ldots,0),\ \mathbf{E}_2 = (0,1,0,\ldots,0),\ \ldots,\ \mathbf{E}_n = (0,\ldots,0,1)$$

are linearly independent, and every vector $\mathbf{X} = (x_1, \ldots, x_n)$ in R^n can be written as

$$\mathbf{X} = x_1\mathbf{E}_1 + \cdots + x_n\mathbf{E}_n\,;$$

hence $\mathbf{E}_1, \ldots, \mathbf{E}_n$ form a basis, called the "standard" or "canonical" basis of R^n. It is not, however, the best basis to use in every case. Problems in vector analysis can be simplified by a good choice of basis, just as problems in physics or traditional analytic geometry are simplified by a good choice of coordinates. We conclude with two theorems (10 and 12) about bases, and two theorems (11 and 13) that depend on a good choice of basis.

Theorem 10. *If* $\mathbf{A}_1, \ldots, \mathbf{A}_n$ *are mutually orthogonal unit vectors in* R^n, *then they form a basis, and any vector* $\mathbf{X}$ *in* R^n *can be written*

$$\mathbf{X} = (\mathbf{X}\cdot\mathbf{A}_1)\mathbf{A}_1 + \cdots + (\mathbf{X}\cdot\mathbf{A}_n)\mathbf{A}_n\,. \tag{9}$$

Proof. By Theorem 7, the vectors $\mathbf{A}_1, \ldots, \mathbf{A}_n$ are linearly independent. By Theorem 9, $\mathbf{X}$ can be written as a linear combination

$$\mathbf{X} = t_1\mathbf{A}_1 + \cdots + t_n\mathbf{A}_n\,. \tag{10}$$

Taking the inner product of each side with $\mathbf{A}_j$, we get

$$\mathbf{X}\cdot\mathbf{A}_j = t_1\mathbf{A}_1\cdot\mathbf{A}_j + \cdots + t_j\mathbf{A}_j\cdot\mathbf{A}_j + \cdots + t_n\mathbf{A}_n\cdot\mathbf{A}_j = t_j$$

since $\mathbf{A}_m\cdot\mathbf{A}_j = 0$ for $m \neq j$ and $\mathbf{A}_j\cdot\mathbf{A}_j = |\mathbf{A}_j|^2 = 1$. The proof is completed by substituting $\mathbf{X}\cdot\mathbf{A}_j$ for t_j in (10).

A basis of the type in Theorem 10 is called "orthonormal"; "ortho-" refers to the orthogonality condition $\mathbf{A}_m\cdot\mathbf{A}_j = 0$ for $m \neq j$, and "-normal" refers to the condition $|\mathbf{A}_j| = 1$, which standardizes or "normalizes" the lengths of the vectors in the basis. Formula (9) expresses $\mathbf{X}$ as the sum of its orthogonal projections on $\mathbf{A}_1, \ldots, \mathbf{A}_n$.

As an application of Theorem 10, we prove some interesting results about the cross product in R^3.

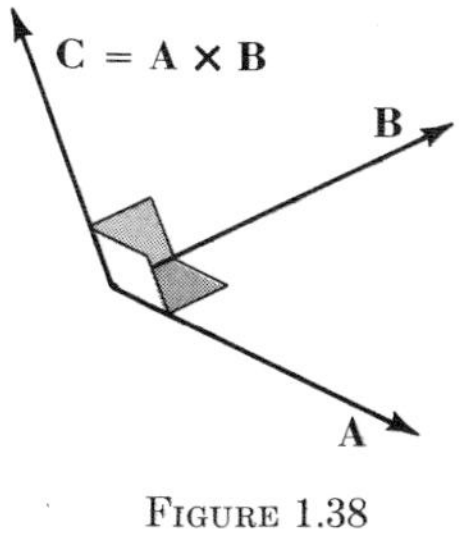

FIGURE 1.38

Theorem 11. *Suppose that* $\mathbf{A}$ *and* $\mathbf{B}$ *are orthogonal unit vectors in* R^3, *and set* $\mathbf{C} = \mathbf{A} \times \mathbf{B}$. *Then*

(i) $\mathbf{A}, \mathbf{B}, \mathbf{C}$ *is an orthonormal basis;*

(ii) $\mathbf{A} = \mathbf{B} \times \mathbf{C}$ *and* $\mathbf{B} = \mathbf{C} \times \mathbf{A}$.

(The formulas in (ii) are suggested by the right-hand rule; see Fig. 38.)

Proof. (i) By assumption, **A** and **B** are orthogonal unit vectors, and by Theorem 2, $\mathbf{C} = \mathbf{A} \times \mathbf{B}$ is orthogonal to **A** and **B**, and

$$|\mathbf{C}|^2 = |\mathbf{A}|^2 \cdot |\mathbf{B}|^2 - |\mathbf{A} \cdot \mathbf{B}|^2 = 1 \cdot 1 - 0 = 1.$$

Hence (i) is proved.

(ii) Applying part (i) to **B** and **C** instead of **A** and **B** shows that **B**, **C**, and $\mathbf{B} \times \mathbf{C}$ are mutually orthogonal unit vectors. Hence by Theorem 10 and Theorem 2, formulas (4) and (6),

$$\begin{aligned} \mathbf{A} &= (\mathbf{A} \cdot \mathbf{B})\mathbf{B} + (\mathbf{A} \cdot \mathbf{C})\mathbf{C} + [\mathbf{A} \cdot (\mathbf{B} \times \mathbf{C})](\mathbf{B} \times \mathbf{C}) \\ &= \quad \mathbf{0} \quad + \quad \mathbf{0} \quad + ([\mathbf{C} \cdot (\mathbf{A} \times \mathbf{B})]\mathbf{B}) \times \mathbf{C} \\ &= ([\mathbf{C} \cdot \mathbf{C}]\mathbf{B}) \times \mathbf{C} = \mathbf{B} \times \mathbf{C}. \end{aligned}$$

Similarly, **C**, **A**, and $\mathbf{C} \times \mathbf{A}$ are mutually orthogonal unit vectors, so

$$\begin{aligned} \mathbf{B} &= (\mathbf{B} \cdot \mathbf{C})\mathbf{C} + (\mathbf{B} \cdot \mathbf{A})\mathbf{A} + [\mathbf{B} \cdot (\mathbf{C} \times \mathbf{A})]\mathbf{C} \times \mathbf{A} \\ &= [\mathbf{C} \cdot (\mathbf{A} \times \mathbf{B})]\mathbf{C} \times \mathbf{A} = \mathbf{C} \times \mathbf{A}. \end{aligned}$$

Q.E.D.

So far we have only two simple ways to identify a basis: (1) in R^2, any pair of nonparallel vectors forms a basis by Theorem 9; (2) in R^n, an orthonormal set of n vectors forms a basis. We add a third way, valid in R^3:

Theorem 12. *Three vectors* **A**, **B**, *and* **C** *in* R^3 *form a basis if and only if* $\mathbf{A} \cdot (\mathbf{B} \times \mathbf{C}) \neq 0$. (*Notice that* $\mathbf{A} \cdot (\mathbf{B} \times \mathbf{C})$ *is* $\pm$ *the volume of the parallelepiped in* Fig. 36.)

Proof. Suppose that $\mathbf{A} \cdot (\mathbf{B} \times \mathbf{C}) \neq 0$, and

$$r\mathbf{A} + s\mathbf{B} + t\mathbf{C} = \mathbf{0}. \tag{11}$$

Taking the dot product with $\mathbf{B} \times \mathbf{C}$ on both sides gives

$$r\mathbf{A} \cdot (\mathbf{B} \times \mathbf{C}) = 0;$$

since $\mathbf{A} \cdot (\mathbf{B} \times \mathbf{C}) \neq 0$, we have $r = 0$. Further, by Theorem 2,

$$\mathbf{B} \cdot (\mathbf{C} \times \mathbf{A}) = \mathbf{A} \cdot (\mathbf{B} \times \mathbf{C}) \neq 0,$$

so taking dot products with $\mathbf{C} \times \mathbf{A}$ on both sides of (11) gives $s = 0$, and similarly taking dot products with $\mathbf{A} \times \mathbf{B}$ gives $t = 0$. Hence if

$$\mathbf{A} \cdot (\mathbf{B} \times \mathbf{C}) \neq 0,$$

then **A**, **B**, **C** is a linearly independent set, so by Theorem 9 it forms a basis.

Conversely, suppose **A**, **B**, **C** is a basis. Then, by definition, these three vectors are linearly independent; it follows that **B**, **C** is a linearly independent set (see Problem 10), so **B** and **C** are not parallel, and $\mathbf{B} \times \mathbf{C} \neq \mathbf{0}$.

Since **A**, **B**, **C** form a basis, we can express $\mathbf{B} \times \mathbf{C}$ as a linear combination

$$\mathbf{B} \times \mathbf{C} = r\mathbf{A} + s\mathbf{B} + t\mathbf{C}.$$

Taking the inner product on both sides with $\mathbf{B} \times \mathbf{C}$, we get

$$r\mathbf{A} \cdot (\mathbf{B} \times \mathbf{C}) = |\mathbf{B} \times \mathbf{C}|^2 \neq 0;$$

hence $\mathbf{A} \cdot (\mathbf{B} \times \mathbf{C}) \neq 0$. *Q.E.D.*

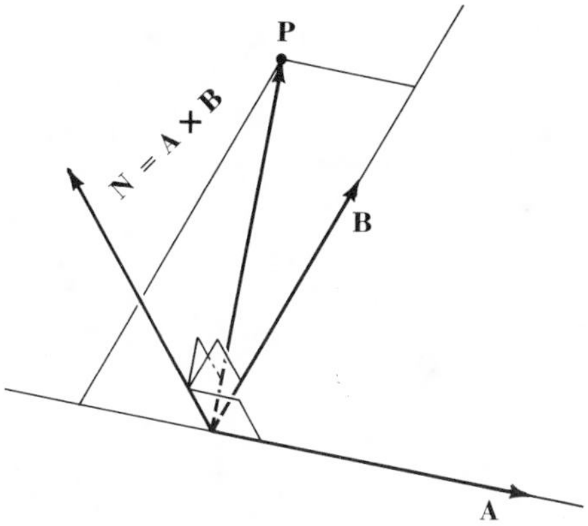

FIGURE 1.39

A typical application of Theorem 12 occurs in the proof of

Theorem 13. *If* **A** *and* **B** *are linearly independent vectors in* R^3, *then their linear combinations form a plane through the origin.*

Proof. From Fig. 39 it seems that the linear combinations of **A** and **B** should coincide with the plane

$$\{\mathbf{P}: \mathbf{P} \cdot \mathbf{N} = 0\}, \tag{12}$$

where $\mathbf{N} = \mathbf{A} \times \mathbf{B}$. The appropriate basis to use in proving this is **N**, **A**, **B**; the first step, then, is to prove that this really is a basis.

Since **A** and **B** are linearly independent, they are not parallel; hence $\mathbf{A} \times \mathbf{B} \neq \mathbf{0}$, and $\mathbf{N} \cdot (\mathbf{A} \times \mathbf{B}) = |\mathbf{A} \times \mathbf{B}|^2 \neq \mathbf{0}$, so by Theorem 12, **N**, **A**, **B** is a basis. Thus every vector **P** can be written uniquely as

$$\mathbf{P} = r\mathbf{N} + s\mathbf{A} + t\mathbf{B}; \tag{13}$$

using this representation of **P**, we find that

$$\begin{aligned} \mathbf{P} \cdot \mathbf{N} = 0 \quad &\Leftrightarrow \quad r|\mathbf{N}|^2 = 0 && (\text{since } \mathbf{A} \cdot \mathbf{N} = 0 = \mathbf{B} \cdot \mathbf{N}) \\ &\Leftrightarrow \quad r = 0 && (\text{since } \mathbf{N} \neq \mathbf{0}) \\ &\Leftrightarrow \quad \mathbf{P} = s\mathbf{A} + t\mathbf{B} && (\text{in view of (13)}) \\ &\Leftrightarrow \quad \mathbf{P} \text{ is a linear combination of } \mathbf{A} \text{ and } \mathbf{B}. \end{aligned}$$

Hence the linear combinations of **A** and **B** coincide with the points of the plane (12). *Q.E.D.*

By a very similar proof, you can show that if $\mathbf{A}$ and $\mathbf{B}$ are linearly independent, and $\mathbf{P}_0$ is any given point in R^3, then

$$\{\mathbf{P}: \mathbf{P} = \mathbf{P}_0 + s\mathbf{A} + t\mathbf{B} \text{ for some real } s \text{ and } t\} \tag{14}$$

coincides with the plane

$$\{\mathbf{P}: (\mathbf{P} - \mathbf{P}_0)\cdot(\mathbf{A} \times \mathbf{B}) = 0\}. \tag{15}$$

The equation $\mathbf{P} = \mathbf{P}_0 + s\mathbf{A} + t\mathbf{B}$ in (14) is called a *parametric equation* of the plane, with s and t as parameters. This is just like the parametric equation of a line $\mathbf{P} = \mathbf{P}_0 + s\mathbf{A}$, except that a plane requires not one but two parameters, and two linearly independent vectors.

Before turning you loose on the problems, we give some simple examples.

Example 1. (2,3) and (1,0) are linearly independent, since they are obviously not parallel; neither one is a scalar multiple of the other.

Example 2. (2,3), (1,0), and (0,1) are linearly dependent, by Theorem 8; they form a set of three vectors in R^2. You can also see directly from the definition that they are dependent, since

$$(2,3) + (-2)(1,0) + (-3)(0,1) = \mathbf{0}.$$

Example 3. (0,0) and (1,0) are linearly *dependent*, since

$$1\cdot(0,0) + 0(1,0) = \mathbf{0}.$$

Example 4. (0,1,0), (0,1,1), and (2,0,1) are linearly *independent*. This can be proved by Theorem 12, but it can also be proved directly:

$$r(0,1,0) + s(0,1,1) + t(2,0,1) = \mathbf{0} \tag{16}$$

is equivalent to

$$\begin{aligned} 2t &= 0 && \text{(equating first components)}\\ r + s &= 0 && \text{(equating second components)}\\ s + t &= 0 && \text{(equating third components).} \end{aligned}$$

It follows that $t = 0$, hence $s = 0$ (from the third equation), hence $r = 0$ (from the second equation). Thus (16) implies that $r = s = t = 0$, so the three vectors are linearly independent.

Example 5. Since (2,3) and (1,0) are two linearly independent vectors in R^2, they form a basis; hence any vector (x,y) can be written as a linear combination of these two. We can find explicitly what the combination is as follows:

$$(x,y) = s(2,3) + t(1,0)$$

means

$$\begin{aligned} x &= 2s + t\\ y &= 3s; \end{aligned}$$

hence $s = y/3$ and $t = x - 2y/3$. Thus

$$(x,y) = \frac{y}{3}\,(2,3) + \left(x - \frac{2y}{3}\right)(1,0)$$

is the desired linear combination.

Example 6'. $\mathbf{A} = (1,1,1)$ and $\mathbf{B} = (2,-1,-1)$ are orthogonal and nonzero, but they do *not* form a basis of R^3. Theorem 9 suggests this, but does not prove it (why not?). To prove it, notice that $\mathbf{C} = \mathbf{A} \times \mathbf{B}$ cannot be written as a linear combination of $\mathbf{A}$ and $\mathbf{B}$; for if $\mathbf{C} = s\mathbf{A} + t\mathbf{B}$, then $\mathbf{C}\cdot\mathbf{C} = s\mathbf{A}\cdot\mathbf{C} + t\mathbf{B}\cdot\mathbf{C} = 0$, which contradicts $|\mathbf{C}| = |\mathbf{A}|\cdot|\mathbf{B}| \sin\theta = |\mathbf{A}|\cdot|\mathbf{B}| \neq 0$. (Problem 8 below shows that in R^n, every basis must have exactly n members; using that result, this example could be done simply by observing that no two vectors can form a basis for R^3.)

PROBLEMS

Problems 1–17 are for practice with the ideas of linear independence, basis, and orthogonal basis. The first five are fairly routine, while Problems 6–17 ask more theoretical questions. Problems 18–20 are geometric (intersection of two planes, conic sections), and 21–28 are algebraic (Cramer's rule for a 3×3 system, partial fractions decomposition).

1. Which of the following sets are linearly dependent? Which are bases in the appropriate space R^n?
(a) $(1,-2)$ and $(-1,2)$
(b) $(1,0)$ and $(1,1)$
(c) $(1,0)$, $(1,1)$, and $(1,-1)$
(d) $(1,-1)$
(e) $(0,0)$
(f) $(0,0,0)$, $(0,1,0)$, and $(0,0,1)$
(g) $(0,1,0)$ and $(0,0,1)$
(h) $(1,0,0)$, $(1,1,0)$, and $(0,0,1)$
(i) $(1,1,0)$, $(1,-1,0)$, and $(0,0,1)$
(j) $(1,1,1)$, $(1,1,0)$, and $(1,0,0)$
(k) $(1,1,1)$, $(1,0,0)$, $(0,1,0)$, and $(0,0,1)$
(l) $(1,1,1,0)$, $(1,0,0,0)$, $(0,1,0,0)$, and $(0,0,1,0)$
(m) $(1,1,1,1)$, $(1,1,1,0)$, $(1,1,0,0)$, and $(1,0,0,0)$. (Hint: Write out $t_1\mathbf{A}_1 + t_2\mathbf{A}_2 + t_3\mathbf{A}_3 + t_4\mathbf{A}_4 = 0$ by components.)

2. (a) Prove that $\mathbf{A}_1 = (1,1)$ and $\mathbf{A}_2 = (1,-1)$ form a basis for R^2.
(b) Express the vector $(2,3)$ as a linear combination of $\mathbf{A}_1$ and $\mathbf{A}_2$. (Write out $(2,3) = t_1\mathbf{A}_1 + t_2\mathbf{A}_2$ by components, and solve for t_1 and t_2.)
(c) Express the general vector (x,y) as a linear combination of $\mathbf{A}_1$ and $\mathbf{A}_2$.

3. (a) Prove that $\mathbf{A}_1 = (1,1,1)$, $\mathbf{A}_2 = (1,-1,0)$, and $\mathbf{A}_3 = (1,1,-2)$ are mutually orthogonal.
(b) Prove that the vectors in part (a) form a basis for R^3.
(c) Express $(1,1,-1)$ as a linear combination of $\mathbf{A}_1$, $\mathbf{A}_2$, $\mathbf{A}_3$. (*Warning:* This basis is not orthonormal; it's "ortho-" but not "-normal." You can use brute force as in Problem 2(b), or be clever and take inner products as in the proof of Theorem 10.)

4. Let $\mathbf{A} = \left(\frac{1}{\sqrt{2}}, \frac{1}{\sqrt{2}}, 0\right)$ and $\mathbf{B} = \left(\frac{1}{\sqrt{2}}, \frac{-1}{\sqrt{2}}, 0\right)$.

(a) Prove that $\mathbf{A}$ and $\mathbf{B}$ are orthogonal unit vectors.
(b) Prove that $\mathbf{A}$ and $\mathbf{B}$ do *not* form a basis of R^3, by finding a vector $\mathbf{C}$ that is not a linear combination of $\mathbf{A}$ and $\mathbf{B}$.
(c) Find a vector $\mathbf{C}$ such that $\mathbf{A}$, $\mathbf{B}$, $\mathbf{C}$ is an orthonormal basis of R^3.
(d) Express $(1,1,1)$ as a linear combination of $\mathbf{A}$, $\mathbf{B}$, and $\mathbf{C}$.

5. Let $\mathbf{A} = (1,1,0)$ and $\mathbf{B} = (1,-1,0)$.
(a) Prove that $\mathbf{A}$, $\mathbf{B}$ is not a basis of R^3 (see Problem 4(b)).
(b) Find a vector $\mathbf{C}$ such that $\mathbf{A}$, $\mathbf{B}$, $\mathbf{C}$ is a basis of R^3.

6. Prove that if $\mathbf{A}$, $\mathbf{B}$, $\mathbf{C}$ are vectors in R^3, all lying in the plane

$$\{\mathbf{P} : \mathbf{P} \cdot \mathbf{N} = 0\},$$

then $\mathbf{A}$, $\mathbf{B}$, $\mathbf{C}$ are linearly dependent. (Hint: If they were independent, they would form a basis, hence $\mathbf{N} = r\mathbf{A} + s\mathbf{B} + t\mathbf{C}$; obtain a contradiction by taking the dot product with $\mathbf{N}$ on both sides of this equation.)

7. Suppose that $\mathbf{B}$ is orthogonal to each of the vectors $\mathbf{A}_1, \ldots, \mathbf{A}_k$. Prove that $\mathbf{B}$ is orthogonal to every linear combination $t_1\mathbf{A}_1 + \cdots + t_k\mathbf{A}_k$.

8. Prove that in R^n no set of k vectors $\mathbf{A}_1, \ldots, \mathbf{A}_k$ forms a basis if $k < n$; i.e. show that there is a vector $\mathbf{B}$ which cannot be written as a linear combination $t_1\mathbf{A}_1 + \cdots + t_k\mathbf{A}_k$. (Use Theorem 5 and the previous problem.)

9. Prove that if *any* of the vectors $\mathbf{A}_1, \ldots, \mathbf{A}_k$ is zero, then the set is linearly dependent. (Hint: For linear dependence, it suffices to have just *one* of $t_1, \ldots, t_k$ different from zero in the sum $t_1\mathbf{A}_1 + \cdots + t_k\mathbf{A}_k = \mathbf{0}$.)

10. Suppose that $\mathbf{A}_1, \ldots, \mathbf{A}_k$ is a linearly dependent set. Prove that any set $\mathbf{A}_1, \ldots, \mathbf{A}_k, \mathbf{A}_{k+1}, \ldots, \mathbf{A}_{k+m}$ containing $\mathbf{A}_1, \ldots, \mathbf{A}_k$ is also linearly dependent.

11. Suppose that $\mathbf{A}_1, \ldots, \mathbf{A}_k$ is an orthonormal set in R^n, i.e. $\mathbf{A}_j \cdot \mathbf{A}_m = 0$

if $j \neq m$, and $|\mathbf{A}_j| = 1$ for every j. Prove that there is an orthonormal basis $\mathbf{A}_1, \ldots, \mathbf{A}_n$ containing the given orthonormal set. (Use Theorem 5.)

12. The *span* of a given set of vectors $\mathbf{A}_1, \ldots, \mathbf{A}_k$ is the set of all linear combinations $t_1\mathbf{A}_1 + \cdots + t_k\mathbf{A}_k$. For example, if $\mathbf{A}_1, \ldots, \mathbf{A}_n$ is a basis of R^n, then the span of this set is all of R^n. Theorem 13 proves that the span of two nonparallel vectors in R^3 is a plane through $\mathbf{0}$.
(a) Choose $\mathbf{A}$, $\mathbf{B}$, $\mathbf{C}$ so that they span all of R^3.
(b) Prove that the span of $(1,0,0)$, $(0,1,0)$, and $(1,1,0)$ is the xy plane.
(c) Choose $\mathbf{A}$, $\mathbf{B}$, $\mathbf{C}$ in R^3 so that they span only a line.
(d) Choose $\mathbf{A}$, $\mathbf{B}$, $\mathbf{C}$ in R^3 so that they span only the origin.
(e) Prove that the span of any three vectors $\mathbf{A}$, $\mathbf{B}$, $\mathbf{C}$ in R^3 is either the *origin*, a *line* through the origin, a *plane* through the origin, or all of R^3. (This is hard, starting from scratch.)

13. Let $\mathbf{A}_1, \ldots, \mathbf{A}_n$ be an orthonormal basis in R^n. Let

$$\mathbf{X} = \sum_1^n t_j\mathbf{A}_j \qquad \text{and} \qquad \mathbf{Y} = \sum_1^n s_k\mathbf{A}_k .$$

(a) Prove that $\mathbf{X}\cdot\mathbf{Y} = \sum_1^n t_j s_j$.

(b) Prove that $|\mathbf{X}| = \sqrt{\sum_1^n t_j^2}$.

14. Let $\mathbf{A}_1, \ldots, \mathbf{A}_n$ be mutually orthogonal nonzero vectors in R^n. Prove that every vector $\mathbf{X}$ can be written as

$$\mathbf{X} = \sum_1^n \frac{\mathbf{X}\cdot\mathbf{A}_j}{|\mathbf{A}_j|^2}\mathbf{A}_j = \sum \mathbf{X}_{\mathbf{A}_j},$$

where $\mathbf{X}_{\mathbf{A}_j}$ is the orthogonal projection of $\mathbf{X}$ on $\mathbf{A}_j$. (Hint: Review the proof of Theorem 10.)

15. Suppose that $\mathbf{A}$, $\mathbf{B}$, $\mathbf{C}$ is a basis of R^3. Prove that $\mathbf{B} \times \mathbf{C}$, $\mathbf{C} \times \mathbf{A}$, $\mathbf{A} \times \mathbf{B}$ is also a basis. (Hint: In $r(\mathbf{B} \times \mathbf{C}) + s(\mathbf{C} \times \mathbf{A}) + t(\mathbf{A} \times \mathbf{B}) = \mathbf{0}$, take dot products with $\mathbf{A}$, $\mathbf{B}$, and $\mathbf{C}$.)

16. Two sets of vectors $\mathbf{A}_1, \ldots, \mathbf{A}_k$ and $\mathbf{B}_1, \ldots, \mathbf{B}_k$ in R^n are called *biorthogonal* if

$$\mathbf{A}_j\cdot\mathbf{B}_m \begin{cases} = 0 & \text{for } j \neq m \\ \neq 0 & \text{for } j = m. \end{cases}$$

(a) Prove that if the two sets are biorthogonal, then each set is linearly independent.
(b) Prove that if the two sets are biorthogonal and $k = n$, then each set is a basis.
(c) With the assumptions in part (b), prove that

$$\mathbf{X} = \sum \frac{\mathbf{X}\cdot\mathbf{B}_j}{\mathbf{A}_j\cdot\mathbf{B}_j}\mathbf{A}_j$$

for every $\mathbf{X}$ in R^n. (This generalizes the formula in Theorem 10. When $\mathbf{A}_j = \mathbf{B}_j$, we have an orthogonal basis, and the formula in part (c) reduces to the one in Problem 14. If we assume further that $|\mathbf{A}_j| = 1$, we have an orthonormal basis, as in Theorem 10.)

17. Suppose that $\mathbf{A}_1, \ldots, \mathbf{A}_k$ is an orthonormal set in R^n, i.e.

$$\mathbf{A}_j\cdot\mathbf{A}_m = \begin{cases} 0 & \text{if } j \neq m \\ 1 & \text{if } j = m. \end{cases}$$

Prove *Bessel's inequality:*

$$|\mathbf{X}|^2 \geq \sum_1^k (\mathbf{X}\cdot\mathbf{A}_j)^2,$$

i.e. $|\mathbf{X}|^2$ is greater than or equal to the sum of the squares of the lengths of the projections of $\mathbf{X}$ on $\mathbf{A}_1, \ldots, \mathbf{A}_k$. (Hint: Show that

$$\left|\mathbf{X} - \sum_1^k (\mathbf{X}\cdot\mathbf{A}_j)\mathbf{A}_j\right|^2 = |\mathbf{X}|^2 - \sum_1^k (\mathbf{X}\cdot\mathbf{A}_j)^2.)$$

18. Suppose that $\mathbf{A}$ and $\mathbf{B}$ are not parallel. Prove that the set

$$\{\mathbf{P}: \mathbf{P} = \mathbf{P}_0 + s\mathbf{A} + t\mathbf{B} \text{ for some } s \text{ and } t\}$$

is the plane $\{\mathbf{P}: (\mathbf{P} - \mathbf{P}_0)\cdot(\mathbf{A} \times \mathbf{B}) = 0\}$.

19. Suppose that $\mathbf{A}$ and $\mathbf{B}$ are not parallel.
(a) Prove that the two planes $\{\mathbf{P}: \mathbf{P}\cdot\mathbf{A} = 0\}$ and $\{\mathbf{P}: \mathbf{P}\cdot\mathbf{B} = 0\}$ intersect in the line $\{\mathbf{P}: \mathbf{P} = t\mathbf{A} \times \mathbf{B} \text{ for some } t\}$. (Hint: Look at the proof of Theorem 13.)
(b) Let $\mathbf{P}_0$ be any point. Prove that the two planes

$$\{\mathbf{P}: (\mathbf{P} - \mathbf{P}_0)\cdot\mathbf{A} = 0\} \quad \text{and} \quad \{\mathbf{P}: (\mathbf{P} - \mathbf{P}_0)\cdot\mathbf{B} = 0\}$$

intersect in the line $\{\mathbf{P}: \mathbf{P} = \mathbf{P}_0 + t(\mathbf{A} \times \mathbf{B})\}$. (Hint: Write $\mathbf{P} - \mathbf{P}_0$ as a linear combination of appropriate basis vectors.)

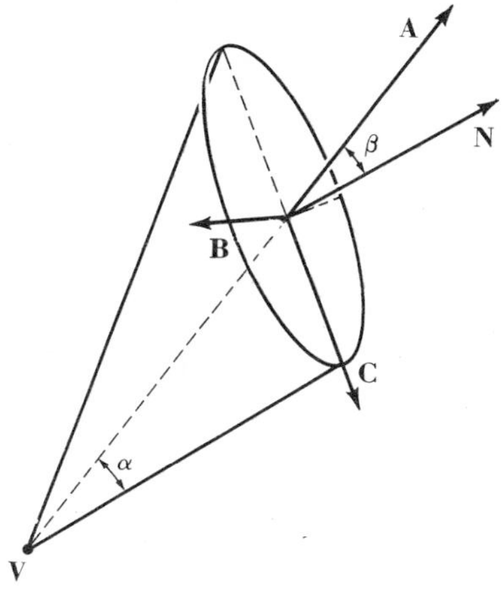

FIGURE 1.40

20. This problem analyzes the intersection of a plane $\{\mathbf{P}: \mathbf{P}\cdot\mathbf{N} = d\}$ and a double cone $\{\mathbf{P}: |(\mathbf{P} - \mathbf{V})\cdot\mathbf{A}| = |\mathbf{P} - \mathbf{V}| \cos\alpha\}$. We assume (without loss of generality) that $|\mathbf{N}| = 1$ and $|\mathbf{A}| = 1$. We also assume that $\mathbf{N}$ and $\mathbf{A}$ are not parallel. Let β be the angle between $\mathbf{N}$ and $\mathbf{A}$.

(a) If $\mathbf{B} = \dfrac{1}{\sin\beta}\mathbf{N} \times \mathbf{A}$ and $\mathbf{C} = \mathbf{N} \times \mathbf{B}$, then $\mathbf{N}, \mathbf{B}, \mathbf{C}$ is an orthonormal basis of R^3 (see Fig. 40).

(b) Prove that $\mathbf{A}\cdot\mathbf{B} = 0$ and $\mathbf{A}\cdot\mathbf{C} = -\sin\beta$. (Use Theorem 2.)

(c) Let $\mathbf{P}_0 = \mathbf{V} + t_0\mathbf{A}$ be the intersection of the given plane and the axis of the cone (the axis is the line $\{\mathbf{P}: \mathbf{P} = \mathbf{V} + t\mathbf{A}$ for some $t\}$). Prove that a point $\mathbf{P}$ is on the plane if and only if $\mathbf{P} = \mathbf{V} + t_0\mathbf{A} + s\mathbf{B} + t\mathbf{C}$ for some real s and t. (See Problem 19.)

(d) Prove that the distance between two points $\mathbf{P} = \mathbf{P}_0 + s\mathbf{B} + t\mathbf{C}$ and $\mathbf{P}' = \mathbf{P}_0 + s'\mathbf{B} + t'\mathbf{C}$ on the plane is given by

$$|\mathbf{P} - \mathbf{P}'|^2 = (s - s')^2 + (t - t')^2.$$

(e) Prove that $\mathbf{P}$ is on both the plane and the cone if and only if

$\mathbf{P} = \mathbf{P}_0 + s\mathbf{B} + t\mathbf{C}$ and

$$(t_0 - t\sin\beta)^2 - (t_0^2 + s^2 + t^2 + 2t_0t\sin\beta)\cos^2\alpha. \qquad (17)$$

(f) Let $e = (\sin\beta)/(\cos\alpha)$. Prove that if $e \neq 1$, then equation (17) is equivalent to

$$\frac{s^2}{1 - e^2} + \left(t + \frac{t_0 \sin\beta \tan^2\alpha}{1 - e^2}\right)^2 = \frac{t_0^2 \tan^2\alpha \cos^2\beta}{(1 - e^2)^2};$$

and if $e = 1$, it is equivalent to

$$s^2 = t_0 \tan^2 \alpha (t_0 - 2t \sin \beta).$$

(In view of part (d), distances on the plane $\{\mathbf{P}: \mathbf{P} \cdot \mathbf{N} = d\}$ are computed in terms of s and t just as distances in the plane R^2 are computed in terms of x and y. Hence, by the methods of elementary analytic geometry, part (f) shows that the curve is an ellipse when $e < 1$, a parabola when $e = 1$, and a hyperbola when $e > 1$.)

21. (Cramer's rule.) Suppose that $\mathbf{A} \cdot (\mathbf{B} \times \mathbf{C}) \neq 0$, and let $\mathbf{D}$ be any vector in R^3. Prove that $\mathbf{D} = r\mathbf{A} + s\mathbf{B} + t\mathbf{C}$ if and only if

$$r = \frac{\mathbf{D} \cdot (\mathbf{B} \times \mathbf{C})}{\mathbf{A} \cdot (\mathbf{B} \times \mathbf{C})}, \qquad s = \frac{\mathbf{D} \cdot (\mathbf{A} \times \mathbf{C})}{\mathbf{B} \cdot (\mathbf{A} \times \mathbf{C})}, \qquad t = \frac{\mathbf{D} \cdot (\mathbf{A} \times \mathbf{B})}{\mathbf{C} \cdot (\mathbf{A} \times \mathbf{B})}.$$

(Hint: Theorem 12 plays an important part in the proof.)

22. Prove that if $a_1 b_2 \neq b_1 a_2$, then the simultaneous equations

$$ra_1 + sb_1 = d_1$$
$$ra_2 + sb_2 = d_2$$

have the unique solution

$$r = \frac{d_1 b_2 - d_2 b_1}{a_1 b_2 - a_2 b_1}, \qquad s = \frac{a_1 d_2 - a_2 d_1}{a_1 b_2 - a_2 b_1}.$$

(Hint: In the previous problem, set $\mathbf{A} = (a_1, a_2, 0)$, $\mathbf{B} = (b_1, b_2, 0)$, $\mathbf{C} = (0,0,1)$, and $\mathbf{D} = (d_1, d_2, 0)$.

23. Show that Theorem 9 is equivalent to the following theorem: *Suppose that the $n \times n$ system of equations*

$$t_1 a_{11} + \cdots + t_n a_{n1} = 0$$
$$t_1 a_{12} + \cdots + t_n a_{n2} = 0$$
$$\vdots \qquad\qquad \vdots \qquad \vdots$$
$$t_1 a_{1n} + \cdots + t_n a_{nn} = 0$$

has no solution other than $t_1 = t_2 = \cdots = t_n = 0$. Then for each choice of the constants $b_1, \ldots, b_n$ the system

$$t_1 a_{11} + \cdots + t_n a_{n1} = b_1$$
$$\vdots \qquad\qquad \vdots \qquad \vdots$$
$$t_1 a_{1n} + \cdots + t_n a_{nn} = b_n$$

has a unique solution $t_1, \ldots, t_n$.

The next five problems prove that partial fraction decompositions are always possible.

24. Prove Theorem 6 for systems of equations where the coefficients (and the solutions) are *complex* numbers.

25. $\mathbf{C}^n$ is the vector space of n-tuples of *complex* numbers; addition and scalar multiplication are defined exactly as in §1.4, except that now the numbers $t, a_1, b_1, \ldots$ are complex. The inner product is defined as $\sum a_j\bar{b}_j$, and the length as $\sqrt{\sum |a_j|^2}$. Prove the analog of Theorem 1 with R^3 replaced by $\mathbf{C}^n$. (The formula $\mathbf{A}\cdot\mathbf{B} = \mathbf{B}\cdot\mathbf{A}$ must be replaced by $\mathbf{A}\cdot\mathbf{B} = \overline{\mathbf{B}\cdot\mathbf{A}}$, and $t(\mathbf{A}\cdot\mathbf{B}) = \mathbf{A}\cdot t\mathbf{B}$ by $t\mathbf{A}\cdot\mathbf{B} = \mathbf{A}\cdot\bar{t}\mathbf{B}$.)

26. A linear combination in $\mathbf{C}^n$ is a sum $t_1\mathbf{A}_1 + \cdots + t_k\mathbf{A}_k$, where the t_j are complex numbers. *Linear dependence* and *basis* are defined for $\mathbf{C}^n$ exactly as for R^n. Prove the analogs of Theorems 8 and 9 for $\mathbf{C}^n$. (See Problem 24.)

27. Prove the analog of Problem 23 for a *complex* system of equations.

28. Let $r_1, \ldots, r_k$ be distinct complex numbers, let $n_1, \ldots, n_k$ be positive integers, and set $n = n_1 + \cdots + n_k$.

(a) Prove that when z is not equal to any of $r_1, \ldots, r_k$, then any linear combination

$$\frac{t_1}{z - r_1} + \frac{t_1}{(z - r_1)^2} + \cdots + \frac{t_{n1}}{(z - r_1)^{n1}} \qquad (n_1 \text{ terms})$$

$$+ \frac{t_{n1+1}}{z - r_2} + \frac{t_{n1+2}}{(z - r_2)^2} + \cdots \qquad (n_2 \text{ terms})$$

$$\vdots \qquad\qquad \vdots$$

$$+ \frac{t_{n-nk+1}}{z - z_k} + \cdots + \frac{t_n}{(z - r_k)^{nk}} \qquad (n_k \text{ terms})$$

can be written in the form

$$\frac{\left(\sum_1^n a_{j1}t_j\right)z^{n-1} + \left(\sum_1^n a_{j2}t_j\right)z^{n-2} + \cdots + \left(\sum_1^n a_{jn}t_j\right)}{(z - r_1)^{n1} \cdots (z - r_k)^{nk}}, \qquad (18)$$

where the a_{jk} are complex numbers depending on $r_1, \ldots, r_k$ and $n_1, \ldots, n_k$, but not on $t_1, \ldots, t_n$.

(b) Prove that if the numerator on the right in (18) is the zero polynomial, then $t_1 = \cdots = t_n = 0$. (Hint: Notice that the numerator N in (18) equals $t_{n_1}(z - r_2)^{n2} \cdots (z - r_k)^{nk}$ + [a polynomial that vanishes when $z = r_1$]; hence if $N \equiv 0$, then $t_{n_1} = 0$. With this established, show that $t_{n_1-1} = 0$, etc. Similarly, all the other coefficients are zero.)

(c) Conclude from Problem 27 that for *any* given complex numbers $b_1, \ldots, b_n$, the constants $t_1, \ldots, t_n$ can be chosen uniquely so that the numerator in (18) equals $b_1 z^{n-1} + \cdots + b_{n-1} z + b_n$.

(d) Prove that if $r_1 = \bar{r}_2$ and $n_1 = n_2$, then

$$\frac{t_1}{z - r_1} + \cdots + \frac{t_{n_1}}{(z - r_1)^{n_1}} + \frac{t_{n_1+1}}{(z - \bar{r}_1)} + \cdots + \frac{t_{2n_1}}{(z - \bar{r}_1)^{n_1}}$$

$$= \frac{t_1' + t_1'' Z}{z^2 - 2\operatorname{Re}(r_1)z + |r_1|^2} + \cdots + \frac{t_{n_1}' + t_{n_1}'' Z}{(z^2 - 2\operatorname{Re}(r_1)z + |r_1|^2)^{n_1}}$$

for uniquely determined constants $t_1', t_1'', \ldots, t_{n_1}', t_{n_1}''$.

(Parts (c) and (d) prove that if

$$Q = (x - a_1)^{r_1} \cdots (x - a_k)^{r_k}(x^2 + b_1 x + c_1)^{s_1} \cdots (x^2 + b_m x + c_m)^{s_m},$$

where $x^2 + b_j x + c_j$ has no real roots, and if R is a polynomial of degree $< n = r_k + 2s_m$, then R/Q can be written uniquely as a linear combination of

$$\frac{1}{x - a_1}, \ldots, \frac{1}{(x - a_1)^{r_1}}, \ldots,$$

$$\frac{1}{(x^2 + b_m x + c_m)^{s_m}}, \frac{x}{(x^2 + b_m x + c_m)^{s_m}}.)$$

29. (a) Prove the Schwarz inequality in $\mathbf{C}^n$:

$$|\mathbf{A} \cdot \mathbf{B}| \leq |\mathbf{A}| \cdot |\mathbf{B}|.$$

(Hint: Minimize $|\theta\mathbf{A} + t\mathbf{B}|^2$, where θ is fixed so that $|\theta| = 1$ and $\theta\mathbf{A} \cdot \mathbf{B}$ is real.)

(b) Prove the triangle inequality in $\mathbf{C}^n$:

$$|\mathbf{A} + \mathbf{B}| \leq |\mathbf{A}| + |\mathbf{B}|.$$

Curves in R^n

The study of curves is interesting in its own right, and moreover provides a useful tool in the study of functions of several variables.

§2.1 gives the basic theory of curves.

§2.2 applies it to some problems of motion (primarily, the motion of an electron) in order to show how certain curves (the helix and the parabola, for example) arise in nature.

§2.3 studies curves from a geometric point of view.

None of §2.2 is used in the rest of the book, nor is much of §2.3, but these sections put some meat on the skeleton given in §2.1.

2.1 DEFINITIONS AND ELEMENTARY PROPERTIES

A function $\mathbf{F}$ that assigns a vector $\mathbf{F}(t)$ to each point t in some interval of the real line is called a *vector function of one real variable.* We write

$$\mathbf{F}: [a,b] \to R^n$$

to show that $\mathbf{F}$ is a function from the interval $[a,b]$ to R^n.

The vector $\mathbf{F}(t)$ has n components $f_1(t), \ldots, f_n(t)$ such that $\mathbf{F}(t) = (f_1(t), \ldots, f_n(t))$; for example, if $\mathbf{F}(t) = (t, e^t, \sin t)$, the components are

$$f_1(t) = t, \qquad f_2(t) = e^t, \qquad f_3(t) = \sin t.$$

If the components of $\mathbf{F}$ are all continuous functions, then $\mathbf{F}$ is called continuous. A continuous vector-valued function defined on an interval is called simply a *curve,* and is usually denoted by the letter $\boldsymbol{\gamma}$, instead of $\mathbf{F}$.

This definition of curve as a function conflicts slightly with the general idea of a curve as a figure in space, but there are good reasons for our terminology. First, we need a reasonable abbreviation for "continuous vector-valued function of one variable." Second, the easiest way to describe analytically a curved line in space is by means of a vector-valued function of one variable, as you will see in the following examples.

The simplest example of a curve is

$$\boldsymbol{\gamma}(t) = \mathbf{A} + t\mathbf{B},$$

where $\mathbf{A}$ and $\mathbf{B}$ are fixed vectors in R^n, $\mathbf{B} \neq \mathbf{0}$. The range of $\boldsymbol{\gamma}$, i.e. the set

$$\{\mathbf{X} : \mathbf{X} = \boldsymbol{\gamma}(t) \text{ for some } t\},$$

is a straight line, by definition (see Fig. 1 and §1.4). When $n = 3$, this curve describes the motion of a particle in space, with constant speed and direction; at time t, the particle is at $\boldsymbol{\gamma}(t)$. If $\mathbf{A} = (a_1, \ldots, a_n)$ and $\mathbf{B} = (b_1, \ldots, b_n)$, then

$$\boldsymbol{\gamma}(t) = (a_1 + tb_1, \ldots, a_n + tb_n);$$

hence the components of $\boldsymbol{\gamma}$ are

$$\begin{aligned} \gamma_1(t) &= a_1 + tb_1 \\ &\vdots \\ \gamma_n(t) &= a_n + tb_n. \end{aligned}$$

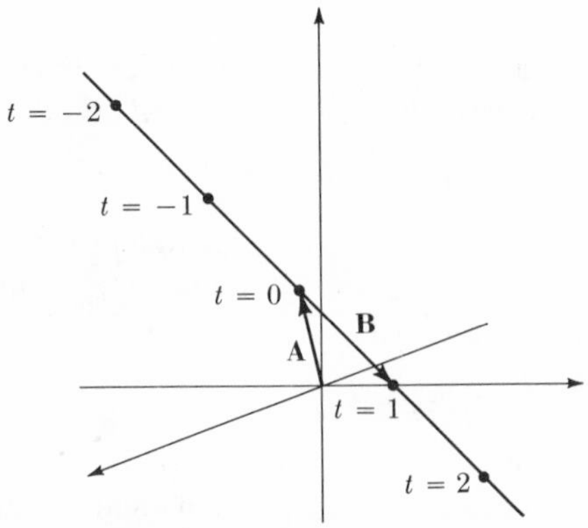

FIGURE 2.1

A more interesting example is the helix

$$\boldsymbol{\gamma}(t) = (a \cos t, a \sin t, bt) \tag{1}$$

which spirals steadily around a circular cylinder of radius a (see Fig. 2). This describes the motion of an electron in a constant magnetic field (see §2.2 below). The components of $\boldsymbol{\gamma}$ are

$$\begin{aligned} \gamma_1(t) &= a \cos t \\ \gamma_2(t) &= a \sin t \\ \gamma_3(t) &= bt. \end{aligned}$$

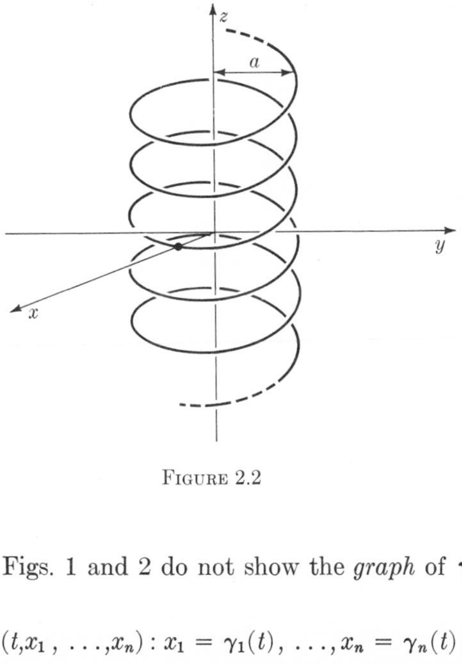

FIGURE 2.2

Notice that Figs. 1 and 2 do not show the *graph* of $\boldsymbol{\gamma}$; this would be the set in R^{n+1}

$$\{(t, x_1, \ldots, x_n) : x_1 = \gamma_1(t), \ldots, x_n = \gamma_n(t)\}.$$

What the figures actually show is the *range* of $\boldsymbol{\gamma}$, the set of points $\{\mathbf{X}: \mathbf{X} = \boldsymbol{\gamma}(t) \text{ for some } t\}$, sometimes called the *trace* of the curve $\boldsymbol{\gamma}$. Any point $\boldsymbol{\gamma}(t)$ in the range of $\boldsymbol{\gamma}$ is called a *point on the curve.*

The *derivative* of a curve $\boldsymbol{\gamma} = (\gamma_1, \ldots, \gamma_n)$ is defined by

$$\boldsymbol{\gamma}'(t) = (\gamma_1'(t), \ldots, \gamma_n'(t)).$$

For example, if $\boldsymbol{\gamma}$ is the helix (1), then

$$\boldsymbol{\gamma}'(t) = (-a \sin t, a \cos t, b).$$

If $\boldsymbol{\gamma}'(t)$ exists at each point where $\boldsymbol{\gamma}(t)$ is defined, then $\boldsymbol{\gamma}$ is called a *differentiable* curve.

The usual formulas for differentiation carry over to curves, as in the following theorem.

Theorem 1. *Let* $\boldsymbol{\gamma}$ *and* $\boldsymbol{\delta}$ *be curves, let* h *be a real-valued function, and suppose that* $\boldsymbol{\gamma}'(c)$, $\boldsymbol{\delta}'(c)$, *and* $h'(c)$ *exist. Then*

$$(\boldsymbol{\gamma}+\boldsymbol{\delta})'(c) = \boldsymbol{\gamma}'(c)+\boldsymbol{\delta}'(c) \tag{2}$$

$$(\boldsymbol{\gamma}\cdot\boldsymbol{\delta})'(c) = \boldsymbol{\gamma}'(c)\cdot\boldsymbol{\delta}(c)+\boldsymbol{\gamma}(c)\cdot\boldsymbol{\delta}'(c) \tag{3}$$

$$(h\boldsymbol{\gamma})'(c) = h'(c)\,\boldsymbol{\gamma}(c)+h(c)\,\boldsymbol{\gamma}'(c). \tag{4}$$

In the case of curves in R^3,

$$(\boldsymbol{\gamma}\times\boldsymbol{\delta})'(c) = \boldsymbol{\gamma}'(c)\times\boldsymbol{\delta}(c)+\boldsymbol{\gamma}(c)\times\boldsymbol{\delta}'(c). \tag{5}$$

Finally, if φ *is a real-valued function such that* $\varphi'(c)$ *exists, and* $\boldsymbol{\gamma}'(\varphi(c))$ *exists, then the chain rule holds:*

$$(\boldsymbol{\gamma}\circ\varphi)'(c) = \varphi'(c)\,\boldsymbol{\gamma}'(\varphi(c)). \tag{6}$$

Each of these formulas is proved simply by writing out the components on both sides of the equation and applying known results for real-valued functions to the individual components. For example, to prove (6), we have

$$(\boldsymbol{\gamma}\circ\varphi)(t) = \boldsymbol{\gamma}(\varphi(t)) = \big(\gamma_1(\varphi(t)),\ \ldots,\ \gamma_n(\varphi(t))\big);$$

hence by the chain rule for real-valued functions

$$\begin{aligned}(\boldsymbol{\gamma}\circ\varphi)'(c) &= \big(\gamma_1'(\varphi(c))\varphi'(c),\ \ldots,\gamma_n'(\varphi(c))\varphi'(c)\big)\\ &= \varphi'(c)\big(\gamma_1'(\varphi(c)),\ \ldots,\gamma_n'(\varphi(c))\big)\\ &= \varphi'(c)\,\boldsymbol{\gamma}'(\varphi(c)).\end{aligned}$$

Notice that the order of the factors in formula (5) for the derivative of the cross product $\boldsymbol{\gamma}\times\boldsymbol{\delta}$ has to be preserved, since generally

$$\boldsymbol{\gamma}'\times\boldsymbol{\delta}\neq\boldsymbol{\delta}\times\boldsymbol{\gamma}'.$$

Example 1. If $\boldsymbol{\gamma}(t)\equiv\mathbf{B}$ (a constant vector), then each component of $\boldsymbol{\gamma}$ is constant; hence $\boldsymbol{\gamma}'(t)=\mathbf{0}$ for all t.

Example 2. Applying formula (4) with $\boldsymbol{\gamma}(t)=\mathbf{B}$ and $h(t)=t$, we find that $t\mathbf{B}$ has the derivative $1\cdot\mathbf{B}+t\cdot\mathbf{0}=\mathbf{B}$.

Example 3. Applying formula (2) with $\boldsymbol{\gamma}(t)=\mathbf{A}$ and $\boldsymbol{\delta}(t)=t\mathbf{B}$, we find $\boldsymbol{\gamma}'\equiv\mathbf{0}$ (by Example 1) and $\boldsymbol{\delta}'\equiv\mathbf{B}$ (by Example 2), hence by (2) the sum $\mathbf{A}+t\mathbf{B}$ has the derivative

$$\mathbf{0}+\mathbf{B}=\mathbf{B}.$$

We have defined continuity and differentiability of a vector function in terms of its components, but these properties can be characterized more intuitively without referring to components.

Theorem 2. *A vector function* $\mathbf{F}: [a,b] \to R^n$ *is continuous at a point* c, $a < c < b$, *if and only if*

$$\lim_{t \to c} |\mathbf{F}(t) - \mathbf{F}(c)| = 0. \tag{7}$$

Similarly, $\mathbf{F}$ *is continuous at the left endpoint* a *if and only if*

$$\lim_{t \to a+} |\mathbf{F}(t) - \mathbf{F}(a)| = 0,$$

and $\mathbf{F}$ *is continuous at the right endpoint* b *if and only if*

$$\lim_{t \to b-} |\mathbf{F}(t) - \mathbf{F}(b)| = 0.$$

Formula (7) says that the distance between $\mathbf{F}(t)$ and $\mathbf{F}(c)$ tends to zero as t tends to c. Intuitively, when $\mathbf{F}$ is continuous, the moving particle does not jump around, but moves continuously from point to point.

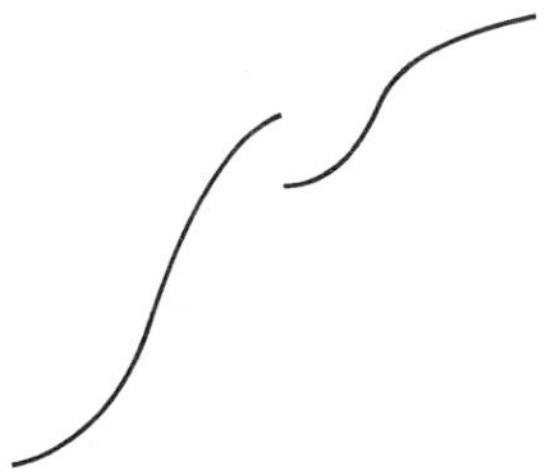

(a) Discontinuous curve

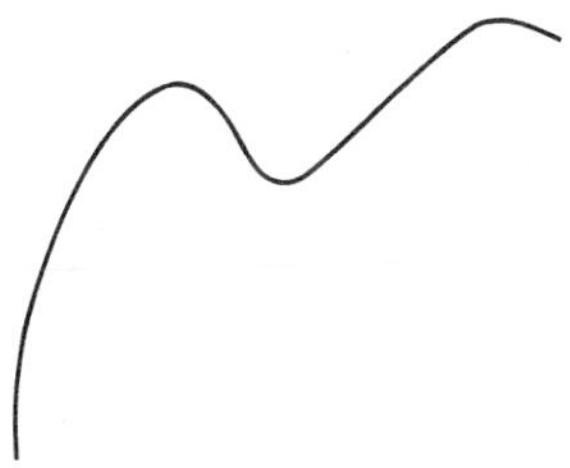

(b) Continuous curve

FIGURE 2.3

Proof of Theorem 2. Suppose that $\mathbf{F}$ is continuous at c; i.e. each component f_j is continuous at c. By Problem 6, §1.4,

$$0 \leq |\mathbf{F}(t) - \mathbf{F}(c)| \leq \sum_{j=1}^{n} |f_j(t) - f_j(c)|. \tag{8}$$

Since f_j is continuous at c, we have $\lim_{t \to c} |f_j(t) - f_j(c)| = 0$ for each j; hence the sum on the right in (8) has limit zero, and (7) follows.

Conversely, suppose (7) holds. Then for each j,

$$\begin{aligned} 0 \leq |f_j(t) - f_j(c)| &= \sqrt{[f_j(t) - f_j(c)]^2} \\ &\leq \sqrt{\sum_{k=1}^{n} [f_k(t) - f_k(c)]^2} = |\mathbf{F}(t) - \mathbf{F}(c)|. \end{aligned} \tag{9}$$

By (7), the last term on the right has limit zero as $t \to c$; hence $|f_j(t) - f_j(c)|$ has limit zero, so f_j is continuous at c.

The corresponding result when c is replaced by an endpoint a or b is proved in the same way.

Theorem 2 characterizes continuity at c by comparing $\mathbf{F}(t)$ to the *constant* vector $\mathbf{F}(c)$. We get an analogous characterization of the derivative $\boldsymbol{\gamma}'(c)$ of a curve $\boldsymbol{\gamma}$ by comparing $\boldsymbol{\gamma}(t)$ to the *straight line* curve $\boldsymbol{\gamma}(c) + (t - c)\boldsymbol{\gamma}'(c)$.

Theorem 3. *$\boldsymbol{\gamma}'(c)$ exists and equals $\mathbf{D}$ if and only if*

$$\lim_{t \to c} \frac{1}{|t - c|} |\boldsymbol{\gamma}(t) - \boldsymbol{\gamma}(c) - (t - c)\mathbf{D}| = 0. \tag{10}$$

Proof. The theorem follows from a chain of equivalent statements, beginning with $\boldsymbol{\gamma}'(c) = \mathbf{D}$. Let $\mathbf{D} = (d_1, \ldots, d_n)$. By definition, $\boldsymbol{\gamma}'(c) = \mathbf{D}$ if and only if $\gamma_j'(c) = d_j$ for every j. Further, $\gamma_j'(c) = d_j$ if and only if the function

$$f_j(t) = \begin{cases} \dfrac{1}{t - c}[\gamma_j(t) - \gamma_j(c)] & t \neq c \\ d_j & t = c \end{cases} \tag{11}$$

is continuous at $t = c$. Let $\mathbf{F} = (f_1, \ldots, f_n)$. By Theorem 2, the functions f_j are all continuous at c if and only if

$$\lim_{t \to c} |\mathbf{F}(t) - \mathbf{F}(c)| = 0. \tag{12}$$

But looking at (11), you can see that

$$|\mathbf{F}(t) - \mathbf{F}(c)| = \frac{1}{|t - c|} |\boldsymbol{\gamma}(t) - \boldsymbol{\gamma}(c) - (t - c)\mathbf{D}|;$$

hence (12) is equivalent to (10). *Q.E.D.*

Notice that if $\boldsymbol{\gamma}$ is continuous at c, then for *any* choice of $\mathbf{D}$ we have the limit relation

$$\lim_{t \to c} |\boldsymbol{\gamma}(t) - \boldsymbol{\gamma}(c) - (t - c)\mathbf{D}| = 0; \tag{13}$$

for

$$\begin{aligned} 0 &\le |\boldsymbol{\gamma}(t) - \boldsymbol{\gamma}(c) - (t - c)\mathbf{D}| \\ &\le |\boldsymbol{\gamma}(t) - \boldsymbol{\gamma}(c)| + |t - c|\,|\mathbf{D}|, \end{aligned} \tag{14}$$

and the right-hand side of (14) tends to zero as $t \to c$, by Theorem 2. However, dividing the expression in (13) by $|t - c|$ leads to the much stronger relation (10) which, by Theorem 3, can be satisfied for *only one* choice of $\mathbf{D}$, namely, for $\mathbf{D} = \boldsymbol{\gamma}'(c)$. The resulting straight line

$$\{\mathbf{X}: \mathbf{X} = \boldsymbol{\gamma}(c) + (t - c)\,\boldsymbol{\gamma}'(c) \text{ for some } t\}$$

is by definition the *tangent line* to $\boldsymbol{\gamma}$ at the point $\boldsymbol{\gamma}(c)$.

A simple rewriting of (10) yields

$$\lim_{t \to c} \left| \frac{\boldsymbol{\gamma}(t) - \boldsymbol{\gamma}(c)}{t - c} - \boldsymbol{\gamma}'(c) \right| = 0; \tag{15}$$

i.e. the difference quotient $\dfrac{\boldsymbol{\gamma}(t) - \boldsymbol{\gamma}(c)}{t - c}$ tends to $\boldsymbol{\gamma}'(c)$ as $t \to c$ (see Fig. 4).

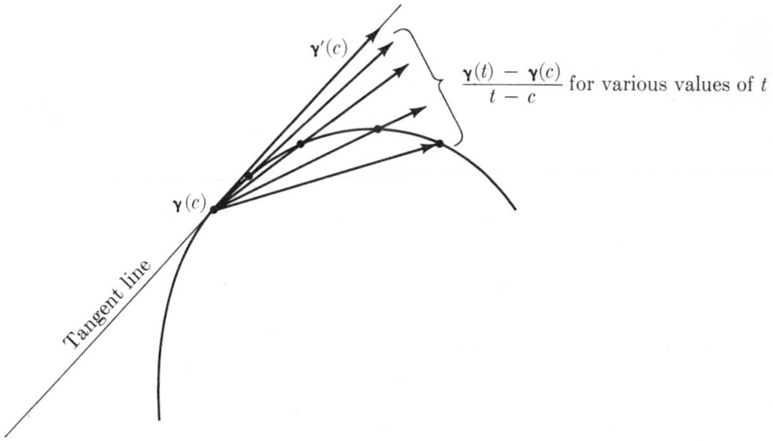

FIGURE 2.4

When $\boldsymbol{\gamma}$ describes the motion of a particle, the ratio

$$\frac{\boldsymbol{\gamma}(t) - \boldsymbol{\gamma}(c)}{t - c}$$

is the average velocity of the particle from time c to time t; hence, in view of (15), $\boldsymbol{\gamma}'(c)$ is called the *instantaneous velocity* at time c. The derivative $\boldsymbol{\gamma}'(c)$ is represented by an arrow beginning at the point $\boldsymbol{\gamma}(c)$ and tangent to the curve at that point, as in Fig. 4. For example, with the helix

$$\boldsymbol{\gamma}(t) = (2 \cos t,\ 2 \sin t,\ t) \tag{16}$$

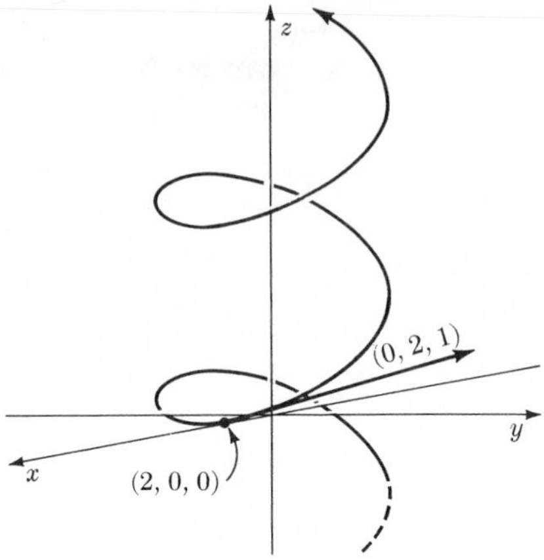

FIGURE 2.5

we have

$$\gamma'(t) = (-2 \sin t, 2 \cos t, 1) \tag{17}$$

and in particular

$$\gamma'(0) = (0,2,1).$$

Figure 5 shows $\gamma'(0)$ as an arrow tangent to the curve at the point $\gamma(0) = (2,0,0)$.

This same helix illustrates an interesting difference between curves in R^1 (i.e. real-valued functions of one variable) and curves in R^n, $n > 1$. In R^1 the mean value theorem holds: *If f: $[a,b] \to R^1$ is continuous, and f is differentiable on (a,b), then*

$$\frac{f(b) - f(a)}{b - a} = f'(t_0)$$

for some t_0 in (a,b). For curves in R^n, $n > 1$, this is no longer true. For example, taking the helix (16), we have

$$\frac{\gamma(2\pi) - \gamma(0)}{2\pi} = (0,0,1),$$

and you can see from (17) that the derivative $\gamma'(t)$ is never equal to $(0,0,1)$; in fact, $\gamma'(t)$ is never even parallel to $(0,0,1)$ (see Fig. 6). In terms of velocity, this shows that the average velocity from time a to time b may *not* equal the instantaneous velocity at any intermediate time.

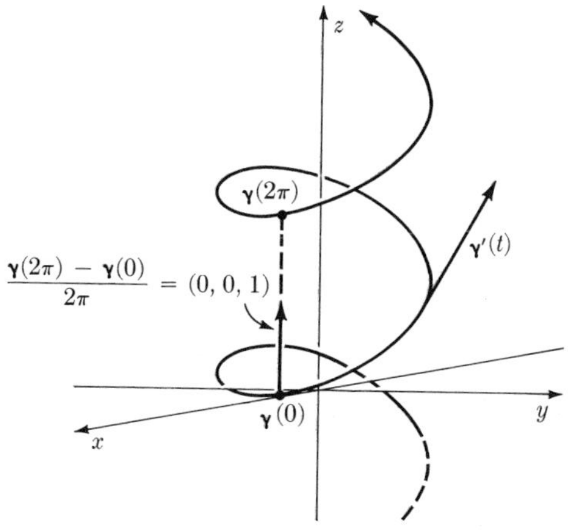

FIGURE 2.6

PROBLEMS

1. (a) Find the derivative of the helix

$$\gamma(t) = \left(\cos\frac{t}{2}, \sin\frac{t}{2}, t\right).$$

(b) Sketch the curve for $-\pi \leq t \leq \pi$, and sketch $\gamma'(0)$ as an arrow beginning at the corresponding point $\gamma(0) = (1,0,0)$ on the curve.

2. Repeat Problem 1 for the "elliptical spiral"

$$\gamma(t) = (\cos t, 2 \sin t, 3t).$$

3. Repeat Problem 1 for the "expanding spiral"

$$\gamma(t) = (t \cos t, t \sin t, t).$$

4. (a) At what points does the curve $\gamma(t) = (t - 1, 3 + t^2, 2t^2)$ intersect the plane with equation $14x + y + 3z = 10$?

(b) Find the angle of intersection in part (a), i.e. the complement of the angle between γ' and the normal to the plane.

5. (a) Find a point of intersection of the two curves γ and $\bar{\gamma}$, where $\gamma(t) = (\cos t, \sin t, 0)$ and $\bar{\gamma}(t) = (0, \cos t, \sin t)$. (Hint: Do not simply set $\cos t = 0$, $\sin t = \cos t$, $0 = \sin t$; the curves may go through the same point at different times.)

(b) Find a parametric equation of a line that is perpendicular to both γ and $\bar{\gamma}$ at the point of intersection found in part (a).

6. For the helix $\boldsymbol{\gamma}(t) = (a \cos t, a \sin t, bt)$, prove that $\boldsymbol{\gamma}'(t)$ is orthogonal to $(a \cos t, a \sin t, 0)$. Draw a sketch illustrating this situation.

7. The *normal plane* to a curve $\boldsymbol{\gamma}$ at a point $\boldsymbol{\gamma}(t_0)$ is the plane through $\boldsymbol{\gamma}(t_0)$ with normal $\boldsymbol{\gamma}'(t_0)$. Find the equation of the normal plane to the helix in Problem 6 at the point $(a,0,0)$.

8. Let $\boldsymbol{\gamma}(t) = \left(\dfrac{2t}{1+t^2}, \dfrac{1-t^2}{1+t^2}\right).$

   (a) Prove that $|\boldsymbol{\gamma}(t)| \equiv 1$.
   (b) Prove that $\boldsymbol{\gamma}$ and $\boldsymbol{\gamma}'$ are orthogonal.

9. (a) Find the derivative of the "twisted cubic" $\boldsymbol{\gamma}(t) = (t,t^2,t^3)$.
   (b) Sketch the curve for $-1 \leq y \leq 1$, and sketch $\boldsymbol{\gamma}'(0)$.
   (c) Is there any point t_0, $0 < t_0 < 1$, such that

$$\boldsymbol{\gamma}'(t_0) = \frac{1}{1-0}[\boldsymbol{\gamma}(1) - \boldsymbol{\gamma}(0)]?$$

   (Compare this equation to the mean value theorem.)
   (d) Is there any point t_0, $0 < t_0 < 1$, such that $\boldsymbol{\gamma}'(t_0)$ is parallel to $\boldsymbol{\gamma}(1) - \boldsymbol{\gamma}(0)$?

10. Repeat Problem 9, but this time use the curve $\boldsymbol{\gamma}(t) = (t,t^3)$ in R^2.

11. Suppose that $\boldsymbol{\gamma}$ has a derivative $\boldsymbol{\gamma}'$, that $\boldsymbol{\gamma}'$ has a derivative $\boldsymbol{\gamma}''$, and that $\boldsymbol{\gamma}''$ has a derivative $\boldsymbol{\gamma}'''$. Prove that

$$[\boldsymbol{\gamma}\cdot(\boldsymbol{\gamma}' \times \boldsymbol{\gamma}'')]' = \boldsymbol{\gamma}\cdot(\boldsymbol{\gamma}' \times \boldsymbol{\gamma}''').$$

12. Suppose that $|\boldsymbol{\gamma}(t)|^2$ is constant. Prove that for every t, $\boldsymbol{\gamma}(t)$ is orthogonal to $\boldsymbol{\gamma}'(t)$. Draw an illustrating sketch when $\boldsymbol{\gamma}$ is a curve in R^2, and another sketch for the case of a curve in R^3. (Hint: Use formula (3) with $\boldsymbol{\gamma} = \boldsymbol{\delta}$.)

13. Let $\mathbf{P}_0 = (0,1,0)$.
   (a) Let $\boldsymbol{\gamma}(t) = \mathbf{P}_1$ be the point on the helix in Problem 6 closest to $\mathbf{P}_0$. Show that $a \cos t = b^2 t$.
   (b) Prove that $\mathbf{P}_0 - \mathbf{P}_1$ is orthogonal to the velocity vector of the helix at $\mathbf{P}_1$.

14. Let $\boldsymbol{\gamma}$ be any differentiable curve and $\mathbf{P}_0$ be any point *not* on the curve. Suppose that there is a point $\mathbf{P}_1$ on the curve, not an endpoint, such that $\mathbf{P}_0$ is closer to $\mathbf{P}_1$ than to any other point on the curve. Prove that $\mathbf{P}_1 - \mathbf{P}_0$ is orthogonal to the curve at $\mathbf{P}_1$. (Hint: If $\mathbf{P}_1 = \boldsymbol{\gamma}(t_1)$, then $|\boldsymbol{\gamma}(t) - \mathbf{P}_0|^2$ has a minimum at $t = t_1$.)

15. Prove the derivative formulas (2), (3), (4), and (5).

16. Prove that if $\boldsymbol{\gamma}(t_0)$ is not zero, then

$$\left(\frac{1}{|\boldsymbol{\gamma}|}\boldsymbol{\gamma}\right)'(t_0) = \frac{1}{|\boldsymbol{\gamma}(t_0)|}\boldsymbol{\gamma}'(t_0) - \frac{\boldsymbol{\gamma}(t_0)\cdot\boldsymbol{\gamma}'(t_0)}{|\boldsymbol{\gamma}(t_0)|^3}\boldsymbol{\gamma}(t_0).$$

17. Suppose that $\boldsymbol{\gamma}$ is a curve in R^3 such that $\boldsymbol{\gamma}(t)$ is never zero and $\boldsymbol{\gamma}'(t)$ is parallel to $\boldsymbol{\gamma}(t)$ for every t.

(a) Prove that $\frac{1}{|\boldsymbol{\gamma}|}\boldsymbol{\gamma}$ is constant. (Hint: Use Problem 16 above and the fact that $\boldsymbol{\gamma}'(t) = c(t)\boldsymbol{\gamma}(t)$.)

(b) Prove that there is a single straight line through the origin which contains $\boldsymbol{\gamma}(t)$ for every t.

2.2 NEWTON'S LAW OF MOTION

Vector functions are perfectly adapted to the study of particles (electrons, for example) moving in space. If $\boldsymbol{\gamma}(t)$ denotes the position of the particle at time t, then the first derivative $\boldsymbol{\gamma}'(t)$ is called the *velocity*, its absolute value $|\boldsymbol{\gamma}'(t)|$ is the *speed*, and the second derivative $\boldsymbol{\gamma}''(t)$ is the *acceleration*. Newton's law of motion says that if a particle of mass m is moved by a force $\mathbf{F}$, then

$$\mathbf{F} = (m\boldsymbol{\gamma}')'.$$

If the mass m is constant, this reduces to the familiar rule that force equals mass times acceleration:

$$\mathbf{F} = m\boldsymbol{\gamma}''.$$

Two examples will suggest the impressive consequences of this simple equation.

First, suppose that the force $\mathbf{F}$ is constant. (This happens, for example, when an electron is moved by an electric field of constant strength and direction.) We write out Newton's law by components, setting $\boldsymbol{\gamma} = (x,y,z)$ and $\mathbf{F} = (a,b,c)$, and find

$$\begin{aligned} mx''(t) &= a \\ my''(t) &= b \\ mz''(t) &= c. \end{aligned}$$

The solutions of these three equations are well known to be

$$x = \frac{a}{2m} t^2 + x_1 t + x_0$$

$$y = \frac{b}{2m} t^2 + y_1 t + y_0$$

$$z = \frac{c}{2m} t^2 + z_1 t + z_0$$

where x_0, x_1, y_0, y_1, z_0, z_1 are constants. These three equations are summed up in the vector equation

$$\boldsymbol{\gamma}(t) = \frac{t^2}{2m} \mathbf{F} + t\mathbf{V}_0 + \mathbf{P}_0$$

where $\mathbf{P}_0 = (x_0, y_0, z_0)$ and $\mathbf{V}_0 = (x_1, y_1, z_1)$ are constant vectors (see Fig. 7). Setting $t = 0$, we find that $\mathbf{P}_0 = \boldsymbol{\gamma}(0)$; differentiating and setting $t = 0$ shows that $\mathbf{V}_0 = \boldsymbol{\gamma}'(0)$. ($\mathbf{P}_0$ is called the *initial position*, and $\mathbf{V}_0$ is called the *initial velocity*. Warning: Remember that the above formula for $\boldsymbol{\gamma}$ is valid *only when the force* $\mathbf{F}$ *is constant.*)

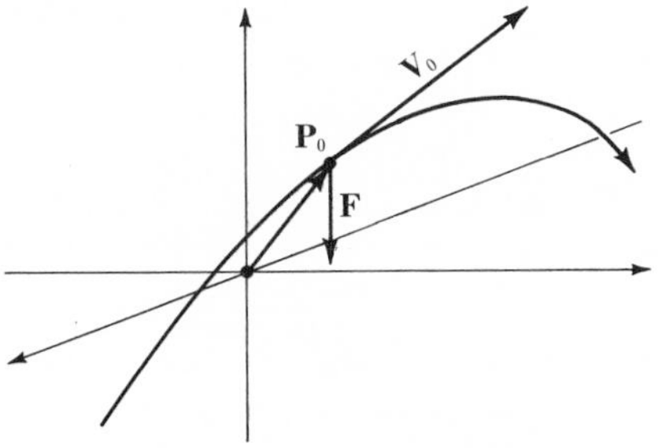

FIGURE 2.7

In particular, when there is no force, i.e. when $\mathbf{F} = \mathbf{0}$, we have

$$\boldsymbol{\gamma}(t) = t\mathbf{V}_0 + \mathbf{P}_0$$

so the particle moves with constant speed and direction along a straight line. This is another of Newton's laws of motion, sometimes called the law of inertia.

Our second example is a little more complicated. Suppose that $\boldsymbol{\gamma}(t)$ is the position at time t and that the force $\mathbf{F}$ has the form $q\mathbf{H} \times \boldsymbol{\gamma}'$, where q is a constant number and $\mathbf{H}$ is a constant vector. (This is the force acting on a particle of charge q in a constant magnetic field $\mathbf{H}$.) We will show that $\boldsymbol{\gamma}$ is either a *straight line*, a *circle*, or a *helix*.

To simplify matters, suppose that $\mathbf{H} = (0,0,h)$, where h is a numerical constant. Then

$$\mathbf{H} \times \boldsymbol{\gamma}' = \left(\begin{vmatrix} 0 & h \\ y' & z' \end{vmatrix}, \ -\begin{vmatrix} 0 & h \\ x' & z' \end{vmatrix}, \ \begin{vmatrix} 0 & 0 \\ x' & y' \end{vmatrix} \right)$$

$$= (-hy', kx', 0),$$

so Newton's law $\mathbf{F} = m\boldsymbol{\gamma}''$ becomes, with $\mathbf{F} = q\mathbf{H} \times \boldsymbol{\gamma}'$,

$$mx'' = -qhy', \qquad my'' = qhx', \qquad mz'' = 0,$$

or

$$\begin{aligned} x'' &= -cy' \\ y'' &= cx' \\ z'' &= 0 \end{aligned}$$

where we have set $c = qh/m$. The equation for z is easy to solve:

$$z = z_0 + z_1 t, \qquad z_0 \text{ and } z_1 \text{ constants.}$$

The other two equations look harder; they are simultaneous linear differential equations in the two unknown functions x and y. Actually, they are not so hard; we simply imitate the solution of simultaneous linear equations in algebra. Write them in the form

$$x'' + cy' = 0 \tag{1}$$

$$cx' - y'' = 0. \tag{2}$$

To eliminate y, differentiate equation (1), multiply equation (2) by c, and add; the result is

$$x''' + c^2x' = 0.$$

This can be regarded as an equation in x', and, as such, its solution is

$$x'(t) = a\cos(ct) + b\sin(ct) \tag{3}$$

for some constants a and b. We integrate to find x, and evaluate the constant of integration by setting $t = 0$ to find

$$x(t) = \frac{a}{c}\sin(ct) - \frac{b}{c}\cos(ct) + \left(x_0 + \frac{b}{c}\right) \tag{4}$$

where $x_0 = x(0)$. Going back to solve for y, we have from equations (1) and (3) that

$$cy' = ac\sin ct - bc\cos ct; \tag{5}$$

hence

$$y = -\frac{a}{c}\cos ct - \frac{b}{c}\sin ct + \left(y_0 + \frac{a}{c}\right) \tag{6}$$

where $y_0 = y(0)$. Finally, relating the constants a and b to the initial velocity, i.e. to $x_1 = x'(0)$ and $y_1 = y'(0)$, we find from (3) that $a = x_1$ and from (5) that $b = -y_1$; hence

$$
\begin{aligned}
x(t) &= \frac{x_1}{c}\sin(ct) + \frac{y_1}{c}\cos(ct) + \left(x_0 - \frac{y_1}{c}\right),\\
y(t) &= -\frac{x_1}{c}\cos(ct) + \frac{y_1}{c}\sin(ct) + \left(y_0 + \frac{x_1}{c}\right),\\
z(t) &= z_0 + z_1 t.
\end{aligned}
\tag{7}
$$

The three equations in (7) can be written as a single vector equation:

$$\boldsymbol{\gamma}(t) = \mathbf{A} + \bar{\boldsymbol{\gamma}}(t)$$

where $\mathbf{A} = \left(x_0 - \frac{y_1}{c},\ y_0 + \frac{x_1}{c},\ z_0\right)$ is a constant vector and

$$\bar{\boldsymbol{\gamma}}(t) = (r\cos(ct - \varphi),\ r\sin(ct - \varphi),\ z_1 t)$$

with

$$r^2 = \frac{x_1^2 + y_1^2}{c^2}, \qquad \frac{x_1}{rc} = \sin\varphi, \qquad \frac{y_1}{rc} = \cos\varphi.$$

The exact shape of the curve depends on the initial velocity $\mathbf{V}_0$.

(a) If $\mathbf{V}_0 = \mathbf{0}$, then $\boldsymbol{\gamma}(t) = \mathbf{P}_0$, and the particle does not move.

(b) If $x_1 = y_1 = 0$, but $z_1 \neq 0$, then $\boldsymbol{\gamma}(t) = \mathbf{P}_0 + t(0,0,z_1)$. The particle moves with constant speed and direction; there is no force acting since $\mathbf{H} \times \boldsymbol{\gamma}' = \mathbf{0}$. (Fig. 8)

(c) If $z_1 = 0$, but $x_1^2 + y_1^2 = r^2c^2 > 0$, then

$$\boldsymbol{\gamma}(t) = \mathbf{A} + (r\cos(ct - \varphi),\ r\sin(ct - \varphi),\ 0)$$

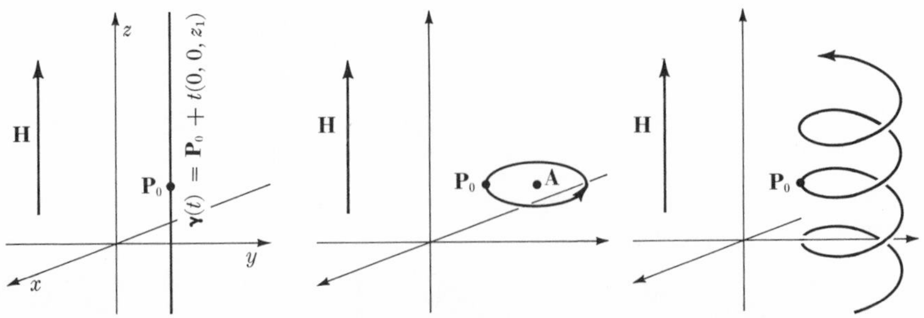

FIGURE 2.8 FIGURE 2.9 FIGURE 2.10

and the particle moves in a circle of radius r, parallel to the xy plane, with center **A**. (Fig. 9)

(d) In the remaining case, the particle moves in a helix spiraling around the line through **A** and parallel to the z axis. (Fig. 10)

PROBLEMS

1. In each of the following problems, find the velocity, the acceleration, and the force.
   (a) $\boldsymbol{\gamma}(t) = (2 \sin t, 3 \cos t, 4t), \quad m(t) = 5$
   (b) $\boldsymbol{\gamma}(t) = (2e^t, 2e^{-t}, 5 \cos t), \quad m(t) = e^{-t}$
   (c) $\boldsymbol{\gamma}(t) = (t^2, 3 + t^3, t^4), \quad m(t) = 1$
   (d) $\boldsymbol{\gamma}(t) = \mathbf{A} + t\mathbf{B}$ (where **A** and **B** are constant vectors in R^n), $m(t) = 1$
   (e) $\boldsymbol{\gamma}(t) = \mathbf{A} + t\mathbf{B}, \quad m(t) = t$

2. Describe the shape of the curve in Problem 1(a).

3. The paths in 1(a) and (c) intersect at $t = 0$. Find the angle between the forces at $t = 0$.

4. Let the constant force $\mathbf{F} = (0,0,e)$ move a particle of constant mass m on a curve $\boldsymbol{\gamma}$, and assume that $\boldsymbol{\gamma}(0) = (1,2,3)$, $\boldsymbol{\gamma}'(0) = (-1,-3,0)$. Find $\boldsymbol{\gamma}(t)$ for all t.

5. Let the variable force $\mathbf{F}(t) = (\cos t,0,1)$ move a particle of constant mass m in a curve $\boldsymbol{\gamma}$ with $\boldsymbol{\gamma}(0) = \boldsymbol{\gamma}'(0) = \mathbf{0}$. Find $\boldsymbol{\gamma}(t)$, and sketch the path.

6. A particle of constant mass m is moved in a curve $\boldsymbol{\gamma}(t) = (x(t),y(t),z(t))$ by a force $\mathbf{F} = (x(t),y(t),z(t))$, with $\boldsymbol{\gamma}(0) = \mathbf{P}_0$ and $\boldsymbol{\gamma}'(0) = \mathbf{V}_0$. Find $\boldsymbol{\gamma}(t)$ for all t. (Hint: The solution of $f'' = cf$ is $f(t) = Ae^{\sqrt{c}t} + Be^{-\sqrt{c}t}$, where A and B are constants.)

7. (a) Prove that if the acceleration $\boldsymbol{\gamma}''$ is always orthogonal to the direction of motion $\boldsymbol{\gamma}'$, then the speed $|\boldsymbol{\gamma}'|$ is constant. (Hint: $|\boldsymbol{\gamma}'|^2 = \boldsymbol{\gamma}' \cdot \boldsymbol{\gamma}'$.)
   (b) Prove the converse of part (a).

8. The acceleration of a curve $\boldsymbol{\gamma}$ is called *central* if $\boldsymbol{\gamma}''$ is always parallel to $\boldsymbol{\gamma}$, i.e. if $\boldsymbol{\gamma}'' \times \boldsymbol{\gamma} \equiv \mathbf{0}$. Suppose that $\boldsymbol{\gamma}$ has central acceleration.
   (a) Prove that $\mathbf{N} = \boldsymbol{\gamma} \times \boldsymbol{\gamma}'$ is constant.
   (b) Assuming $\mathbf{N} \neq \mathbf{0}$, prove that $\boldsymbol{\gamma}(t)$ always lies on the plane through the origin with normal **N**. (See Fig. 11.)

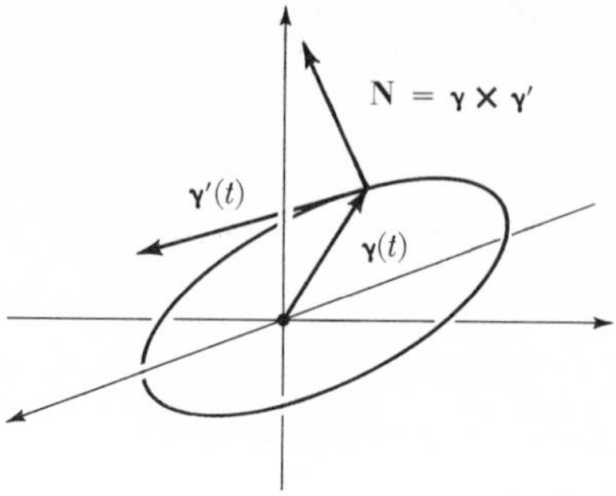

FIGURE 2.11

9. A moving point $\boldsymbol{\gamma}(t)$ has a constant acceleration $\mathbf{A}$, initial velocity $\mathbf{V}_0 = \boldsymbol{\gamma}'(0)$, and initial position $\mathbf{P}_0 = \boldsymbol{\gamma}(0)$.

(a) Prove that

$$\boldsymbol{\gamma}(t) = \frac{t^2}{2}\mathbf{A} + t\mathbf{V}_0 + \mathbf{P}_0 .$$

(b) If $\mathbf{A}$ and $\mathbf{V}_0$ are parallel, prove that $\boldsymbol{\gamma}(t)$ moves in a straight line (though not necessarily with constant speed).

(c) Assuming $\mathbf{A}$ and $\mathbf{V}_0$ are not parallel, prove that $\boldsymbol{\gamma}(t)$ lies in the plane through $\mathbf{P}_0$ with normal $\mathbf{A} \times \mathbf{V}_0$. (See Fig. 12.)

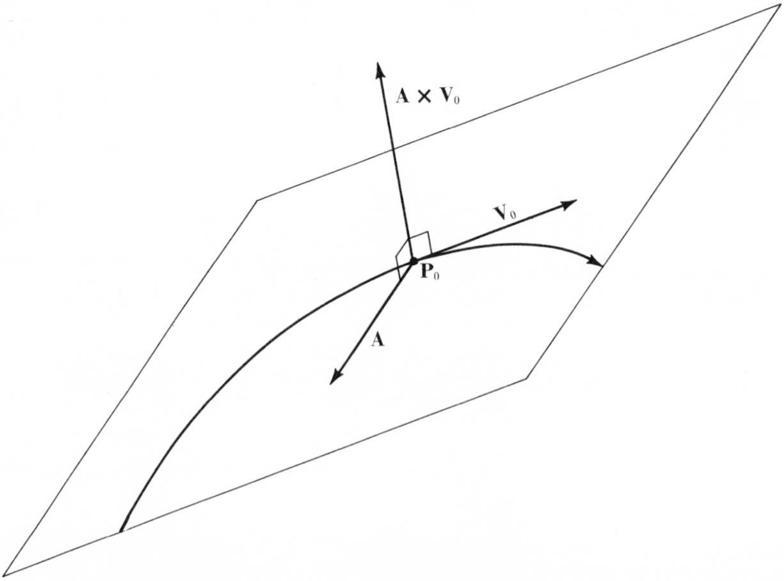

FIGURE 2.12

(d) The *speed* of the particle at time t is $|\boldsymbol{\gamma}'(t)|$. Assuming that $\mathbf{A} \neq \mathbf{0}$, find the time t at which the speed is minimum.

(e) Show that the minimum speed is zero if and only if the acceleration $\mathbf{A}$ is parallel to the initial velocity $\mathbf{V}_0$.

(f) Show that the velocity $\boldsymbol{\gamma}'(t)$ is orthogonal to the acceleration $\mathbf{A}$ when $|\boldsymbol{\gamma}'(t)|$ is minimum.

(g) Assume that the acceleration $\mathbf{A}$ and the initial velocity $\mathbf{V}_0$ are orthogonal, and let $\mathbf{F}$ be the point

$$\mathbf{F} = \mathbf{P}_0 + \frac{|\mathbf{V}_0|^2}{2|\mathbf{A}|^2}\mathbf{A}.$$

Prove that for every t, $|\mathbf{F} - \boldsymbol{\gamma}(t)|$ equals the distance from $\boldsymbol{\gamma}(t)$ to the line $\{\mathbf{Q}: \mathbf{Q} = \mathbf{B} + s\mathbf{V}_0 \text{ for some } s\}$ where

$$\mathbf{B} = \mathbf{P}_0 - \frac{|\mathbf{V}_0|^2}{2|\mathbf{A}|^2}\mathbf{A}.$$

(See Fig. 13. Hint: Recall that the distance d from a point $\mathbf{P}$ to the line $\{\mathbf{Q}: \mathbf{Q} = \mathbf{B} + s\mathbf{V}_0\}$ is given by

$$d^2 = |\mathbf{Q} - \mathbf{B}|^2 - \frac{1}{|\mathbf{V}_0|^2}((\mathbf{Q} - \mathbf{B})\cdot\mathbf{V}_0)^2,$$

and recall the Pythagorean theorem for orthogonal vectors.)

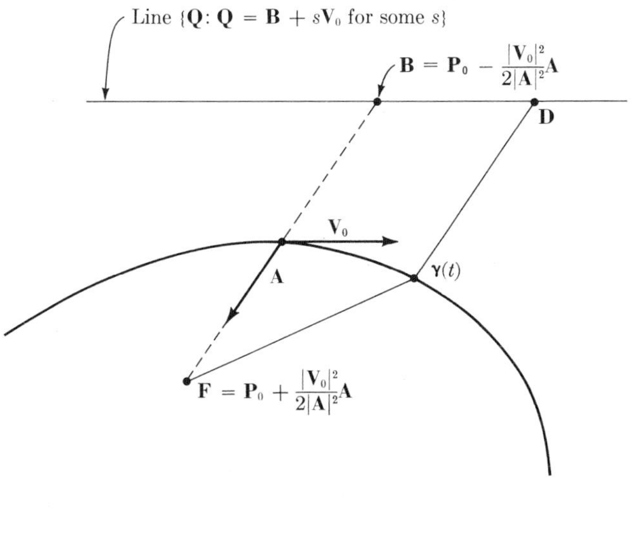

FIGURE 2.13 $|\boldsymbol{\gamma}(t) - \mathbf{F}| = |\boldsymbol{\gamma}(t) - \mathbf{D}|$

(*Remarks:* Part (f) shows that by shifting the time scale (i.e. by considering $\bar{\boldsymbol{\gamma}}(t) = \boldsymbol{\gamma}(t - t_0)$, where t_0 is the time at which $|\boldsymbol{\gamma}'(t_0)|$ is minimum) we can assume that $\mathbf{V}_0$ and $\mathbf{A}$ are orthogonal. Parts (c) and (g) show that $\boldsymbol{\gamma}(t)$ lies on a parabola whose focus is

$$\mathbf{F} = \mathbf{P}_0 + \frac{|\mathbf{V}_0|^2}{2|\mathbf{A}|^2}\mathbf{A}$$

and whose directrix is the line $\{\mathbf{Q}\colon \mathbf{Q} = \mathbf{B} + s\mathbf{V}_0\}$, where

$$\mathbf{B} = \mathbf{P}_0 - \frac{|\mathbf{V}_0|^2}{2|\mathbf{A}|^2}\mathbf{A}.)$$

10. A cathode ray tube lies in a constant magnetic field $\mathbf{H} = (0,0,h)$ parallel to the axis of the tube. (See Fig. 14.) At time $t = 0$ an electron of charge q and mass m leaves the origin 0 with velocity $(x_1, 0, z_1)$. The electron is intercepted by the face of the tube, which lies in the plane $\{(x,y,z) : z = d\}$.

(a) When, and at what point, is the electron intercepted? (Hint: In equation (7), recall that $c = qh/m$.)

(b) Show that the electron hits the face of the tube along the line through $(0,0,d)$ in the direction

$$\left(\sin\frac{dqh}{mz_1},\ 1 - \cos\frac{dqh}{mz_1},\ 0\right). \qquad (*)$$

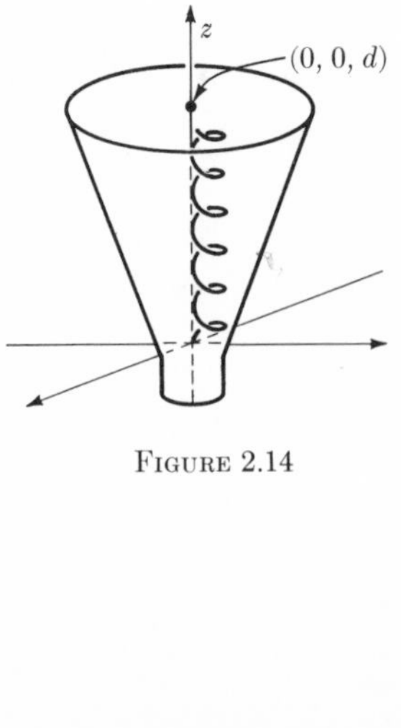

FIGURE 2.14

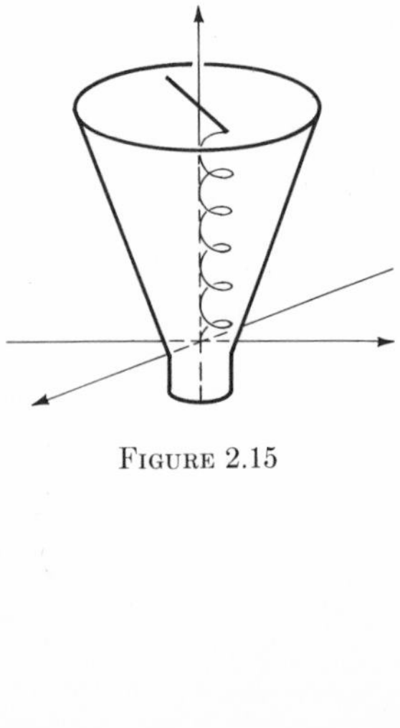

FIGURE 2.15

(*Remark:* When the electron hits the face of the tube, a luminous spot appears briefly at the point of impact. In practice, electrons are sent in a steady stream, all having the same value of z_1 but varying values of x_1; thus as the stream hits the face of the tube a segment of the line in part (b) is illuminated. (See Fig. 15.) The ratio q/m of charge to mass for the electron can be determined by the direction of this line segment because:

(i) the distance d from the origin to the face of the tube is known;

(ii) the constant z_1 equals $a\sqrt{q/m}$, where a is a constant determined by the construction of the tube.

Thus the number dqh/mz_1 in (*) has the form $Ah\sqrt{q/m}$, where A is a known constant. Suppose now that a certain value h_1 of the magnetic field h produces a line of slope m on the cathode ray tube. If h is increased gradually to the next larger value h_2 that produces the same slope m, then it follows from the equation (*) that

$$Ah_2\sqrt{q/m} = Ah_1\sqrt{q/m} + 2\pi,$$

and this equation determines $\sqrt{q/m}$.)

11. Solve the following systems of differential equations. (Note: x' and y' denote dx/dt and dy/dt.)

(a) $$\begin{aligned} y' &= x \\ x' &= y \end{aligned}$$

(b) $$\begin{aligned} x' - y &= 0 \\ x + y' &= 0 \end{aligned}$$

(c) $$\begin{aligned} x' + 2y + 3y' &= 0 \\ x + 3x' - y &= 0 \end{aligned}$$

(Hint: Write the equations (c) in the form

$$\begin{aligned} \mathbf{D}x + (2 + 3\mathbf{D})y &= 0 \\ (1 + 3\mathbf{D})x \qquad - y &= 0.) \end{aligned}$$

2.3 THE GEOMETRY OF CURVES IN R^3

In the study of motion, the first and second derivatives with respect to time (the velocity and acceleration) are crucial. From a geometric point of view, however, the time is irrelevant; what matters is the figure traced out, and particularly the features listed below (see Fig. 16):

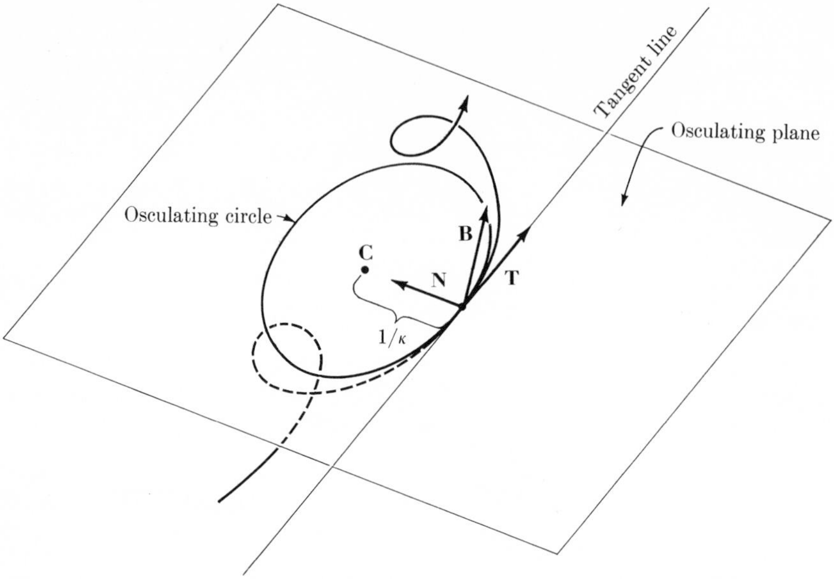

Center of osculating circle $= \mathbf{C}$

Radius of osculating circle $= \dfrac{1}{\kappa} = \dfrac{1}{\text{curvature}}$

Normal to osculating plane $= \mathbf{B} = \mathbf{T} \times \mathbf{N}$

FIGURE 2.16

Arc length
Tangent line (line of best fit)
Osculating* plane (plane of best fit)
Osculating circle (circle of best fit)
Unit tangent vector **T** (direction the curve is going)
Principal normal vector **N** (direction toward which the curve is turning)
Curvature (rate of change of direction per unit length)
Torsion (rate of "twisting" of the curve per unit length)

---

* Look that up in your Funk and Wagnalls.

The development of these ideas begins with the tangent line.

Let $\boldsymbol{\gamma}$ be a curve. If $\boldsymbol{\gamma}'(t_0) \neq 0$, the *tangent line* at $\boldsymbol{\gamma}(t_0)$ is given parametrically as the set

$$\{\mathbf{P}:\mathbf{P} = \boldsymbol{\gamma}(t_0) + (t - t_0)\boldsymbol{\gamma}'(t_0)\}.$$

When $\boldsymbol{\gamma}'(t_0) = 0$, on the other hand, there is generally no way to define the tangent, and Fig. 17 suggests why. Both curves shown there are differentiable everywhere, but neither curve has a tangent line at $\boldsymbol{\gamma}(0)$; the moving point comes in to the origin, stops there ($\boldsymbol{\gamma}'(0) = 0$), and goes off in a new direction. In the rest of this section we rule out such "corners" by requiring that $\boldsymbol{\gamma}' \neq 0$. We also rule out the irregularities which arise when $\boldsymbol{\gamma}'(t)$ does not exist or is not continuous; in fact, we shall assume that $\boldsymbol{\gamma}'$, $\boldsymbol{\gamma}''$, and $\boldsymbol{\gamma}'''$ all exist and that $\boldsymbol{\gamma}'$ is never zero.

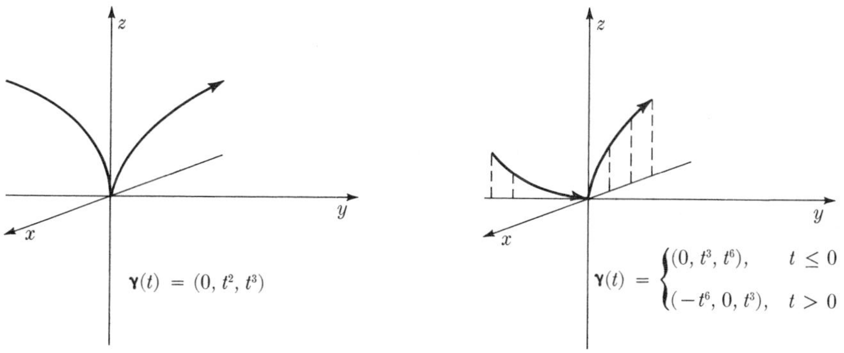

FIGURE 2.17

The length of curve, or *arc length* traversed by the curve $\boldsymbol{\gamma}$ from $t = t_0$ to $t = t_1$, is given by the integral

$$\int_{t_0}^{t_1} |\boldsymbol{\gamma}'|.$$

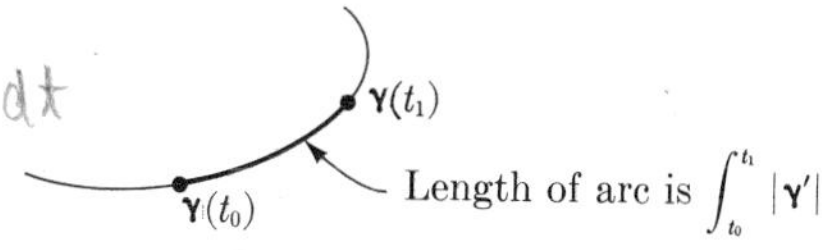

FIGURE 2.18

(See Fig. 18. We use this integral as a definition of the arc length, although it can be derived from a more intuitive definition based on "inscribed polygons," as in our *Calculus of One Variable*, Appendix I.10.) Since we assume that γ'' exists, it follows that γ' is continuous, so $|\gamma'|$ is continuous, and the integral exists. Since

$$\int_{t_0}^{t_1} |\gamma'|$$

gives the length of path traversed, it follows that $|\gamma'(t)|$ (the speed) is the rate at which the path is traversed. The speed is precisely what is irrelevant from the geometric point of view, though essential in the study of motion. By an appropriate change of variable, we can replace the given curve γ by a new curve $\mathbf{G}$ which traces out the same points but does not contain this geometrically irrelevant information.

Taking any "base point" t_0, we define an *arc length function*

$$\ell(t) = \int_{t_0}^{t} |\gamma'|.$$

From the fundamental theorem of calculus, $\ell' = |\gamma'|$. Since γ' is assumed to be different from zero, we have $\ell' > 0$, hence ℓ is strictly increasing. It follows that there is a differentiable inverse function, call it g, such that $\ell(g(s)) = s$ for every s in the range of ℓ. We now define a new vector function

$$\mathbf{G}(s) = \gamma(g(s)).$$

Since the range of g is the domain of ℓ, and g is monotone increasing, the function $\mathbf{G}$ traces out exactly the same points as γ and in the same order; but now the parameter s has a geometric significance, namely, it is the arc length. To prove this, notice that $\mathbf{G}'(s) = \gamma'(g(s))g'(s)$ and $g'(s) = 1/\ell'(g(s)) = 1/|\gamma'(g(s))|$; hence $\mathbf{G}'(s) = \gamma'(g(s))/|\gamma'(g(s))|$. It follows that $|\mathbf{G}'(s)| = 1$; hence the arc length traversed by $\mathbf{G}$ as s varies from 0 to s_1 is

$$\int_0^{s_1} 1 = s_1 ;$$

in other words, s gives the arc length on the curve $\mathbf{G}$ measured from the point $\mathbf{G}(0) = \gamma(t_0)$.

In the rest of this section we study $\mathbf{G}$ instead of γ. The vector $\mathbf{G}'(s)$ is a unit vector (since $|\mathbf{G}'(s)| = 1$) giving the direction of the curve; it is generally denoted $\mathbf{T}(s)$.*

Example 1. Take the helix $\gamma(t) = (\cos t, \sin t, t)$, and the base point $t_0 = 0$. Compute $\ell(t)$, $g(s)$, $\mathbf{G}(s)$, and $\mathbf{T}(s)$. *Solution*:

$$\gamma'(t) = (-\sin t, \cos t, 1), \qquad |\gamma'(t)| = \sqrt{2}$$

$$\ell(t) = \int_0^t \sqrt{2} = t\sqrt{2}\,.$$

* The rest of this section is not required in any other part of the text.

To find g, use the defining equation $\ell(g(s)) = s$, i.e.

$$g(s)\sqrt{2} = s, \qquad g(s) = \frac{s}{\sqrt{2}}.$$

Hence

$$\mathbf{G}(s) = \boldsymbol{\gamma}(g(s)) = \boldsymbol{\gamma}\left(\frac{s}{\sqrt{2}}\right) = \left(\cos\frac{s}{\sqrt{2}}, \sin\frac{s}{\sqrt{2}}, \frac{s}{\sqrt{2}}\right).$$

It is obvious that $\mathbf{G}$ traces the same path as $\boldsymbol{\gamma}$. Finally,

$$\mathbf{T}(s) = \mathbf{G}'(s) = \left(-\frac{1}{\sqrt{2}}\sin\frac{s}{\sqrt{2}}, \frac{1}{\sqrt{2}}\cos\frac{s}{\sqrt{2}}, \frac{1}{\sqrt{2}}\right)$$

$$= \frac{1}{\sqrt{2}}\left(-\sin\frac{s}{\sqrt{2}}, \cos\frac{s}{\sqrt{2}}, 1\right).$$

Curvature. Since $\mathbf{T}(s)$ is a unit vector giving the direction of the curve, its derivative $\mathbf{T}'(s)$ gives the *rate of change of direction with respect to arc length.* We define the length of this derivative to be the *curvature* κ,

$$\kappa(s) = |\mathbf{T}'(s)|.$$

Moreover, since $\mathbf{T}$ has constant length, the derivative $\mathbf{T}'$ is orthogonal to $\mathbf{T}$ (see Problem 12, §2.1). When $\mathbf{T}'(s) \neq \mathbf{0}$, we can divide by $|\mathbf{T}'(s)|$ to obtain a unit vector orthogonal to $\mathbf{T}(s)$, called the *principal normal vector* $\mathbf{N}$:

$$\mathbf{N}(s) = \frac{1}{|\mathbf{T}'(s)|}\mathbf{T}'(s) = \frac{1}{\kappa}\mathbf{T}'. \tag{1}$$

(See Fig. 16.) To simplify the rest of the discussion, we restrict our attention to points where $\mathbf{T}'(s) \neq \mathbf{0}$. Geometrically, $\mathbf{T} = \mathbf{G}'$ gives the direction of the curve, and $\mathbf{N} = (1/\kappa)\mathbf{T}'$ gives the direction toward which the curve is turning.

Suppose that $\mathbf{G}$ describes a circle of radius r. Then it is easy to show that the curvature $\kappa = 1/r$; the smaller the radius, the greater the curvature. Moreover, the principal normal $\mathbf{N}$ points toward the center of the circle (see Fig. 19), so the center is located at $\mathbf{C} = \mathbf{G} + (1/\kappa)\mathbf{N}$. (See Problems 9 and 11.)

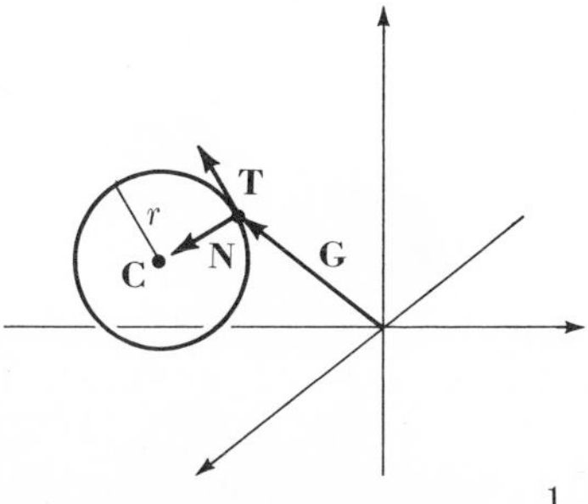

FIGURE 2.19 $\mathrm{C} = \mathrm{G} + r\mathrm{N} + \mathrm{G} + \frac{1}{\kappa}\mathrm{N}$

For a general curve, the point

$$\mathbf{C}(s_0) = \mathbf{G}(s_0) + \frac{1}{\kappa(s_0)}\mathbf{N}(s_0)$$

is called the *center of curvature* at $\mathbf{G}(s_0)$. This point together with the tangent line determines a plane, the *osculating plane* (see Fig. 16). The circle lying in this plane with center $\mathbf{C}(s_0)$ and radius $1/\kappa(s_0)$ is the *osculating circle*; it matches the curve both in direction and in curvature at the point $\mathbf{G}(s_0)$.

The cross product of $\mathbf{T}$ and $\mathbf{N}$ is a normal to the osculating plane, called the *binormal* $\mathbf{B}$:

$$\mathbf{B}(s_0) = \mathbf{T}(s_0) \times \mathbf{N}(s_0).$$

Since $\mathbf{T}$ and $\mathbf{N}$ are orthogonal unit vectors, $\mathbf{B} = \mathbf{T} \times \mathbf{N}$ is a unit vector orthogonal to both $\mathbf{T}$ and $\mathbf{N}$. Just as the line to which the curve adheres most closely at $\mathbf{G}(s_0)$ is the tangent line, the plane to which the curve adheres most closely at $\mathbf{G}(s_0)$ is the osculating plane. (See Fig. 16 and Problem 16 below.)

Torsion. Change in the binormal $\mathbf{B}$ amounts geometrically to a "twist" in the curve. If your intuition about space curves is very good, it may occur to you that this change in $\mathbf{B}$ must be directed toward $\pm\mathbf{N}$ and is perpendicular to $\mathbf{T}$ and $\mathbf{B}$, as the following theorem proves:

Theorem 5. *For each s where* $\mathbf{T}'(s) \neq \mathbf{0}$, *there is a number* $\tau(s)$ *such that* $\mathbf{B}'(s) = \tau(s)\mathbf{N}(s)$.

Proof. Since $\mathbf{T}$, $\mathbf{N}$, and $\mathbf{B}$ are mutually orthogonal unit vectors in R^3, we have

$$\mathbf{B}' = (\mathbf{B}'\cdot\mathbf{T})\mathbf{T} + (\mathbf{B}'\cdot\mathbf{N})\mathbf{N} + (\mathbf{B}'\cdot\mathbf{B})\mathbf{B},$$

by Theorem 10, §1.5. But $\mathbf{B}$ is a unit vector, so $\mathbf{B}'\cdot\mathbf{B} = 0$. And

$$\mathbf{B}' = (\mathbf{T} \times \mathbf{N})' = \mathbf{T}' \times \mathbf{N} + \mathbf{T} \times \mathbf{N}' = \mathbf{T} \times \mathbf{N}',$$

since $\mathbf{T}' \times \mathbf{N} = \kappa\mathbf{N} \times \mathbf{N} = \mathbf{0}$. Hence $\mathbf{B}'\cdot\mathbf{T} = 0$, and we have proved that $\mathbf{B}' = \tau\mathbf{N}$, with $\tau = \mathbf{B}'\cdot\mathbf{N}$. *Q.E.D.*

The number τ in Theorem 5 is called the *torsion* of the curve at the point in question. The torsion τ, like κ, $\mathbf{T}$, $\mathbf{N}$, and $\mathbf{B}$, is a function of the arc length s. Since $\mathbf{B}'$ describes the twisting of the curve and $|\mathbf{B}'| = |\tau\mathbf{N}| = |\tau|$, the torsion τ measures the amount of twisting; the sign of τ determines whether the curve is twisted toward $\mathbf{N}$ or toward $-\mathbf{N}$.

We now have two important derivative formulas. By the definition of $\mathbf{N}$,

$$\mathbf{T}' = \kappa\mathbf{N}, \qquad \kappa = \text{curvature}, \tag{2}$$

and by Theorem 5,

$$\mathbf{B}' = \tau\mathbf{N}, \qquad \tau = \text{torsion}. \tag{3}$$

There is a similar formula for $\mathbf{N}'$, namely,

$$\mathbf{N}' = -\kappa\mathbf{T} - \tau\mathbf{B}. \tag{4}$$

Formulas (2), (3), and (4) are the three *Frenet-Serret formulas.* The last one, (4), can be easily derived from the other two, as outlined in Problem 8 below.

We conclude this brief exposition with a few examples of the general theorems that can be proved about space curves.

Theorem 6. *If the curvature* $\kappa = |\mathbf{T}'|$ *is identically zero, then the curve* $\mathbf{G}$ *is a straight line.*

Proof. Since $\mathbf{T}' \equiv \mathbf{0}$, $\mathbf{T}$ is a constant vector. Since $\mathbf{G}'(s) = \mathbf{T}$ and $\mathbf{T}$ is constant, we have $\mathbf{G}(s) = s\mathbf{T} + \mathbf{C}$ for some constant vector $\mathbf{C}$, and the theorem is proved.

Theorem 7. *If the torsion* τ *is identically zero, then the curve lies in a plane, and this is the osculating plane at every point of the curve.*

Proof. If $\tau \equiv 0$, then $\mathbf{B}' \equiv \mathbf{0}$ by (3); hence $\mathbf{B}$ is constant. Let $\mathbf{G}(s_0)$ be any point on the curve; we want to prove that the curve lies in the osculating plane

$$\{\mathbf{P}: [\mathbf{P} - \mathbf{G}(s_0)]\cdot\mathbf{B} = 0\},$$

in other words, that the function $d(s) = [\mathbf{G}(s) - \mathbf{G}(s_0)]\cdot\mathbf{B}$ is zero for every s. But $d(s_0) = 0$, and

$$\begin{aligned} d'(s) &= \mathbf{G}'(s)\cdot\mathbf{B} && \text{(since } \mathbf{B} \text{ and } \mathbf{G}(s_0) \text{ are constant)} \\ &= \mathbf{T}(s)\cdot\mathbf{B} = 0 && \text{(since } \mathbf{T} \text{ and } \mathbf{B} \text{ are orthogonal);} \end{aligned}$$

hence d is identically zero, as was to be proved.

Theorem 8. *If the torsion* $\tau \equiv 0$ *and the curvature* κ *is a nonzero constant, then the curve is a circle of radius* $1/\kappa$.

Proof. Since $\tau = 0$, the curve lies in a plane. Thus, to prove that it is a circle of radius $1/\kappa$, all we have to do is find a fixed point $\mathbf{C}$ such that

$$|\mathbf{C} - \mathbf{G}(s)| = \frac{1}{\kappa} \quad \text{for all } s.$$

Clearly, **C** should be the center of curvature, so it is natural to look at the function

$$\mathbf{C}(s) = \mathbf{G}(s) + \frac{1}{\kappa}\mathbf{N}(s).$$

Differentiate this equation, and apply the Frenet-Serret formula (4). Since κ is constant and $\tau = 0$, the result is

$$\mathbf{C}'(s) = \mathbf{G}'(s) + \frac{1}{\kappa}\mathbf{N}'(s) = \mathbf{T}(s) - \mathbf{T}(s) = \mathbf{0}.$$

Hence **C** is constant; and from its definition,

$$|\mathbf{C} - \mathbf{G}(s)| = \left|\frac{1}{\kappa}\mathbf{N}(s)\right| = \frac{1}{\kappa},$$

so the theorem is proved.

PROBLEMS

1. Write parametric equations for the tangent line to the given curve at the given point.
(a) $\boldsymbol{\gamma}(t) = (t, \sin 4t, \cos 4t)$ at the point $\boldsymbol{\gamma}(\pi/8)$
(b) $\boldsymbol{\gamma}(t) = (2t, t^2, t)$ at the point $(2,1,1)$
(c) $\boldsymbol{\gamma}(t) = (e^{3t}, e^{-3t}, 3\sqrt{2}t)$ at $\boldsymbol{\gamma}(1)$
(d) $\boldsymbol{\gamma}(t) = (t, t^4, t^5)$ at $(1,1,1)$

2. For each curve in Problem 1, find the unit tangent vector $\mathbf{T} = \boldsymbol{\gamma}'/|\boldsymbol{\gamma}'|$ at the given point.

3. Find the length of the given curve over the given interval:
(a) The curve in Problem 1(a) from $t = 0$ to $t = \pi$
(b) The curve in Problem 1(b) from $t = 0$ to $t = 1$
(c) The curve in Problem 1(c) from $t = -1$ to $t = 2$

4. For the curve in Problem 1(a):
(a) Find the arc length function $\ell(t)$.
(b) Solve the equation $s = \ell(t)$ for t, and thus find the inverse g to ℓ.
(c) Write the curve with arc length as parameter, $\mathbf{G}(s) = \boldsymbol{\gamma}(g(s))$.

5. Repeat Problem 4 for the curve in Problem 1(c).

6. (a) For the helix $\boldsymbol{\gamma}(t) = (a\cos(kt), a\sin(kt), bkt)$, where a, b, and k are constants, find the arc length function $\ell(t) = \int_0^t |\boldsymbol{\gamma}'|$.

(b) Show that the inverse function g is

$$g(s) = \frac{s}{k\sqrt{a^2 + b^2}}.$$

(c) Show that the equation of the helix with arc length as parameter is

$$\mathbf{G}(s) = \left(a \cos \frac{s}{c}, a \sin \frac{s}{c}, \frac{bs}{c}\right),$$

where $c = \sqrt{a^2 + b^2}$.

7. For the helix $\mathbf{G}$ in Problem 6(c):
(a) find $\mathbf{T}(s)$
(b) find $\kappa(s)$ and $\mathbf{N}(s)$
(c) find $\mathbf{B}(s)$
(d) find $\tau(s)$
(e) Show that the Frenet-Serret formulas (2)–(4) are true for this particular curve.

8. For the helix in Problem 6, prove that $\mathbf{T}$, $\mathbf{N}$, and $\mathbf{B}$ all make constant angles with the vector $(0,0,1)$.

9. $\boldsymbol{\gamma}(t) = (r \cos t, r \sin t, 0)$ describes a circle of radius r in the xy plane. Show that its curvature is $1/r$.

10. Suppose that $\boldsymbol{\gamma}$ is a curve, ℓ the arc length function, g its inverse function, and $\mathbf{G}$ the corresponding curve with arc length as parameter. Suppose further that $s = \ell(t)$. Prove that

(a) $g'(s) = \dfrac{1}{\ell'(t)}$

(b) $\mathbf{T}(s) = \dfrac{1}{|\boldsymbol{\gamma}'(t)|}\,\boldsymbol{\gamma}'(t)$

(c) $\mathbf{T}'(s) = \dfrac{|\boldsymbol{\gamma}'(t)|^2\boldsymbol{\gamma}''(t) - [\boldsymbol{\gamma}'(t) \cdot \boldsymbol{\gamma}''(t)]\boldsymbol{\gamma}'(t)}{|\boldsymbol{\gamma}'(t)|^4}$ $\left(\text{Hint: } \dfrac{d\mathbf{T}}{ds} = \dfrac{d\mathbf{T}/dt}{ds/dt}\right)$

(d) $\kappa(s) = \dfrac{|\boldsymbol{\gamma}'(t) \times \boldsymbol{\gamma}''(t)|}{|\boldsymbol{\gamma}'(t)|^3}$

(Hint: Compute the length of the numerator in part (c) by taking its inner product with itself.)

11. The general circle of radius r about a given center $\mathbf{C}$ and perpendicular to a given unit vector $\mathbf{B}$ has parametric equations

$$\boldsymbol{\gamma}(t) = \mathbf{C} + (r \cos t)\mathbf{D} + (r \sin t)\mathbf{E},$$

where $\mathbf{D}$ is a unit vector orthogonal to $\mathbf{B}$, and $\mathbf{E} = \mathbf{B} \times \mathbf{D}$. Prove that the curvature of this circle is $1/r$. (There are two ways: (i) rewrite the circle with arc length as parameter, or (ii) use Problem 10(d). Note that $\mathbf{D}$ and $\mathbf{E}$ are orthogonal unit vectors.)

12. Recall that the center of curvature at $\mathbf{G}(s_0)$ is

$$\mathbf{C}(s_0) = \mathbf{G}(s_0) + \frac{1}{\kappa(s_0)}\mathbf{N}(s_0).$$

(a) For the helix $\mathbf{G}$ in Problem 6(c) prove that the center of curvature $\mathbf{C}(s)$ describes a helix. (See Fig. 20.)

(b) Prove that the curvature of $\mathbf{C}$ is the same as that of $\mathbf{G}$. (*Caution:* s is *not* the arc length on the curve $\mathbf{C}$.)

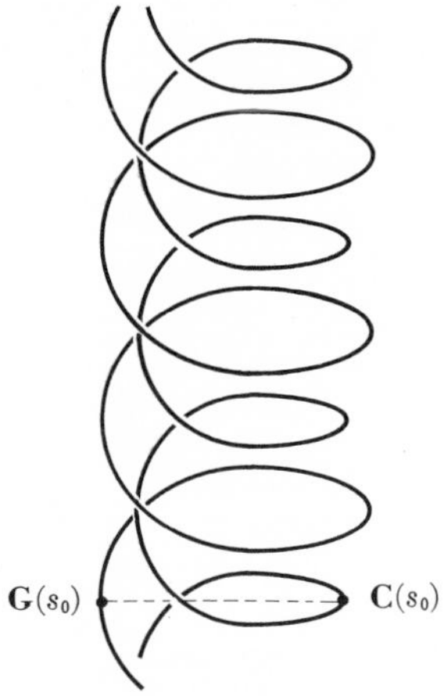

FIGURE 2.20

13. Derive the Frenet-Serret formula (4). (Hint: Use Theorem 11, §1.5, together with (2) and (3).)

14. Suppose that the curve $\mathbf{G}$ lies in a plane $\{\mathbf{P}: (\mathbf{P} - \mathbf{P}_0)\cdot\mathbf{A} = 0\}$.

(a) Prove that the tangent vector $\mathbf{T}$ is orthogonal to $\mathbf{A}$.

(b) Prove that the principal normal $\mathbf{N}$ is orthogonal to $\mathbf{A}$.

(c) Prove that $\mathbf{A} = (\mathbf{A}\cdot\mathbf{B})\mathbf{B}$, where $\mathbf{B}$ is the binormal. (See Theorem 10, §1.5.)

(d) Prove that

$$\mathbf{B} = \frac{\pm 1}{|\mathbf{A}|}\mathbf{A}.$$

(e) Prove that where $\mathbf{B}'$ exists, $\mathbf{B}' = \mathbf{0}$. (Hint: $\mathbf{B}(s) = b(s)\mathbf{A}$, where $b(s) = \pm 1/|\mathbf{A}|$; and $\mathbf{B}'(s_0)$ exists $\Leftrightarrow$ $b'(s_0)$ exists $\Leftrightarrow$ b has constant sign in an open interval about s_0.)

(*Remark:* The difficulty with the $\pm$ sign here can be eliminated only by using a more subtle definition of the principal normal $\mathbf{N}$. To see what the problem is, look at the curve $\boldsymbol{\gamma}(t) = (t,t^3,0)$ in Fig. 21, and compare the vectors $\mathbf{N}$ and $\mathbf{B}$ for $t < 0$ with the corresponding vectors for $t > 0$; at $t = 0$, they both switch signs.)

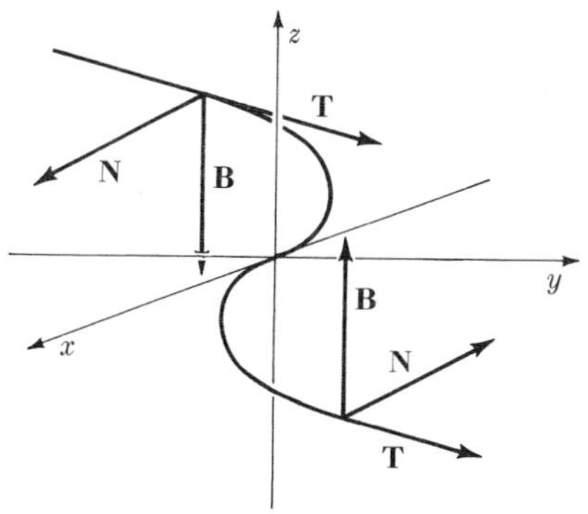

FIGURE 2.21

15. Suppose that $\mathbf{G}$, $\mathbf{G}'$, and $\mathbf{G}''$ are continuous in an open interval containing s_0. Prove that

$$\mathbf{G}(s) = \mathbf{G}(s_0) + (s - s_0)\mathbf{T}(s_0) + \tfrac{1}{2}(s - s_0)^2\kappa(s_0)\mathbf{N}(s_0) + (s - s_0)^2\mathbf{R}(s),$$

where $\lim_{s\to s_0} |\mathbf{R}(s)| = 0$. (Hint: Replace each component of $\mathbf{G}$ by a Taylor expansion of the form

$$f(s) = f(s_0) + (s - s_0)f'(s_0) + \tfrac{1}{2}(s - s_0)^2 f''(s_0) + (s - s_0)^2\frac{f''(\bar{s}) - f''(s_0)}{2},$$

with $\bar{s}$ between s and s_0.)

16. The signed distance from a point $\mathbf{P}_1$ to a plane

$$\pi = \{\mathbf{P}: (\mathbf{P} - \mathbf{P}_0)\cdot\mathbf{A} = 0\}$$

is given by

$$d(\mathbf{P}_1, \pi) = \frac{(\mathbf{P}_1 - \mathbf{P}_0)\cdot\mathbf{A}}{|\mathbf{A}|}.$$

(a) Prove that if π is the osculating plane to $\mathbf{G}$ at $\mathbf{G}(s_0)$, then

$$\lim_{s\to s_0} \frac{d(\mathbf{G}(s), \pi)}{(s - s_0)^2} = 0. \tag{5}$$

(Hint: Use Problem 15.)

(b) Prove that if $\pi = \{\mathbf{P}: (\mathbf{P} - \mathbf{P}_0)\cdot\mathbf{A} = 0\}$ is any plane and $\lim_{s\to s_0} d(\mathbf{G}(s), \pi) = 0$, then $\mathbf{G}(s_0)$ lies on π.

(c) Prove that if $\pi = \{\mathbf{P}: (\mathbf{P} - \mathbf{G}(s_0))\cdot\mathbf{A} = 0\}$ is any plane containing $\mathbf{G}(s_0)$, and

$$\lim_{s\to s_0} \frac{d(\mathbf{G}(s), \pi)}{|s - s_0|} = 0, \tag{6}$$

then $\mathbf{A}\cdot\mathbf{T}(s_0) = 0$.

(d) Prove that if π is any plane and (5) holds, and $\mathbf{G}''(s_0) \neq \mathbf{0}$, then π is the osculating plane. (Parts (a) and (d) together show that the osculating plane is the "plane of best fit"; it is the only plane π for which (5) is valid.)

Chapter III

Differentiation of Functions of Two Variables

Functions of several variables present some new and interesting questions that do not arise in the one-variable theory, not even in the theory of curves in R^n. Since most of these new questions are rather easy to visualize in the case of two variables, we begin by studying that case in detail, proceeding quickly through the parts that are close to the one-variable theory and dwelling on the new features. This chapter covers differentiation, and the next one combines the derivative theory with integration.

§3.1 Definitions, examples, and elementary theorems
§3.2 Polynomials of degree one
Appendix: Two-dimensional linear programming
§3.3 Partial derivatives, gradient, chain rule
§3.4 Computations with the chain rule
§3.5 The implicit function theorem
§3.6 Derivatives of higher order
§3.7 The Taylor expansion
§3.8 Maxima and minima.

3.1 DEFINITIONS, EXAMPLES, AND ELEMENTARY THEOREMS

The *domain* of a function of two real variables is a set in the plane R^2, that is, a set of ordered pairs of real numbers. To each point (x,y) in its domain, the function f assigns a real number, denoted $f(x,y)$, for example,

$f(x,y) = \sqrt{1 - x^2 - y^2}$	the domain of f is $\{(x,y) : x^2 + y^2 \leq 1\}$
$g(x,y) = xy/(x^2 + y^2)$	the domain of g is all points except $(0,0)$
$h(x,y) = e^x \cos y$	the domain of h is all points in the plane
$\varphi(x,y) = 1/\sqrt{xy}$	the domain of φ is $\{(x,y) : xy > 0\}$.

Nonmathematical examples are just as easy to find. For instance, the latitudes x and longitudes y of all points on the island of Bali form a set of ordered pairs (x,y). If the height above sea level at the point (x,y) is denoted $A(x,y)$, then A is a function of two variables, which we call the altitude function.

The *range* of a function f is the set of values assumed by f, the set

$$\{z: z = f(x,y) \text{ for some } (x,y) \text{ in the domain of } f\}.$$

In the examples listed above, the range of the first function f is the interval $[0,1]$ on the real line, the range of g is $[-\frac{1}{2},\frac{1}{2}]$, the range of h is $(-\infty,+\infty)$, and the range of φ is $(0,+\infty)$. The range of the Balinese altitude function is $[0,3142]$, if altitude is measured in meters.

The *graph* of a function f of two variables is defined to be the set of points in R^3 given by

$$\{(x,y,z): z = f(x,y) \text{ for some } (x,y) \text{ in the domain of } f\}. \tag{1}$$

This definition is virtually the same as for one variable, but sketching the graph is something else again. In general, the graph is a surface in R^3; for instance, the graph of the altitude function A is part of the surface of the earth. (This is a slight oversimplification neglecting the curvature of the earth, but the general idea is right.) The graph of the function

$$f(x,y) = \sqrt{1 - x^2 - y^2} \tag{2}$$

is the upper half of a sphere of radius 1, sketched in Fig. 1(a). (Notice that the z axis points up; this is a standard convention in sketching a graph (1), just as the y axis generally points up for the graph of a function of one variable.) The graph of (2) is a hemisphere because

$$\begin{aligned} z = \sqrt{1 - x^2 - y^2} \quad &\Leftrightarrow \quad z^2 = 1 - x^2 - y^2 \quad \text{and} \quad z \geq 0, \\ &\Leftrightarrow \quad x^2 + y^2 + z^2 = 1 \quad \text{and} \quad z \geq 0, \\ &\Leftrightarrow \quad |\mathbf{P}| = 1 \quad \text{and} \quad z \geq 0, \end{aligned}$$

where $\mathbf{P} = (x,y,z)$. The condition $|\mathbf{P}| = 1$ puts $\mathbf{P}$ on a sphere, and $z \geq 0$ puts $\mathbf{P}$ on or above the xy plane, i.e. on the upper half of the sphere.

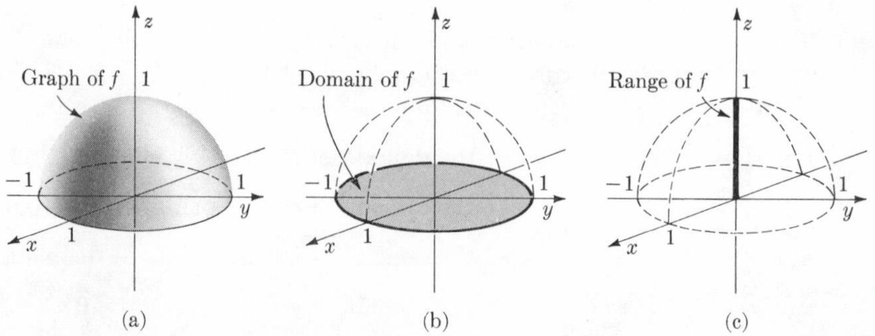

FIGURE 3.1

The *domain* of f is obtained by projecting the graph onto the xy plane; in Fig. 1(b) this projection is the unit disk $\{(x,y) : x^2 + y^2 \leq 1\}$. The *range* of f is obtained by projecting the graph onto the z axis; in Fig. 1(c) this projection is the interval $[0,1]$.

The graph of a function can be illustrated on paper by a perspective drawing like Fig. 1, but this is a severe artistic challenge to most of us. Another way to present the graph, calling for less artistic ability in the grapher but more visual imagination in the beholder, is to draw a "contour map"; that is, draw an xy plane, and show the curves along which f assumes various equally spaced values. Figure 2(a) does this for the Balinese altitude function, and Fig. 2(b) for the function f in (2). The result is called a "contour graph." Figure 3 gives three more contour graphs, and Fig. 4 gives the corresponding perspective drawings. The lines in Fig. 3 along which the function is constant are called *contour lines*, or *level lines*. Notice that the graph is steeper where the contour lines are closer together. The contour line where f assumes the value c shows exactly where the graph of f intersects the plane $\{(x,y,z) : z = c\}$ (see Fig. 5).

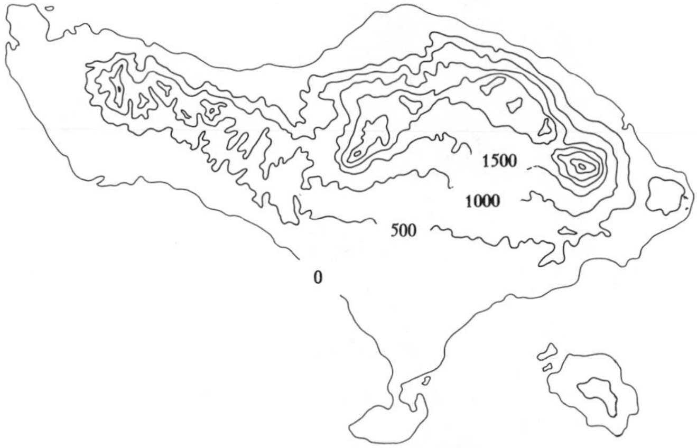

FIGURE 3.2 (a) Topographic map of Bali

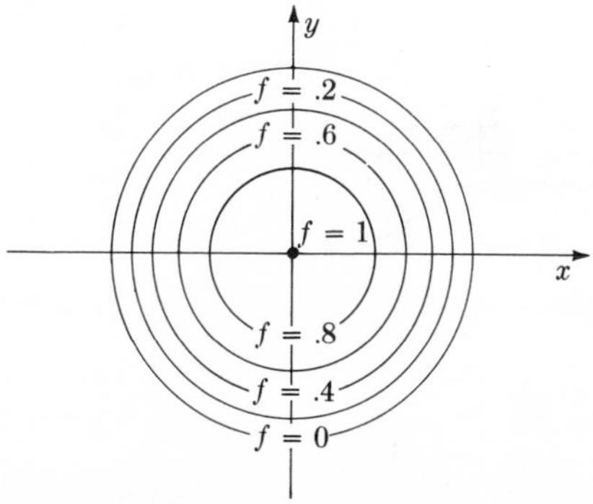

FIGURE 3.2 (b)

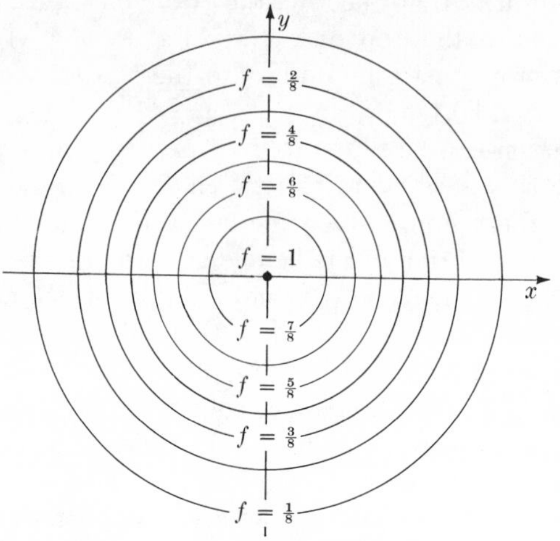

3.3(a) $f(x,y) = \exp\left[-\frac{1}{2}(x^2 + y^2)\right]$

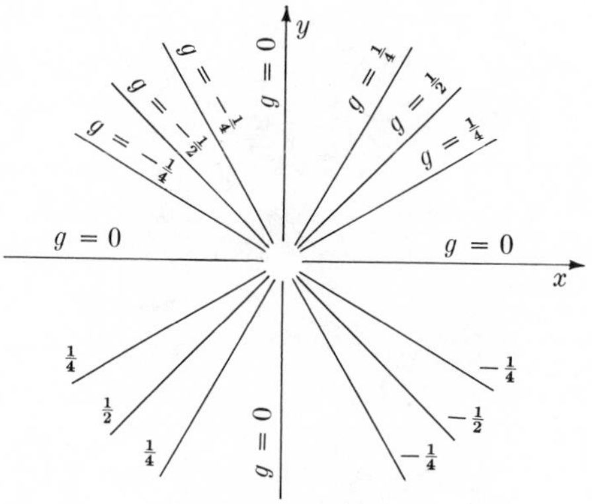

3.3(b) $g(x,y) = \dfrac{xy}{x^2 + y^2}$

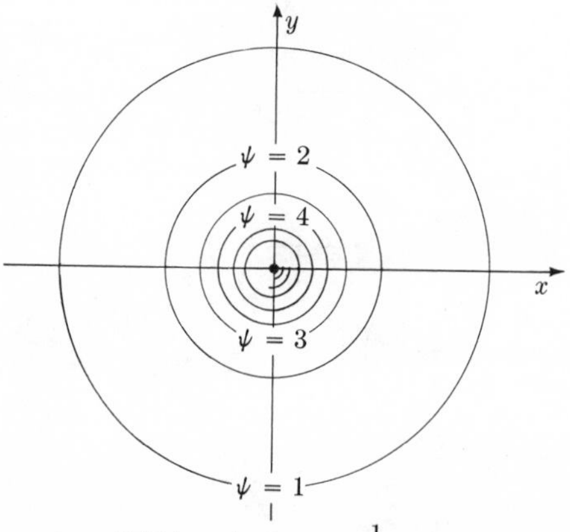

3.3(c) $\psi(x,y) = \dfrac{1}{\sqrt{x^2 + y^2}}$

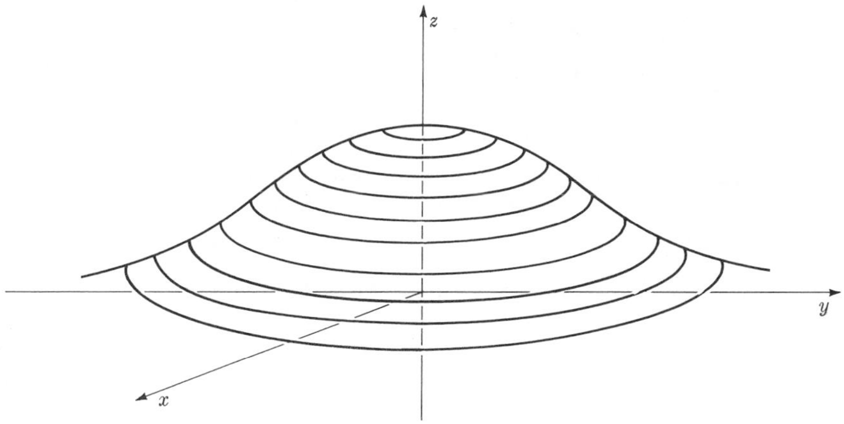

3.4(a)

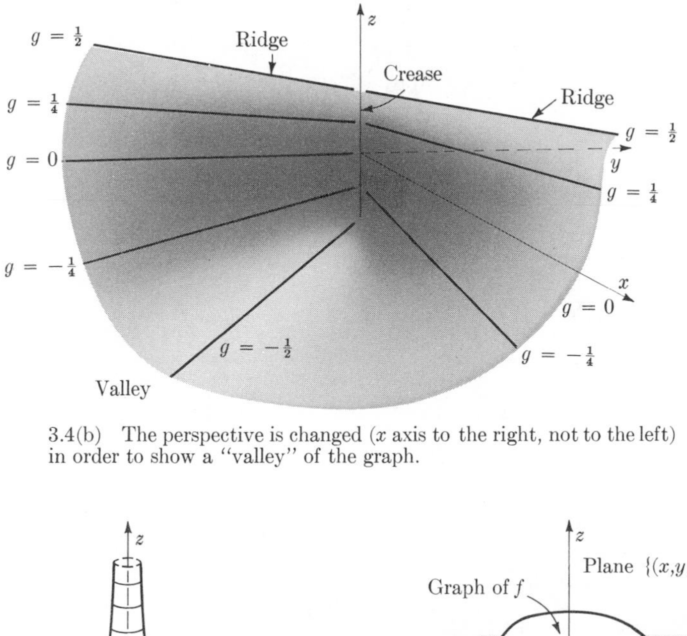

3.4(b) The perspective is changed (x axis to the right, not to the left) in order to show a "valley" of the graph.

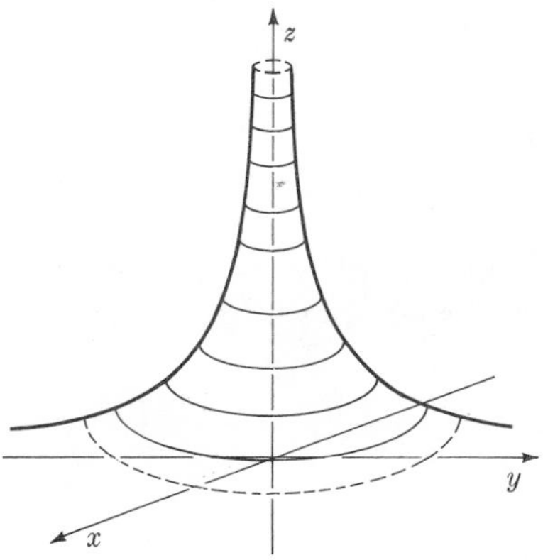

3.4(c)

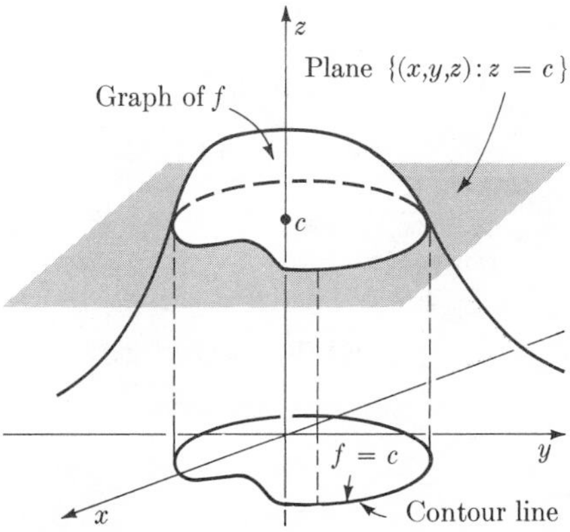

3.5

The ideas of limit and continuity carry over immediately from functions of one variable. We will state the definitions and theorems, but give no proofs, since they are exactly the same as before. We use the letter $\mathbf{P}$ to stand for (x,y), and $\mathbf{P}_0$ to stand for (x_0,y_0).

Definition 1. $\lim_{\mathbf{P}\to\mathbf{P}_0} f(\mathbf{P}) = L$ if and only if, for every $\epsilon > 0$, there is a number $\delta > 0$ such that

$$0 < |\mathbf{P} - \mathbf{P}_0| < \delta \;\Rightarrow\; f(\mathbf{P}) \text{ is defined and } |f(\mathbf{P}) - L| < \epsilon;$$

that is,

$$0 < \sqrt{(x - x_0)^2 + (y - y_0)^2} < \delta \;\Rightarrow\; f(x,y) \text{ is defined and } |f(x,y) - L| < \epsilon.$$

An alternate notation for $\lim_{\mathbf{P}\to\mathbf{P}_0} f(\mathbf{P})$ is

$$\lim_{(x,y)\to(x_0,y_0)} f(x,y),$$

which is clumsy but sometimes convenient.

A given function f can have at most one limit at a given point $\mathbf{P}_0$. Moreover, limits obey the usual algebraic rules:

Theorem 1. *If* $\lim_{\mathbf{P}\to\mathbf{P}_0} f(\mathbf{P}) = a$ *and* $\lim_{\mathbf{P}\to\mathbf{P}_0} g(\mathbf{P}) = b$, *then*

$$\lim_{\mathbf{P}\to\mathbf{P}_0} (f(\mathbf{P}) + g(\mathbf{P})) = a + b,$$

$$\lim_{\mathbf{P}\to\mathbf{P}_0} f(\mathbf{P})g(\mathbf{P}) = ab,$$

$$\lim_{\mathbf{P}\to\mathbf{P}_0} cf(\mathbf{P}) = ca \qquad (\textit{where } c \textit{ is any constant}),$$

$$\lim_{\mathbf{P}\to\mathbf{P}_0} \frac{f(\mathbf{P})}{g(\mathbf{P})} = \frac{a}{b} \qquad (\textit{if } b \neq 0).$$

Definition 2. f is *continuous* at $\mathbf{P}_0$ if and only if $\mathbf{P}_0$ is in the domain of f and, for every $\epsilon > 0$, there is $\delta > 0$ such that for all points $\mathbf{P}$ in the domain of f,

$$|\mathbf{P} - \mathbf{P}_0| < \delta \;\Rightarrow\; |f(\mathbf{P}) - f(\mathbf{P}_0)| < \epsilon;$$

that is,

$$\sqrt{(x - x_0)^2 + (y - y_0)^2} < \delta \;\Rightarrow\; |f(x,y) - f(x_0,y_0)| < \epsilon.$$

Theorem 2. *If f and g are continuous at $\mathbf{P}_0$, then so are $f + g$, fg, and cf (where c is any constant). If, in addition, $g(\mathbf{P}_0) \neq 0$, then f/g is continuous at $\mathbf{P}_0$.*

Theorem 3. Composition of Continuous Functions. *Let f be continuous at $\mathbf{P}_0$.*

(i) *If g is continuous at $f(\mathbf{P}_0)$, then $g \circ f$ is continuous at $\mathbf{P}_0$. (Here, g is a function of* one *real variable, and $g \circ f$ is the composite function defined by $(g \circ f)(\mathbf{P}) = g(f(\mathbf{P}))$.)*

(ii) *If $\boldsymbol{\gamma}$ is a curve in the plane which is continuous at t_0, and $\boldsymbol{\gamma}(t_0) = \mathbf{P}_0$, then $f \circ \boldsymbol{\gamma}$ is continuous at t_0.*

The functions we ordinarily encounter are continuous at "most" of the points where they are defined; the exceptional points of discontinuity show up on the contour graph where contour lines for different values of f come together (*example:* the point (0,0) in Fig. 3(b)) or where contour lines pile up (*example:* the point (0,0) in Fig. 3(c)). The first possibility corresponds to a "crinkly" part of the graph (Fig. 4(b)), and the second to a place where the graph "blows up" (Fig. 4(c)).

The domains of functions of one variable are generally taken to be intervals, but in several variables they may be more complicated. The plane sets most nearly analogous to open intervals are *open rectangles*

$$R = \{(x,y) : a < x < b,\ c < y < d\}$$

(Fig. 6) and *open disks*

$$D = \{\mathbf{P} : |\mathbf{P} - \mathbf{A}| < r\}.$$

But these are too special. The general concept we need is that of an *open set.*

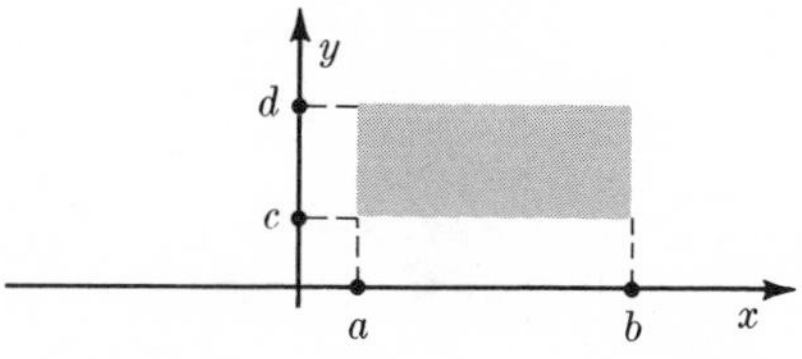

Rectangle $\{(x,y): a < x < b, c < y < d\}$

FIGURE 3.6

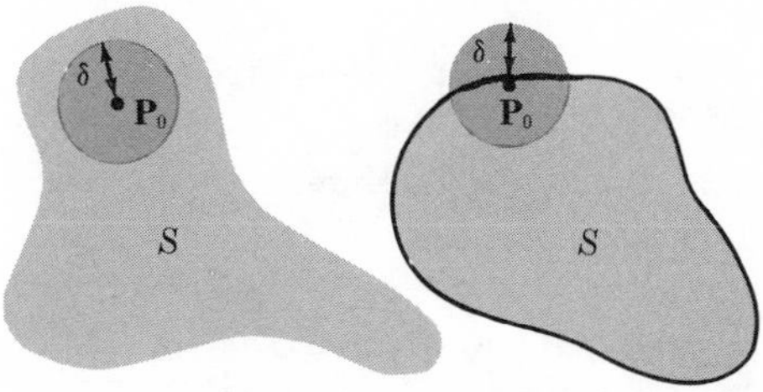

Open Not open

FIGURE 3.7

A set S in R^2 is called *open* if every point $\mathbf{P}_0$ in S is the center of an open disk of positive radius contained entirely in S. (See Fig. 7.) More formally:

Definition 3. A set S in R^2 is *open* if for every point $\mathbf{P}_0$ in S there is a number $\delta > 0$ such that

$$|\mathbf{P} - \mathbf{P}_0| < \delta \quad \Rightarrow \quad \mathbf{P} \text{ is in } S.$$

Intuitively, a set S is open if it contains none of the points on its boundary. Every open disk $S = \{\mathbf{P}: |\mathbf{P} - \mathbf{A}| < r\}$ is an open set in the sense of Definition 3. To prove it, let $\mathbf{P}_0$ be any point in S. Then

$$\delta = r - |\mathbf{P}_0 - \mathbf{A}|$$

is a positive number, and the disk

$$\{\mathbf{P}: |\mathbf{P} - \mathbf{P}_0| < \delta\}$$

is contained entirely in S, since by the triangle inequality

$$|\mathbf{P} - \mathbf{P}_0| < \delta \quad \Rightarrow \quad |\mathbf{P} - \mathbf{A}| \le |\mathbf{P} - \mathbf{P}_0| + |\mathbf{P}_0 - \mathbf{A}| < \delta + |\mathbf{P}_0 - \mathbf{A}| = r$$
$$\Rightarrow \quad \mathbf{P} \quad \text{is in } S.$$

(See Fig. 8.) As you might expect, the *closed* disk $\{\mathbf{P}: |\mathbf{P}| \le 1\}$ is not an open set. Any boundary point $\mathbf{P}_0$ violates the condition in Definition 3; no matter how small $\delta > 0$ is chosen, the disk

$$\{\mathbf{P}: |\mathbf{P} - \mathbf{P}_0| < \delta\}$$

contains points $\mathbf{P}$ that are *not* in the closed unit disk. (See Fig. 9.)

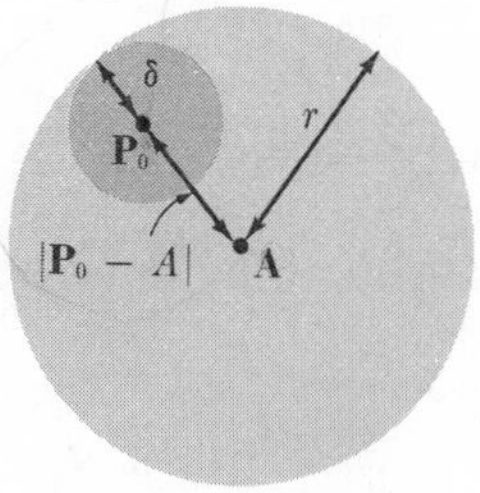

FIGURE 3.8

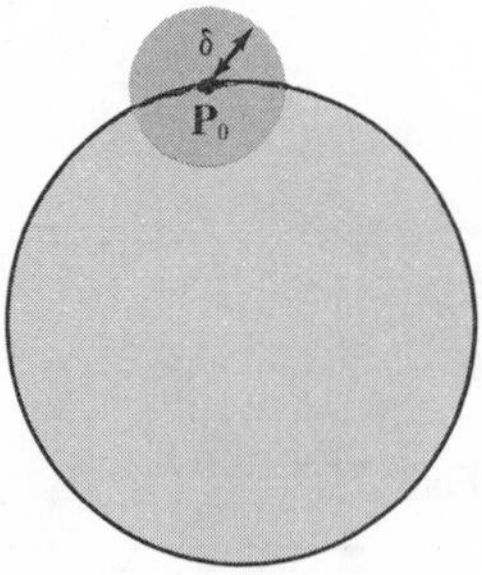

FIGURE 3.9

Similarly, the set $\{(x,y): xy > 0\}$ is open, but the set $\{(x,y): xy \geq 0\}$ is not. Roughly speaking, sets defined by strict inequalities ($<$ or $>$) are open, and sets defined by $\leq$, $\geq$, or $=$ are generally not open.

One advantage of considering functions defined on open sets shows up in

Theorem 4. *If the domain of f is an open set, then f is continuous at $\mathbf{P}_0$ if and only if* $\lim_{\mathbf{P}\to\mathbf{P}_0} f(\mathbf{P}) = f(\mathbf{P}_0)$.

Proof. The only difference between the two statements

$$f \text{ is continuous at } \mathbf{P}_0$$

and

$$\lim_{\mathbf{P}\to\mathbf{P}_0} f(\mathbf{P}) = f(\mathbf{P}_0)$$

is that the second statement requires f to be defined in some disk of radius $\delta > 0$ about $\mathbf{P}_0$ (see Definitions 1 and 2). Since the domain of f is an open set, f is in fact defined in such a disk, so the two statements about f are equivalent.

We conclude with some examples of limits, continuity, and open sets.

Example 1. If $f(\mathbf{P}) = c$ (a constant), then $\lim_{\mathbf{P}\to\mathbf{P}_0} f(\mathbf{P}) = c$.

Proof. Given $\epsilon > 0$, *every* $\delta > 0$ satisfies the conditions of Definition 1, since

$$0 < |\mathbf{P} - \mathbf{P}_0| < \delta \Rightarrow |f(\mathbf{P}) - f(\mathbf{P}_0)| = |c - c| = 0 < \epsilon.$$

Example 2. $\lim_{(x,y)\to(x_0,y_0)} x = x_0$.

Proof. Given $\epsilon > 0$, choose $\delta = \epsilon$. Since $|x - x_0| \leq \sqrt{|x - x_0|^2 + |y - y_0|^2}$, we have

$$0 < \sqrt{|x - x_0|^2 + |y - y_0|^2} < \delta \Rightarrow |x - x_0| < \delta \Rightarrow |x - x_0| < \epsilon;$$

hence Definition 1 is satisfied.

A similar proof shows that $\lim_{(x,y)\to(x_0,y_0)} y = y_0$. These results combine with Theorems 2, 3, and 4 to prove the continuity of functions given by simple expressions such as $x^2 + y^2$, $e^{x^2+y^2}$, $\sin(xe^y)$, and so on.

Example 3. The set $S = \{(x,y): |y| > 1\}$ is open.

Proof. If $|y_0| > 1$, then $\delta = |y_0| - 1 > 0$, and the disk of radius δ lies in S (see Fig. 10) since

$$\sqrt{(x - x_0)^2 + |y - y_0|^2} < \delta \Rightarrow |y - y_0| < \delta \Rightarrow |y| > |y_0| - \delta = 1.$$

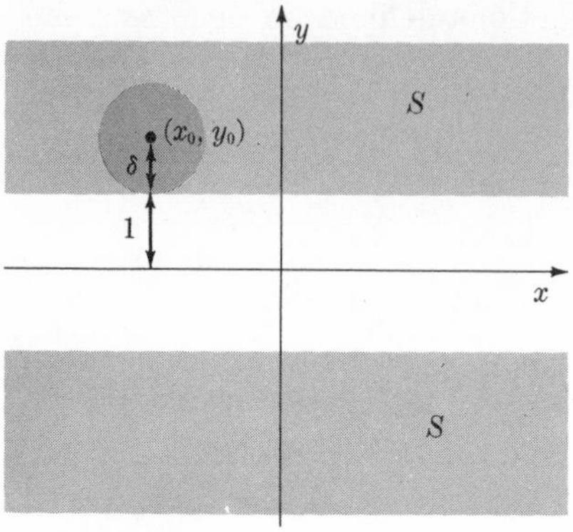

FIGURE 3.10 $S = \{(x,y): |y| > 1\}$, $\delta = |y_0| - 1$

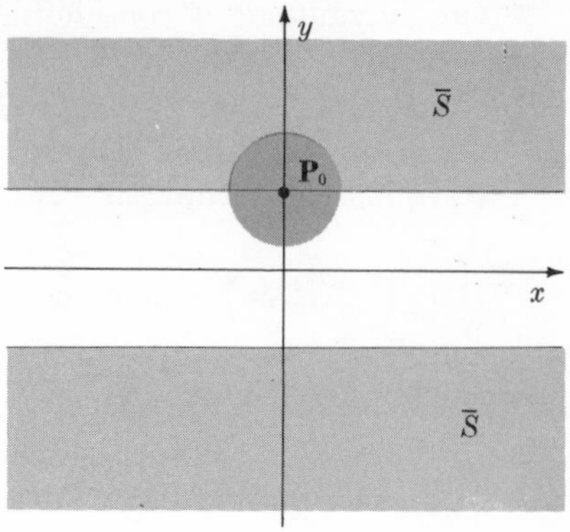

3.11 $\bar{S} = \{(x,y): |y| \geq 1\}$, $\mathbf{P}_0 = (0,1)$

Example 4. The set $\bar{S} = \{(x,y): |y| \geq 1\}$ is *not* open. Intuitively, the reason for this is that it contains boundary points along the lines $y = \pm 1$. To prove that $\bar{S}$ is not open, we take the point $\mathbf{P}_0$ in Definition 3 to be one of these boundary points, say $\mathbf{P}_0 = (0,1)$. It is clear from Fig. 11 that *every* open disk about $\mathbf{P}_0$ contains points which are not in $\bar{S}$; hence, by Definition 3, $\bar{S}$ is not open. (To make a rigorous analytic proof, suppose there *is* $\delta > 0$ such that

$$|\mathbf{P} - \mathbf{P}_0| < \delta \implies \mathbf{P} \text{ is in } \bar{S}. \tag{*}$$

Choose a number h such that $0 < h < 2$ and $h < \delta$, and let $\mathbf{P} = (0,1-h)$. Since $0 < h < 2$, we get $|1-h| < 1$, so $\mathbf{P}$ is *not* in $\bar{S}$. Since $0 < h < \delta$, we have $|\mathbf{P} - \mathbf{P}_0| = |(0,1-h) - (0,1)| = h < \delta$; hence, by (*), $\mathbf{P}$ *is* in $\bar{S}$. This contradiction shows that $\bar{S}$ is not open, after all.)

Example 5. If $g(x,y) = xy/(x^2 + y^2)$ for $(x,y) \neq 0$ (see Figs. 3(b) and 4(b)), then $\lim_{\mathbf{P}\to\mathbf{0}} g(\mathbf{P})$ does not exist. The reason for this, intuitively, is that $g(\mathbf{P})$ approaches *different* values as $\mathbf{P} \to \mathbf{0}$ from different directions. For example, if $\mathbf{P} \to \mathbf{0}$ along either axis, then $g(\mathbf{P}) \to 0$, but if $\mathbf{P} \to \mathbf{0}$ along the main diagonal (where $x = y$), then $g(\mathbf{P}) \to 1/2$, since $g(x,x) = x^2/2x^2 = 1/2$. To prove analytically that $\lim_{\mathbf{P}\to\mathbf{0}} g(\mathbf{P})$ does not exist, suppose on the contrary that $\lim_{\mathbf{P}\to\mathbf{0}} g(\mathbf{P}) = L$ for some L. Then the function

$$\bar{g}(\mathbf{P}) = \begin{cases} \dfrac{xy}{x^2 + y^2}, & (x,y) \neq \mathbf{0} \\ L, & (x,y) = \mathbf{0} \end{cases}$$

is continuous at $\mathbf{0}$, by Theorem 4. Now let $\boldsymbol{\gamma}(t) = (0,t)$. Then $\boldsymbol{\gamma}(0) = \mathbf{0}$, so

$$\begin{aligned} L &= \bar{g}(\boldsymbol{\gamma}(0)) && \text{(by definition of } \bar{g}\text{)} \\ &= \lim_{t\to 0} \bar{g}(\boldsymbol{\gamma}(t)) && \text{(by Theorem 3, since } \boldsymbol{\gamma} \text{ is continuous at 0 and } \bar{g} \text{ is continuous at } \boldsymbol{\gamma}(0)\text{)} \\ &= 0 && \left(\text{since } \bar{g}(\boldsymbol{\gamma}(t)) = \frac{0\cdot t}{0+t^2} = 0 \text{ for } t \neq \mathbf{0}\right); \end{aligned}$$

hence $L = 0$. On the other hand, if we take $\boldsymbol{\gamma}(t) = (t,t)$, the same argument shows that $L = \frac{1}{2}$, and this contradiction shows that $\lim_{\mathbf{P}\to\mathbf{0}} g(\mathbf{P}) = L$ is impossible.

This example shows that when $\lim_{\mathbf{P}\to\mathbf{P}_0} f(\mathbf{P}) = L$, then $f(\mathbf{P})$ must tend to L as $\mathbf{P}$ approaches $\mathbf{P}_0$ *from any direction.* Moreover, it could happen that $f(\mathbf{P})$ tends to L along every straight line through $\mathbf{P}_0$, and yet $\lim_{\mathbf{P}\to\mathbf{P}_0} f(\mathbf{P}) \neq L$ because $f(\mathbf{P})$ does not tend to L along certain curves through $\mathbf{P}_0$. (See Problem 14 below.)

PROBLEMS

1. Sketch contour graphs (and, when practical, perspective graphs) of the following functions:

(a) $f(x,y) = x^2 + y^2$. (Sketch the contour lines for $f = 0, \frac{1}{2}, 1, \frac{3}{2}, 2$.)

(b) $f(x,y) = \dfrac{1}{x^2+y^2}$. (Sketch the contour lines for $f = 1, 2, \ldots$.)

(c) $f(x,y) = xy$. (Sketch the contour lines for $f = 0, \pm\frac{1}{2}, \pm 1, \pm\frac{3}{2}, \pm 2$.)

(d) $f(x,y) = \dfrac{x}{x^2+y^2}$. (Sketch the contour lines for $f = 0, \pm 1, \pm 2$. Notice that the contour lines are circles.)

(e) $f(x,y) = x^2 + 3y^2$.

(f) $f(x,y) = e^x \cos y$. (Sketch the contour lines for $f = 0, \pm\frac{1}{2}, \pm 1, \pm\frac{3}{2}$.)

2. From the graphs in Problem 1, which of the functions appear to be continuous at $(0,0)$?

3. (a) Prove that $\lim_{(x,y)\to(x_0,y_0)} y = y_0$.

(b) Prove that if $Q(x,y)$ is a polynomial in x and y, then Q is continuous at every point (x_0,y_0). (Use part (a), Examples 1 and 2, and Theorems 2 and 4.)

(c) Prove that if f is a rational function, i.e. if $f = Q/R$ where Q and R are polynomials, then f is continuous at every point where $R \neq 0$.

4. Prove that the following functions are continuous at every point. (Use Problem 3 and the theorems given above.)

(a) $f(x,y) = e^{xy}$

(b) $g(x,y) = \cos(x^2 + y^2)$

(c) $h(x,y) = xe^{xy}$

For Problems 5–7 review the corresponding proof for functions of one variable, if necessary.

5. Prove Theorem 1.

6. Prove Theorem 2.

7. Prove Theorem 3.

8. Prove that $S = \{\mathbf{P}: |\mathbf{P}| > 0\}$ is open. (Hint: Prove that if $\mathbf{P}_0$ is in S, then the open disk about $\mathbf{P}_0$ of radius $|\mathbf{P}_0|$ is contained entirely in S.)

9. Is the set $\{(x,y): |y| > 0\}$ open or not? Prove your answer.

10. Prove that the x axis is not open.

11. Suppose that f is continuous and its domain is an open set. Prove that the set $\{\mathbf{P}: f(\mathbf{P}) > 0\}$ is open. (Hint: Use Theorem 4 and the definition of limit with $\epsilon = f(\mathbf{P}_0)$.)

12. Suppose that f is continuous and its domain is an open set. Prove that for any numbers a and b, the set $\{\mathbf{P}: a < f(\mathbf{P}) < b\}$ is open. (Hint: $a < z < b \Leftrightarrow (b - z)(z - a) > 0$.)

13. Use Problem 12 to show that the following sets are open:

(a) $\{\mathbf{P}: |\mathbf{P}| < r\}$ (r a constant)

(b) $\{\mathbf{P}: 1 < |\mathbf{P}| < 2\}$

(c) $\{(x,y): x^2 + y^2 < 1 \text{ and } y > 0\}$. (Hint: Consider the function $f(x,y) = y$ defined only on the open unit disk.)

(d) $\{(x,y): x^2 + y^2 < 1 \text{ and } 0 < y < \frac{1}{2}\}$

(e) $\{(x,y): \sin^2 x < \frac{1}{2}\}$

14. Let

$$f(x,y) = \begin{cases} 1 & \text{if } x^2 < y < 2x^2 \\ 0 & \text{otherwise.} \end{cases}$$

Figure 12(a) shows a "contour graph"; $f = 1$ in the shaded area, and $f = 0$ elsewhere. Prove that this function has the following properties:

(a) $f(\mathbf{P})$ tends to zero along every straight line through the origin; that is, $\lim_{t \to 0} f(t \cos \theta, t \sin \theta) = 0$. (See Fig. 12(b).)

(b) $f(\mathbf{P})$ tends to 1 along certain curves through the origin; for example, $\lim_{t \to 0} f(2t, 6t^2) = 1$. (See Fig. 12(b).)

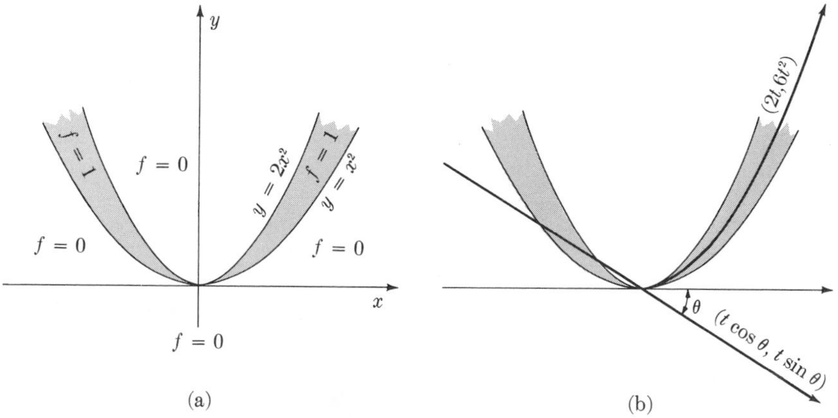

FIGURE 3.12

3.2 POLYNOMIALS OF DEGREE ONE

The study of functions of one variable begins, as you know, with the general first degree polynomial $f(x) = mx + b$. The graph of f, the set $\{(x,y) : y = mx + b\}$, is a straight line in R^2. The number m, called the *slope*, tells how steeply the line is tipped, and in which direction.

Our starting point for two variables is exactly the same. A first degree polynomial is a function of the form $f(x,y) = ax + by + c$, where a, b, and c are constants. More concisely, $f(\mathbf{P}) = \mathbf{M} \cdot \mathbf{P} + c$, where $\mathbf{P} = (x,y)$ and $\mathbf{M} = (a,b)$. The graph of f is the set $\{(x,y,z) : z = ax + by + c\}$, which is a plane in R^3. The vector $\mathbf{M} = (a,b)$ is called the *slope* of the plane. To see the geometric meaning of the slope, think of the plane as a hillside with the z axis pointing straight up, as in Fig. 13. Then *the slope* $\mathbf{M}$ *points in the direction of steepest ascent, and its length gives the rate of ascent in this direction.* This slightly vague statement can be made precise as follows: moving from point $\mathbf{P}_0$ to point $\mathbf{P}$ causes f to increase by $f(\mathbf{P}) - f(\mathbf{P}_0)$, and the *rate* of increase is

$$\frac{f(\mathbf{P}) - f(\mathbf{P}_0)}{|\mathbf{P} - \mathbf{P}_0|} = \frac{\mathbf{M}\cdot\mathbf{P} + c - (\mathbf{M}\cdot\mathbf{P}_0 + c)}{|\mathbf{P} - \mathbf{P}_0|}$$

$$= \frac{\mathbf{M}\cdot(\mathbf{P} - \mathbf{P}_0)}{|\mathbf{P} - \mathbf{P}_0|} = |\mathbf{M}| \cos \theta, \qquad (1)$$

where θ is the angle between $\mathbf{P} - \mathbf{P}_0$ and $\mathbf{M}$. Our italicized claim about the slope follows immediately from (1): the rate of increase of f is maximum when $\cos \theta = 1$ (that is, when $\mathbf{P} - \mathbf{P}_0$ has the same direction as $\mathbf{M}$), and the maximum rate is $|\mathbf{M}|$.

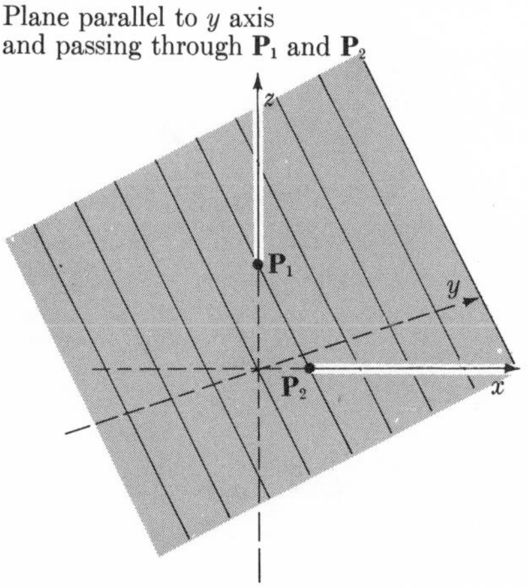

FIGURE 3.13 $f(x,y) = -2x + 1$

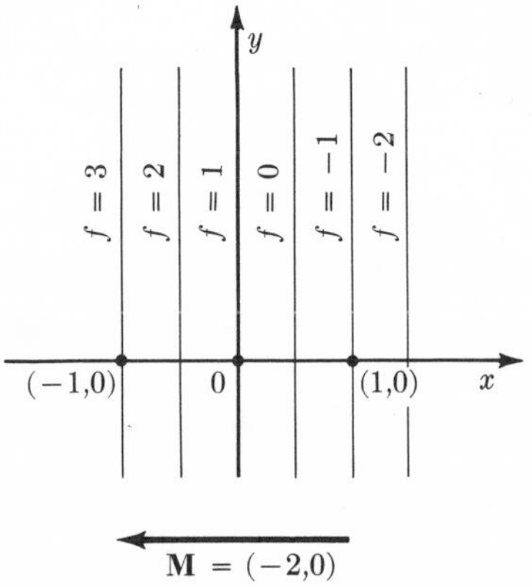

FIGURE 3.14 $f(x,y) = -2x + 1$

Figure 13 illustrates this for the function $f(x,y) = -2x + 1$. The slope $\mathbf{M} = (-2,0)$ points directly to the left, which is clearly the direction of steepest ascent; and the length of $\mathbf{M}$ is 2, which corresponds to the fact that moving one unit to the left causes f to increase by 2 units (see contour graph in Fig. 14).

Another important fact shows up in Fig. 14, namely, *the slope is orthogonal to the contour lines.* This is nothing new; it is basic in analytic geometry that the vector (a,b) is a normal to the line $\{(x,y): ax + by + c = d\}$. In other words, the slope vector (a,b) is orthogonal to the level curve $f(x,y) = ax + by + c = d$.

So far we have discussed the slope vector as a whole, but each component has its own interpretation as well. In the polynomial $f(x,y) = ax + by + c$, suppose we hold y fixed, but increase x by some amount h. Then f is increased by

$$f(x + h,y) - f(x,y) = a(x + h) + by + c - ax - by - c = ah,$$

which shows that a is the rate of increase of f per unit increase in x, with y fixed. Geometrically, this is the slope in the x direction. (See Fig. 15.) Similarly, b is the slope in the y direction.

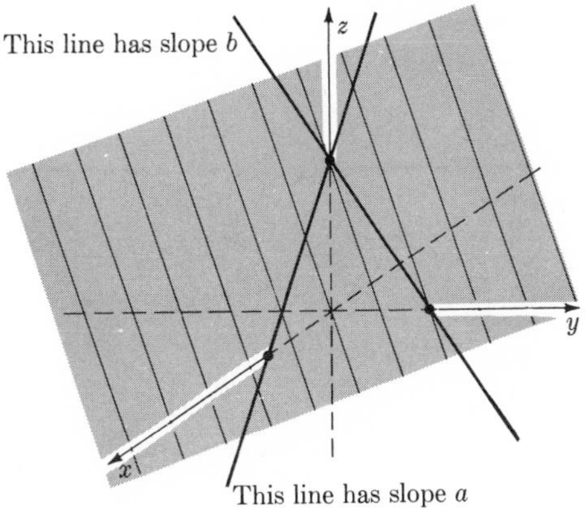

FIGURE 3.15

To summarize: The graph of the first degree polynomial $f(x,y) = ax + by + c$ is a plane. The vector $\mathbf{M} = (a,b)$ is its slope; the first component, a, is the slope in the x direction, and the second component, b, is the slope in the y direction. The slope vector $\mathbf{M}$ points in the direction of maximum increase of f. The contour lines of f are precisely the lines orthogonal to $\mathbf{M}$.

This connection between contour lines and slope can be used to solve maximum problems for any first degree polynomial f. Let R be a given region in the plane; then $\max_R f = d$ means that

(i) $f(\mathbf{P}) \leq d$ for every point $\mathbf{P}$ in R

and

(ii) $f(\mathbf{P}) = d$ for *some* point $\mathbf{P}$ in R.

To see the geometric meaning of (i), notice that the contour line

$$\{\mathbf{P}: f(\mathbf{P}) = d\} \tag{2}$$

divides the plane into two open half-planes, namely,

$$\{\mathbf{P}: f(\mathbf{P}) > d\} \quad \text{and} \quad \{\mathbf{P}: f(\mathbf{P}) < d\}.$$

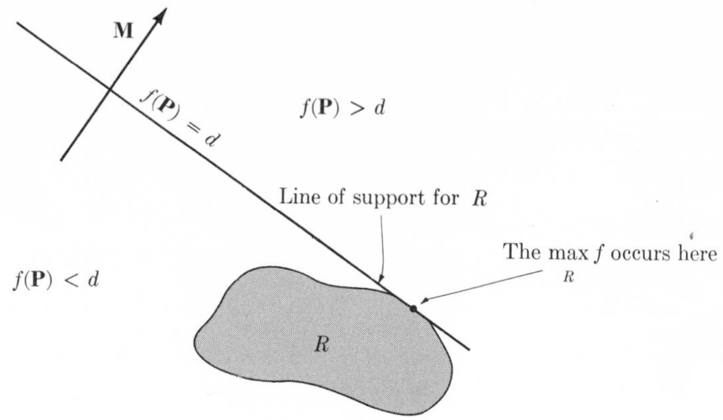

FIGURE 3.16

The first, called the *positive* half-plane, is the one toward which the slope **M** points (see Fig. 16). The second, naturally, is called the *negative* half-plane. Thus condition (i) above means that R lies on the *negative* side of the contour line (2), and (ii) means that at least one point of R lies *on* the contour line itself. A line (2) with these two properties is called a *line of support for R orthogonal to* **M**.

We have shown that finding the maximum $\max_R f$ is equivalent to finding such a line of support; this can often be done simply by drawing an accurate picture of R and **M**. The appendix following this section gives many examples of simple "managerial" problems (maximizing profit, for example) that can be solved in this way.

Example 1. Find the maximum of $f(x,y) = 3x + 4y - 10$ over the disk $\{(x,y): x^2 + y^2 \leq 1\}$. *Solution.* Figure 17 shows the region R, the slope vector $\mathbf{M} = (3,4)$, and a line of support orthogonal to **M**. By elementary geometry, this line of support must be tangent to the unit circle at $(\frac{3}{5},\frac{4}{5})$. Hence the maximum of f over the unit disk is $f(\frac{3}{5},\frac{4}{5}) = -5$. (This result, found by graphical means, can be proved analytically by observing that the expression $3x + 4y$ is a dot product. Thus

$$\begin{aligned} 3x + 4y = (3,4)\cdot(x,y) &= |(3,4)|\cdot|(x,y)| \cos\theta \\ &= 5\sqrt{x^2 + y^2}\cos\theta, \end{aligned} \tag{3}$$

where θ is the angle between (3,4) and (x,y). Hence the maximum of the expression (3) under the restriction $x^2 + y^2 \leq 1$ is achieved by taking $x^2 + y^2 = 1$ and $\cos\theta = 1$, and this maximum is 5. Since $3x + 4y$ has a maximum of 5, it follows that $3x + 4y - 10$ has a maximum of -5.)

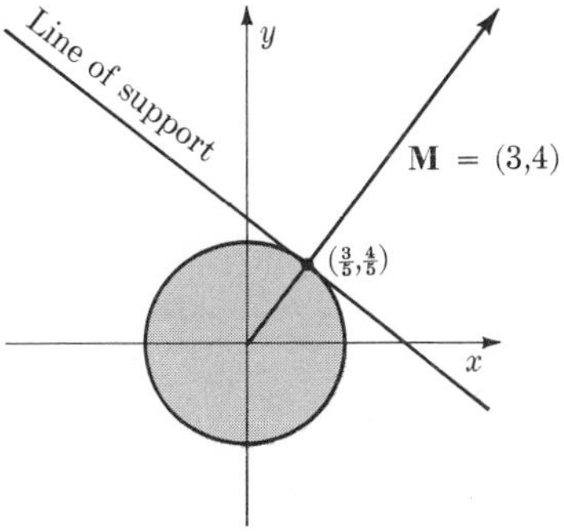

FIGURE 3.17

PROBLEMS

1. Show that the equation of a plane through a given point (x_0, y_0, z_0) with given slope $\mathbf{M} = (a,b)$ is

$$f(\mathbf{P}) = z_0 + (\mathbf{P} - \mathbf{P}_0) \cdot \mathbf{M},$$

where $\mathbf{P}_0 = (x_0, y_0)$.

2. Find the slope of the plane defined by the given equation:
(a) $z = x - y + 100$ (d) $4z + 5x = 1$
(b) $z = 2$ (e) $x + 2y + 3z = 0$
(c) $z = x - y + 100$ (f) $x + y = 1$
(Notice that in part (b) the slope is (0,0); the graph is horizontal and there is no "uphill" direction. Notice that in part (f) *no slope is defined*; the plane is vertical.)

3. For each of the following functions f, sketch a contour graph (as in Fig. 14), and sketch the slope vector.
(a) $f(x,y) = 2x + 3y - 1$ (c) $f(x,y) = -5x + 4y$
(b) $f(x,y) = 10x - 5y + 3$ (d) $f(x,y) = -x - y + 10$

4. Let $f(x,y) = ax + by + c$. Show that $\mathbf{N} = (a,b, -1)$ is a normal vector to the graph of f.

5. For each of the functions f in Problem 3, find (by graphical means) the maximum value of f over the unit circle $\{(x,y) : x^2 + y^2 \leq 1\}$.

6. Repeat Problem 5, but find the minimum instead of the maximum.

7. Find the maximum of f over the rectangle $\{(x,y): |x| \leq 1, |y| \leq 2\}$. Use graphical methods.
(a) $f(x,y) = 10x - 3y$
(b) $f(x,y) = -4x + 5y + 6$

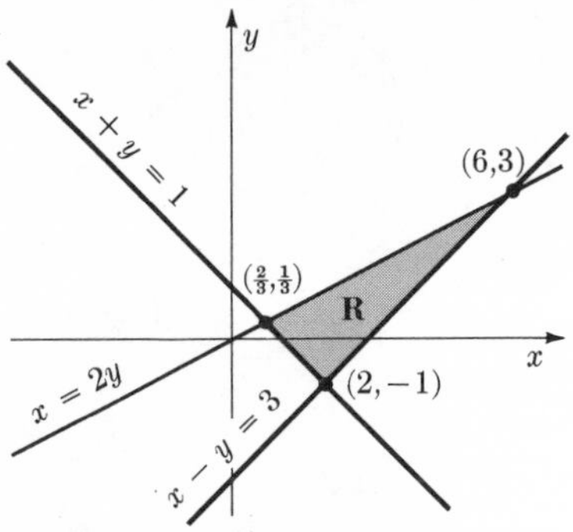

FIGURE 3.18

8. Figure 18 shows the region R in the (x,y) plane determined by the inequalities $x \geq 2y$, $x + y \geq 1$, $x - y \leq 3$. For each of the functions in Problem 7, find (by graphical means) the maximum value over R.

9. What happens in Problem 8 if R is defined by the strict inequalities $x > 2y$, $x + y > 1$, $x - y < 3$? Is there still a maximum?

10. Find (graphically) the maximum of $f(x,y) = x + y$ over the ellipse $\{(x,y): x^2 + 2y^2 \leq 2\}$.

11. Suppose a hillside is sloped like the plane $\{(x,y,z): z = x\}$, and a man is going "northeast" up the hill, i.e. in the direction of the vector $(1,1)$. Show that he rises 1 unit whenever he moves $\sqrt{2}$ units toward the northeast; i.e. the upward slope of his path is $1/\sqrt{2}$.

12. Suppose a hillside is sloped like the plane $\{(x,y,z): z = ax + by + c\}$, and a man is walking on the hillside in the direction of the unit vector $\mathbf{V} = (v_1,v_2)$. Find the upward slope of his path, i.e. the increase of altitude due to his going one unit in the direction $\mathbf{V}$. (The answer can be expressed as a dot product.)

13. Under what conditions on the slope $\mathbf{M}$ does the first degree polynomial $f(\mathbf{P}) = \mathbf{M}\cdot\mathbf{P} + c$ achieve a maximum in the region $R = \{(x,y): y \geq x^2\}$?

APPENDIX: TWO-DIMENSIONAL LINEAR PROGRAMMING

In the maximum problems solved by "linear programming," we find the maximum of a first degree polynomial over a region R, where R itself is defined by inequalities involving first degree polynomials. The following example shows how these problems arise, and how to solve them in the simple case of two variables.

Example 1. A trucker going from farm to city has room for only 100 bushels of fruit in his truck. The farm will sell up to 75 bushels of apples at \$1 a bushel, and up to 65 bushels of peaches at \$2 a bushel. The trucker has \$150 to spend on the fruit, and he can make a profit of \$1 a bushel on peaches, and \$.75 a bushel on apples. Exactly how should he divide the load between peaches and apples to make the maximum profit?

We have to sort out the information and express it mathematically. Let p be the number of bushels of peaches he takes, and a the number of bushels of apples. Then the restrictions on what he can take are

$$p + a \leq 100 \tag{1}$$

$$0 \leq a \leq 75 \tag{2}$$

$$0 \leq p \leq 65 \tag{3}$$

$$2p + a \leq 150. \tag{4}$$

The profit which he wants to maximize is

$$P(p,a) = p + \tfrac{3}{4}a. \tag{5}$$

The conditions (1)–(4) define a certain region R in the (p, a) plane, and we want to maximize the profit P on that region. So we sketch the region R, the slope vector of P, and a typical contour line, and then locate the maximum.

To see what the restriction (1) means geometrically, notice that the graph of $a + p = 100$ is the straight line in Fig. 19, and the inequality $a + p \leq 100$ says that (p,a) lies *on or below* this line; thus $\{(p,a)\colon (1) \text{ is satisfied}\}$ is the shaded area in Fig. 19. Taking account of the other restrictions (2)–(4) as well, we find the shaded region R in Fig. 20 representing the trucker's buying possibilities. Finally, we sketch a vector parallel to the slope $\mathbf{M} = (1,\frac{3}{4})$ of the profit function P in (5), sketch a line of support orthogonal to $\mathbf{M}$, and thus find the point marked with a heavy dot in Fig. 20 to yield the maximum profit, given the trucker's possibilities. This point lies at the intersection of the two lines

$$p + a = 100$$

$$2p + a = 150;$$

subtracting the first from the second, we find $p = 50$, hence $a = 50$. Hence the trucker should buy 50 bushels each of apples and peaches, thus spending all his money, filling his truck, and maximizing his profit.

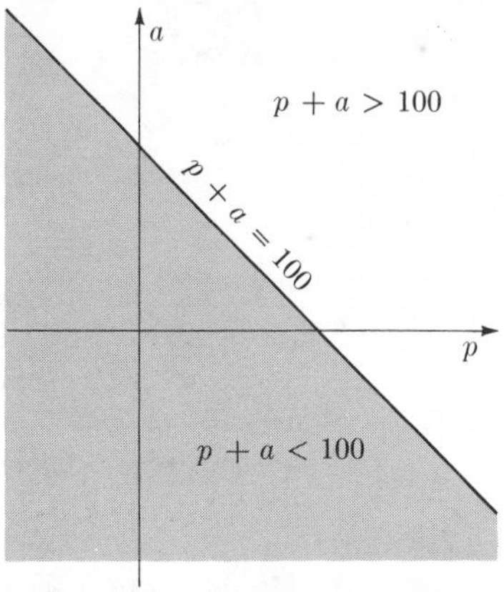

FIGURE 3.19

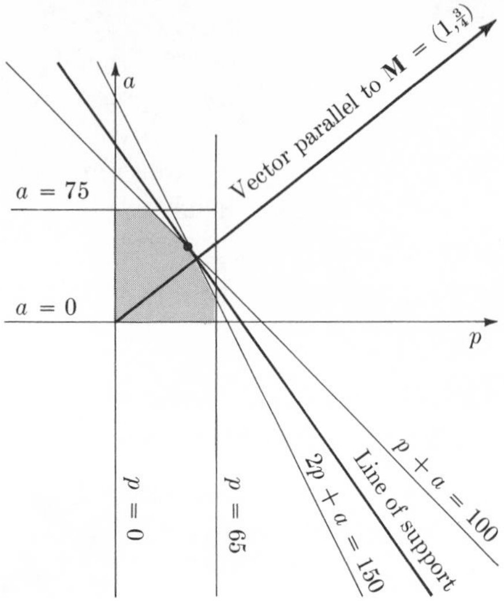

FIGURE 3.20

Remark 1. It is worth comparing our graphical solution to a plausible "common sense" solution. The trucker might reason as follows: "The profit is highest on peaches, so I'll buy as many peaches as possible; 65 bushels at \$2 a bushel comes to \$130, so with the \$20 left over I'll buy 20 bushels of apples. But look, now I have only 85 bushels, and the truck has room for 15 more. Maybe I should try to fill up the truck, but with as high a proportion of peaches as possible. That means I spend \$150 to buy 100 bushels. Let's see, ..." Thus, eventually, he may arrive at our solution; then he has to compare the profit made by buying 65 bushels of peaches to the profit made by buying 50 bushels of each. The virtue of Fig. 20 is that it shows *all* the possibilities at a glance, and you can immediately pick out the best one without weighing each possibility.

Remark 2. Graphical solutions of mathematical problems are convenient, but not completely satisfactory. Fortunately, there is an analytic solution to the problems of linear programming, suitable for use on computers. In the example above, notice that the maximum was found at a vertex of the polygonal region R; this is also true in all the problems below, and in fact it can be proved that the maximum is generally found at a vertex. More important yet, it can always be found by solving systems of linear equations, something computers do rather well. We will describe the method in detail for the case of two variables.

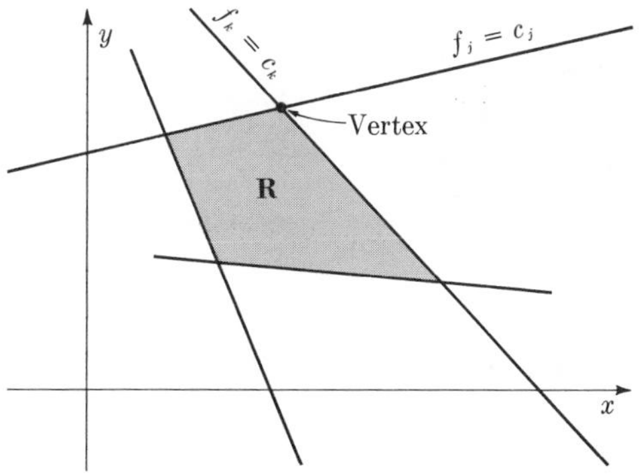

FIGURE 3.21

Let $f(x,y) = ax + by + c$ be the function to be maximized, and let the region R be defined by the inequalities $f_1 \leq c_1, \ldots, f_n \leq c_n$, where $f_j(x,y) = a_jx + b_jy$. Notice that $f_j \leq c_j$ defines a half-plane and $f_j = c_j$ defines its boundary line; the region R consists of the points in common to all these half-planes. A point (x,y) in R is called a *boundary point* if at least one of the equations $f_j(x,y) = c_j$ is satisfied, and a *vertex* if two of these equations are satisfied. Thus, a vertex is a point in R lying on two boundary lines (Fig. 21).

Let $\mathbf{M} = (a,b)$ denote the slope vector for f, and $\mathbf{M}_j = (a_j,b_j)$ the slope for f_j. To avoid uninteresting "degenerate" cases, we assume that none of the vectors $\mathbf{M}, \mathbf{M}_1, \ldots, \mathbf{M}_n$ is zero.

Proposition 1.* *Suppose that none of* $\mathbf{M}, \mathbf{M}_1, \ldots, \mathbf{M}_n$ *is zero, and that* $\mathbf{V}$ *is a point in* R *lying on the two lines* $f_j = c_j$ *and* $f_k = c_k$, *and that*

$$\mathbf{M} = t_j\mathbf{M}_j + t_k\mathbf{M}_k \quad \text{with constants } t_j \geq 0,\ t_k \geq 0. \tag{6}$$

Then $f(\mathbf{P}) \leq f(\mathbf{V})$ *for every point* $\mathbf{P}$ *in* R.

The proof of this is outlined in the problems below. Condition (6) is easy to interpret geometrically; it means that $\mathbf{M}$ lies between $\mathbf{M}_j$ and $\mathbf{M}_k$, as in Fig. 22(a). If (6) held with $t_k < 0$ (as in Fig. 22(b)), we could find larger values of f to one side of $\mathbf{V}$ along the line $f_j = c_j$, and if t_j were < 0 there would be larger values of f to the other side of $\mathbf{V}$ along the line $f_k = c_k$; in either case, $f(\mathbf{V})$ would not be a maximum.

* This fact is labeled "proposition" instead of "theorem" because it is not part of the main line of development of the chapter.

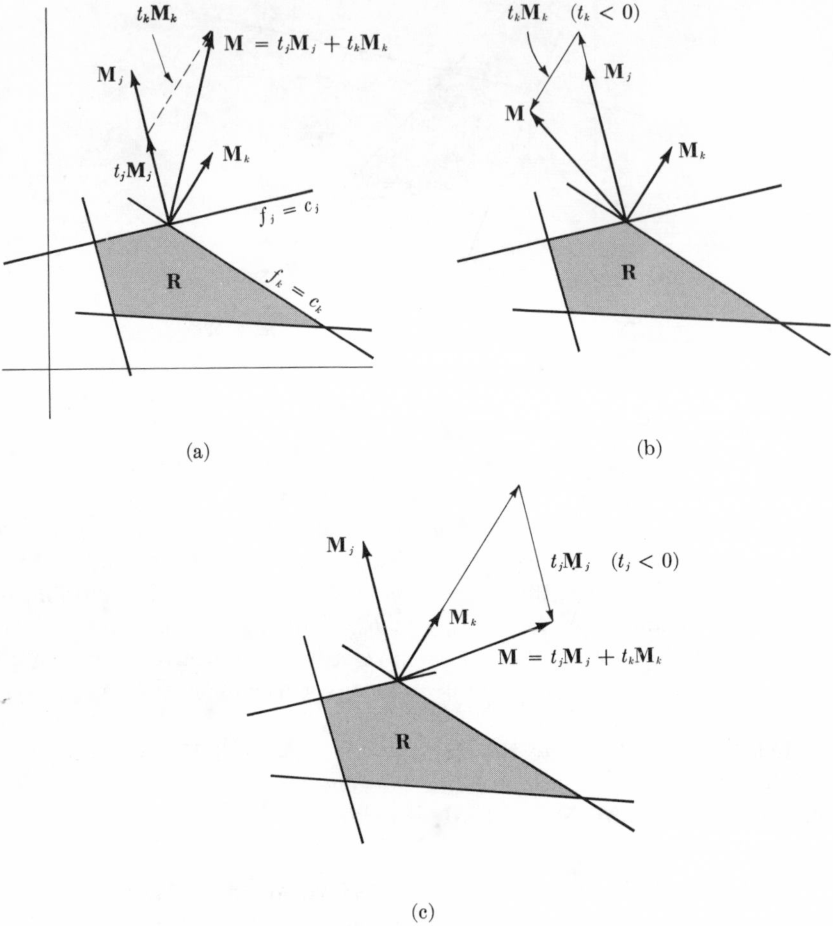

FIGURE 3.22

It may not be clear in a given case how to decide analytically whether (6) holds or not. Fortunately, (6) can be rewritten in a form that is easily decided:

Proposition 2. *Let* $\mathbf{M} = (a,b)$, $\mathbf{M}_j = (a_j, b_j)$, *and* $\mathbf{M}_k = (a_k, b_k)$. *Then condition* (6) *is equivalent to:*

$$ab_j - ba_j = t_k(a_kb_j - b_ka_j) \text{ and } a_kb - b_ka = t_j(a_kb_j - b_ka_j) \tag{6'}$$
$$\text{for some constants } t_k \geq 0 \text{ and } t_j \geq 0.$$

The proof of this is left as a problem. Propositions 1 and 2 complement the graphical method of finding maxima; once you have found $\mathbf{V}$ graphically, you can prove that $f(\mathbf{V})$ is maximum by verifying (6′).

Example 2. Prove that the point found in the solution of Example 1 actually does give maximum profit. *Solution.* We found graphically that the function

$$f(x,y) = x + \tfrac{3}{4}y$$

has a maximum in R at the intersection of the two lines

$$\begin{aligned} x + y &= 100 \\ 2x + y &= 150. \end{aligned} \tag{7}$$

Thus the various slopes we have to consider are

$$\begin{aligned} \mathbf{M} &= (a,b) = (1,\tfrac{3}{4}) \\ \mathbf{M}_1 &= (a_1,b_1) = (1,1) \\ \mathbf{M}_2 &= (a_2,b_2) = (2,1). \end{aligned}$$

We find

$$ab_1 - ba_1 = 1 - \tfrac{3}{4} = \tfrac{1}{4}, \qquad ab_2 - ba_2 = 1 - \tfrac{3}{2} = -\tfrac{1}{2}$$

$$a_1b_2 - b_1a_2 = 1 - 2 = -1, \qquad a_2b_1 - b_2a_1 = 1;$$

hence

$$ab_1 - ba_1 = \tfrac{1}{4}(a_2b_1 - b_2a_1) \qquad \text{and} \qquad ab_2 - ba_2 = \tfrac{1}{2}(a_1b_2 - b_1a_2),$$

so (6′) is satisfied by the nonnegative constants $t_1 = \frac{1}{2}$ and $t_2 = \frac{1}{4}$. Thus by Propositions 1 and 2, the point (x,y) solving (7) does give a maximum of f over the region R.

One question remains: What if *no* vertex of R satisfies the conditions (6) or (6′)? In most cases, this implies that f has *no* maximum in R. The precise statement in this situation is a little complicated, and we will not give the (tedious and uninspiring) proof, but we will at least state the result:

Proposition 3. *If the vectors* $\mathbf{M}, \mathbf{M}_1, \ldots, \mathbf{M}_n$ *are nonzero and not all parallel, and if no vertex of R satisfies* (6) *or* (6′), *then f has no maximum in R. If* $\mathbf{M}, \mathbf{M}_1, \ldots, \mathbf{M}_n$ are *all parallel, and R is not empty, then there are two cases:*

Case (i) *For some k,* $\mathbf{M} = t_k\mathbf{M}_k$ *with* $t_k > 0$, *and the line*

$$\{\mathbf{P}: \mathbf{P}\cdot\mathbf{M}_k = c_k\} \tag{8}$$

lies in R; in this case, f is constant on the line (8) *and every point on this line gives a maximum value of f.*

Case (ii) *For every k, $\mathbf{M} = t_k\mathbf{M}_k$ with $t_k < 0$. In this case, R is one of the half-planes $\{\mathbf{P}: \mathbf{P}\cdot\mathbf{M}_j \le c_j\}$, and $\mathbf{M}$ points "into" R; f has no maximum in R, but it has a minimum along the line $\{\mathbf{P}: \mathbf{P}\cdot\mathbf{M}_j = c_j\}$.*

PROBLEMS

1. In Example 1 in the text, suppose that the profit on peaches were \$.75 and the profit on apples were \$1. How should the trucker maximize his profit then? (You will find that he fills the truck, but does *not* spend all his money.)

2. Superduper Farms, Inc. has a square feet of livestock storage, and B cubic feet of feed storage. Each cow requires c square feet of room, and C cubic feet of feed storage, while each sheep requires s square feet of room and S cubic feet of feed storage. The net income per year from a cow is I_c, and the net income from a sheep is I_s. Superduper's farm is to have x cows and y sheep.

(a) Set up the inequalities governing Superduper's possibilities, and the function giving their income.

(b) Determine x and y to give maximum income, when $a = 1{,}000$, $B = 12{,}500$, $c = 20$, $C = 200$, $s = 10$, $S = 150$, $I_c = \$200$, and $I_s = \$120$.

3. A dealer has space for 50 appliances: washing machines, stoves, or refrigerators. He is sure to sell more washers than refrigerators, and more refrigerators than stoves; and he must fill orders for 3 stoves, 5 refrigerators, and 10 washers. Beyond these facts, he has no idea how many of each item he will sell in a given time. However, he does know that his profit is \$50 per stove, \$60 per refrigerator, and \$30 per washer. He wants to order 50 appliances in such a way that his profit will be maximum if they are all sold.

(a) Suppose he orders w washers, s stoves, and r refrigerators. Write down all the conditions that w, s, and r must satisfy, and write the profit P as a function of w, s, and r. (There are five inequalities, one equality, and one equation giving the profit P.)

(b) Use the equality found in part (a) to express w in terms of r and s, and rewrite all the other expressions in terms of r and s.

(c) Sketch the region in the (r,s) plane determined by the inequalities found in part (b).

(d) Find the maximum profit for the region found in part (c). How many of each appliance does the dealer order?

4. A manufacturer has 52 workers, each provided with adequate machines. Twenty are skilled, earning \$5/hour, and 32 are unskilled, earning

\$2/hour. The manufacturer can make either of two products. Product X takes 10 man-hours of skilled labor, 5 man-hours of unskilled labor, and brings a net profit of \$120, *not counting* labor costs. Product Y takes 4 man-hours of skilled and 8 man-hours of unskilled labor, and brings a net profit of \$80, again *not counting* labor costs. How much of each product should be made per hour to maximize the profit, taking into account labor costs? Assume that the skilled laborers will not do unskilled work.

(a) Suppose the manufacturer produces x items per hour of product X, and y items per hour of product Y. Taking into account the fixed labor cost

$$20 \times \$5/\text{hour} + 32 \times \$2/\text{hour} = \$164/\text{hour},$$

show that the net hourly profit in dollars is

$$P(x,y) = 120x + 80y - 164.$$

(b) Show that the total number of skilled man-hours required is $10x + 4y$, and deduce the restriction $10x + 4y \leq 20$.

(c) Taking into account the supply of unskilled labor, show that $5x + 8y \leq 32$.

(d) Sketch the region R determined by the inequalities in parts (b) and (c), and by the obvious restrictions $x \geq 0$, $y \geq 0$.

(e) Find the maximum in R of the function P given in part (a). (Hint: The slope vector itself is much too long to sketch. All you need is a vector in the right direction, so scale down the slope vector; for instance, divide it by 40.)

5. Rework Problem 4 above, but now assume that there are 20 unskilled workers and 32 skilled workers.

6. Rework Problem 4 above, but now assume that the skilled laborers will do unskilled work, as long as they are still paid \$5/hour. Show that the inequality in part (c) of Problem 4 should be replaced by $5x + 8y + 10x + 4y \leq 52$.

7. Find three first-degree polynomials f, f_1, and f_2 such that f does not assume a maximum in the region $R = \{\mathbf{P}: f_1(\mathbf{P}) \leq 0 \text{ and } f_2(\mathbf{P}) \leq 0\}$.

8. Prove Proposition 2. (Treat separately the two cases $a_kb_j - b_ka_j \neq 0$ and $a_kb_j - b_ka_j = 0$.)

9. This problem outlines the proof of Proposition 1 under the assumption that $\mathbf{M}_j$ and $\mathbf{M}_k$ are not parallel. Without loss of generality, we assume that $j = 1$ and $k = 2$.

(a) Let $\mathbf{A}_1$ and $\mathbf{A}_2$ be nonzero, and $\mathbf{A}_1 \cdot \mathbf{M}_2 = 0$, $\mathbf{A}_2 \cdot \mathbf{M}_1 = 0$. Prove that $\mathbf{A}_1 \cdot \mathbf{M}_1 \neq 0$ and $\mathbf{A}_2 \cdot \mathbf{M}_2 \neq 0$. (Hint: $\mathbf{M}_1$ and $\mathbf{M}_2$ form a basis of R^2: see §1.5).

(b) Let $\mathbf{B}_1 = \dfrac{1}{\mathbf{A}_1 \cdot \mathbf{M}_1} \mathbf{A}_1$ and $\mathbf{B}_2 = \dfrac{1}{\mathbf{A}_2 \cdot \mathbf{M}_2} \mathbf{A}_2$. Prove that

$$\mathbf{B}_l \cdot \mathbf{M}_m = \begin{cases} 0 & \text{if } l \neq m \\ 1 & \text{if } l = m \end{cases}$$

and that $\mathbf{B}_1$ and $\mathbf{B}_2$ form a basis of R^2. (See Fig. 23).

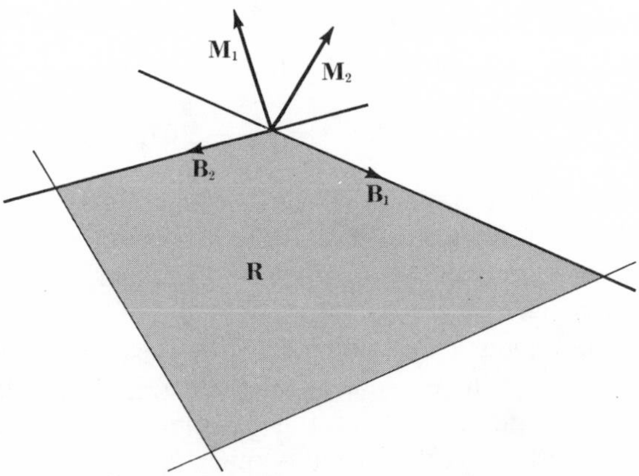

FIGURE 3.23

(c) Let $\mathbf{M}_1 \cdot \mathbf{V} = c_1$ and $\mathbf{M}_2 \cdot \mathbf{V} = c_2$ (i.e. $\mathbf{V}$ is the vertex in the statement of Proposition 1.) By part (b), any point $\mathbf{P}$ in R^2 can be written in the form $\mathbf{P} = \mathbf{V} + s_1\mathbf{B}_1 + s_2\mathbf{B}_2$. Prove that if $\mathbf{P}$ is in the given region R, then $s_1 \leq 0$ and $s_2 \leq 0$. (Compute $f_1(\mathbf{P}) = \mathbf{M}_1 \cdot \mathbf{P}$ and $f_2(\mathbf{P}) = \mathbf{M}_2 \cdot \mathbf{P}$.)

(d) Using parts (b) and (c), prove that if $f(\mathbf{P}) = \mathbf{M} \cdot \mathbf{P} + c$, and $\mathbf{M}$ satisfies (6), then $f(\mathbf{P}) \leq f(\mathbf{V})$ for every point $\mathbf{P}$ in R.

10. This problem proves Proposition 1 in the remaining case, where $\mathbf{M}_j$ and $\mathbf{M}_k$ are assumed to be parallel.

(a) Suppose that $\mathbf{M}_j$ and $\mathbf{M}_k$ are parallel and nonzero, and

$$\mathbf{M} = t_j\mathbf{M}_j + t_k\mathbf{M}_k$$

with $t_j \geq 0$ and $t_k \geq 0$. Prove that either $\mathbf{M} = t\mathbf{M}_j$ or $\mathbf{M} = t\mathbf{M}_k$, with $t \geq 0$.

(b) Suppose that $\mathbf{M} = t\mathbf{M}_j$, $t \geq 0$, and let $\mathbf{V} \cdot \mathbf{M}_j = c_j$. Prove that $\mathbf{P} \cdot \mathbf{M}_j \leq c_j \Rightarrow f(\mathbf{P}) \leq f(\mathbf{V})$, where $f(\mathbf{P}) = \mathbf{M} \cdot \mathbf{P} + c$.

(c) Conclude that $f(\mathbf{P}) \leq f(\mathbf{V})$ for $\mathbf{P}$ in R.

3.3 PARTIAL DERIVATIVES, THE GRADIENT, AND THE CHAIN RULE

We come at last to the question of differentiating functions of two variables. In general, a derivative is a rate of change. For a function $f(x,y)$ there are two easily computed rates of change, one with respect to x, and one with respect to y. The first of these is the *partial derivative with respect to* x, whose value at a point (x_0, y_0) is

$$\lim_{x \to x_0} \frac{f(x,y_0) - f(x_0,y_0)}{x - x_0}, \tag{1}$$

and the second is the partial derivative with respect to y, whose value at (x_0, y_0) is

$$\lim_{y \to y_0} \frac{f(x_0,y) - f(x_0,y_0)}{y - y_0}. \tag{2}$$

There are at least three current notations for partial derivatives: for the x derivative (1) they are

$$\frac{\partial f}{\partial x}(x_0,y_0), \qquad f_x(x_0,y_0), \qquad \text{or} \qquad D_1 f(x_0,y_0),$$

and for the y derivative (2)

$$\frac{\partial f}{\partial y}(x_0,y_0), \qquad f_y(x_0,y_0), \qquad \text{or} \qquad D_2 f(x_0,y_0).$$

The $\partial f/\partial x$ version (read "*dfdx*" or "partial f partial x") depends on the conventional use of x for the first variable, and shares some (but not all!) of the advantages of the Leibniz notation df/dx for functions of one variable. The f_x version is the easiest to write, and $D_1 f$ is the safest when the conventions about x and y become ambiguous. (What does $f_x(y_0, x_0)$ mean?) Figure 24 shows the geometric meaning of partial derivatives. The vertical plane $\{(x,y,z) : y = y_0\}$ intersects the graph of f in a curve which is essentially the graph of $f(x,y_0)$ considered as a function of the one variable x. The limit (1) is precisely the derivative of this function of one variable, and thus $f_x(x_0, y_0)$ is the slope of the line tangent to this curve at $Q_0 = (x_0, y_0, f(x_0, y_0))$, as shown in Fig. 24(a). Similarly, $\dfrac{\partial f}{\partial y}(x_0, y_0)$ is the slope of the line in Fig. 24(b).

To compute $f_x(x_0, y_0)$ simply think of $y = y_0$ as a constant, and take the derivative with respect to x. For example, if $f(x,y) = x^2 + y^2$, then $f_x(x_0, y_0) = 2x_0$; if $g(x,y) = 2x + 3xy$, then $g_x(x_0, y_0) = 2 + 3y_0$. Similarly, to compute f_y, think of x as constant and differentiate with respect to y. The functions f and g just given have the derivatives

$$f_y(x_0,y_0) = \frac{\partial f}{\partial y}(x_0,y_0) = 2y_0, \qquad \frac{\partial g}{\partial y}(x_0,y_0) = 3x_0.$$

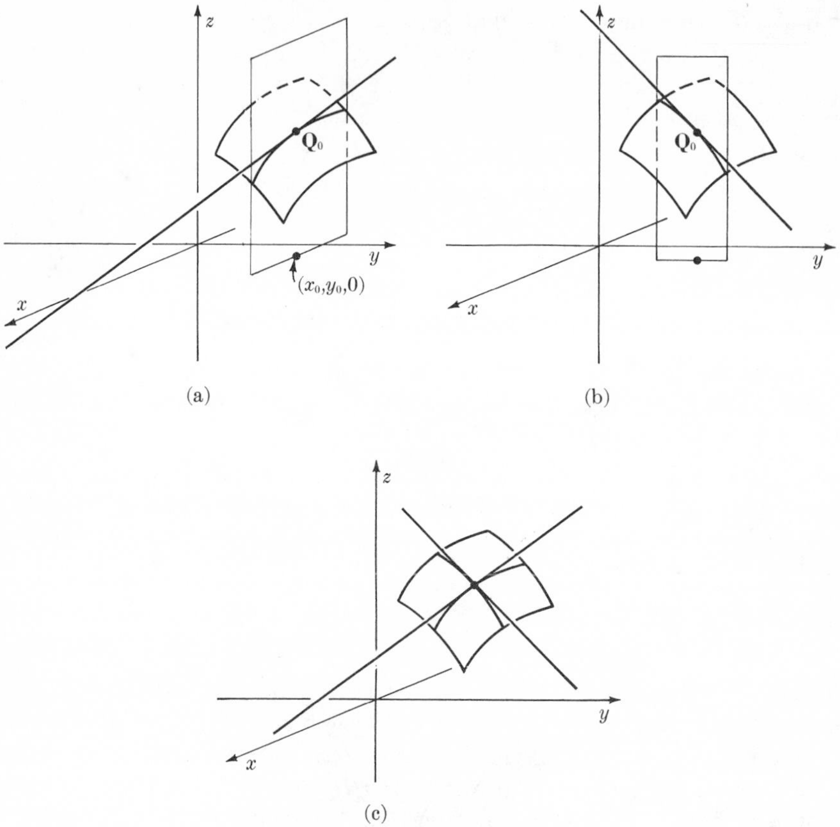

FIGURE 3.24

A less trivial example is the function graphed in Fig. 25,

$$h(x,y) = \begin{cases} \dfrac{xy}{x^2 + y^2}, & x^2 + y^2 \neq 0 \\ 0, & x^2 + y^2 = 0. \end{cases}$$

When $(x,y) \neq (0,0)$, you can easily find the partial derivatives

$$D_1h(x,y) = \frac{y^3 - x^2y}{(x^2 + y^2)^2} \quad \text{and} \quad D_2h(x,y) = \frac{x^3 - y^2x}{(x^2 + y^2)^2}.$$

At the origin these formulas do not apply, but a direct application

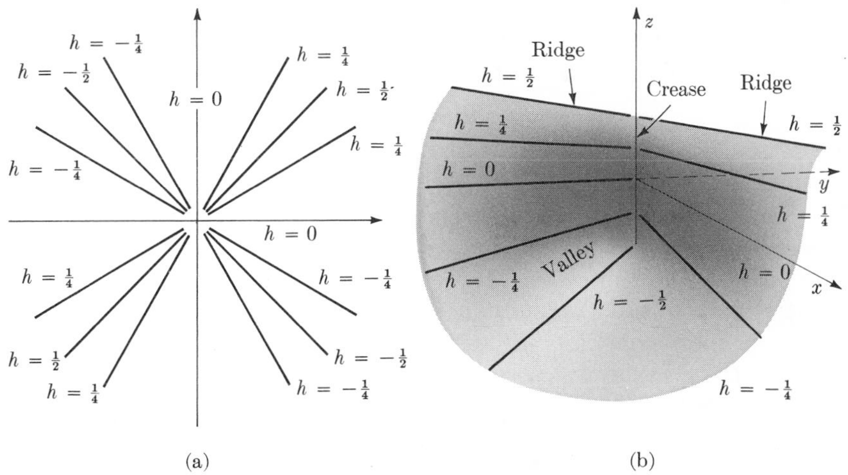

FIGURE 3.25

of the definition of D_1 yields

$$D_1h(0,0) = \lim_{x \to 0} \frac{h(x,0) - h(0,0)}{x - 0} = \lim_{x \to 0} \frac{0 - 0}{x} = 0.$$

This reflects the fact that when h is restricted to the x axis (this is the effect of setting $y = 0$), then it is a "nice" function at $x = 0$; in fact, h is identically zero along the x axis. Similarly, h is identically zero along the y axis, so $D_2h(0,0) = 0$. Thus the *partial derivatives of h exist at every point, even though h itself is not continuous at* $(0,0)$. (See Fig. 25 and Example 5, §3.1.)

Thus the mere existence of the partial derivatives does not tell very much about the function. For this reason, the term "differentiable" is *not* taken to mean "having partial derivatives", but is given a more sophisticated definition. The existence of $f_x(x_0, y_0)$ and $f_y(x_0, y_0)$ depends only on the behaviour of f along the lines $x = x_0$ and $y = y_0$. By contrast, differentiability takes into account *all* points near (x_0, y_0).

Definition 4. A function f is *differentiable at* $\mathbf{P}_0$ if and only if there is a first degree polynomial $g(\mathbf{P}) = f(\mathbf{P}_0) + (\mathbf{P} - \mathbf{P}_0)\cdot\mathbf{M}$ such that

$$\lim_{\mathbf{P} \to \mathbf{P}_0} \frac{f(\mathbf{P}) - g(\mathbf{P})}{|\mathbf{P} - \mathbf{P}_0|} = 0, \qquad (3)$$

that is,

$$\lim_{(x,y) \to (x_0,y_0)} \frac{f(x,y) - f(x_0,y_0) - a(x - x_0) - b(y - y_0)}{\sqrt{(x - x_0)^2 + (y - y_0)^2}} = 0. \qquad (3')$$

This definition is modeled on a simple result about functions of one variable. Elementary algebra shows that the relation

$$\lim_{x \to x_0} \frac{F(x) - F(x_0)}{x - x_0} = a \qquad (\text{i.e. } F'(x_0) = a)$$

is equivalent to

$$\lim_{x \to x_0} \frac{F(x) - F(x_0) - a(x - x_0)}{x - x_0} = 0.$$

The similarity between this last limit and (3′) suggests that Definition 4 is at least a reasonable one. However, the real importance of the definition lies in its consequences, and the most efficient course now is to develop these consequences, point out their geometric significance, and finally apply the whole theory to specific examples. (The theoretical development is a little heavy, so on a first reading you may prefer to skip to the summary and examples below, beginning on p. 125.)

First of all we prove that differentiability implies continuity, and also implies the existence of the partial derivatives.

Theorem 5. *Suppose that* $g(\mathbf{P}) = f(\mathbf{P}_0) + (\mathbf{P} - \mathbf{P}_0)\cdot\mathbf{M}$ *is a first degree polynomial satisfying* (3). *Then* f *is continuous at* $\mathbf{P}_0$, *the partial derivatives* $D_1 f$ *and* $D_2 f$ *exist at* $\mathbf{P}_0$, *and* g *has the slope*

$$\mathbf{M} = (D_1 f(\mathbf{P}_0), D_2 f(\mathbf{P}_0)).$$

The proof takes three easy steps.

(i) $\lim_{\mathbf{P} \to \mathbf{P}_0} f(\mathbf{P}) = f(\mathbf{P}_0)$. For

$$f(\mathbf{P}) = g(\mathbf{P}) + |\mathbf{P} - \mathbf{P}_0| \frac{f(\mathbf{P}) - g(\mathbf{P})}{|\mathbf{P} - \mathbf{P}_0|}; \tag{4}$$

since g is a polynomial and $g(\mathbf{P}_0) = f(\mathbf{P}_0)$, we have $\lim_{\mathbf{P} \to \mathbf{P}_0} g(\mathbf{P}) = f(\mathbf{P}_0)$, so (3) shows that the right-hand side of (4) tends to $f(\mathbf{P}_0) + 0\cdot 0$ as $\mathbf{P} \to \mathbf{P}_0$.

(ii) If $\mathbf{M} = (a,b)$, then

$$\lim_{x \to x_0} \left| \frac{f(x,y_0) - f(x_0,y_0)}{x - x_0} - a \right| = 0. \tag{5}$$

To prove this, let $\mathbf{P}_0 = (x_0,y_0)$ and $\mathbf{P} = (x,y_0)$. Then $g(\mathbf{P}) = f(x_0,y_0) + a(x - x_0)$, and $|\mathbf{P} - \mathbf{P}_0| = |x - x_0|$, so

$$\left| \frac{f(x,y_0) - f(x_0,y_0)}{x - x_0} - a \right| = \frac{|f(x,y_0) - f(x_0,y_0) - a(x - x_0)|}{|x - x_0|}$$

$$= \frac{|f(\mathbf{P}) - g(\mathbf{P})|}{|\mathbf{P} - \mathbf{P}_0|}. \tag{6}$$

As x tends to x_0, then $\mathbf{P}$ tends to $\mathbf{P}_0$, so the right-hand side of (6) tends to zero, and (5) is proved.

(iii) If $\mathbf{M} = (a,b)$, then

$$\lim_{y\to y_0}\left|\frac{f(x_0,y) - f(x_0,y_0)}{y - y_0} - b\right| = 0.$$

The proof of this is just like (ii).

This completes the theorem, for (i) says that f is continuous at $\mathbf{P}_0$, (ii) says $D_1 f(\mathbf{P}_0) = a$, and (iii) says $D_2 f(\mathbf{P}_0) = b$, so $\mathbf{M} = (a,b) = (D_1 f(\mathbf{P}_0), D_2 f(\mathbf{P}_0))$.

An immediate consequence of Theorem 5 is that *there is only one vector* $\mathbf{M}$ such that $g(\mathbf{P}) = \mathbf{P}_0 + (\mathbf{P} - \mathbf{P}_0)\cdot\mathbf{M}$ satisfies (3), namely

$$\mathbf{M} = (f_x(\mathbf{P}_0), f_y(\mathbf{P}_0)).$$

This vector is called the *gradient* of f at $\mathbf{P}_0$, denoted $\nabla f(\mathbf{P}_0)$ (read "del f of $\mathbf{P}_0$"). Thus, when f is differentiable at $\mathbf{P}_0$ we have the limit relation

$$\lim_{\mathbf{P}\to\mathbf{P}_0}\frac{f(\mathbf{P}) - f(\mathbf{P}_0) - (\mathbf{P} - \mathbf{P}_0)\cdot\nabla f(\mathbf{P}_0)}{|\mathbf{P} - \mathbf{P}_0|} = 0, \tag{7}$$

where $\nabla f(\mathbf{P}_0) = (f_x(\mathbf{P}_0), f_y(\mathbf{P}_0))$.

In many respects the gradient $\nabla f(\mathbf{P}_0)$ replaces the ordinary derivative $F'(x_0)$ of a function F of one variable. For example, the graph of

$$G(x) = F(x_0) + (x - x_0)F'(x_0)$$

is defined to be the tangent line to the graph of F at the point $(x_0, F(x_0))$. Analogously, we define the graph of

$$g(\mathbf{P}) = f(\mathbf{P}_0) + (\mathbf{P} - \mathbf{P}_0)\cdot\nabla f(\mathbf{P}_0)$$

to be the *tangent plane* to the graph of f at the point $(\mathbf{P}_0, f(\mathbf{P}_0))$. Notice that $\nabla f(\mathbf{P}_0)$ is the *slope* of the tangent plane, and the *equation* of the tangent plane is

$$z = f(\mathbf{P}_0) + (\mathbf{P} - \mathbf{P}_0)\cdot\nabla f(\mathbf{P}_0)$$

or

$$z = f(x_0,y_0) + (x - x_0)f_x(x_0,y_0) + (y - y_0)f_y(x_0,y_0).$$

Another analogy between ∇f and F' shows up in the following important *chain rule.*

Theorem 6. *Let* $\boldsymbol{\gamma}$ *be a curve in* R^2 *and* f *a function of two variables. If* f *is differentiable at* $\mathbf{P}_0 = \boldsymbol{\gamma}(t_0)$, *and if* $\boldsymbol{\gamma}'(t_0)$ *exists, then* $f\circ\boldsymbol{\gamma}$ *is differentiable at* t_0 *and*

$$(f\circ\boldsymbol{\gamma})'(t_0) = \nabla f(\mathbf{P}_0)\cdot\boldsymbol{\gamma}'(t_0). \tag{8}$$

Proof. Let

$$Q(\mathbf{P}) = \begin{cases} \dfrac{f(\mathbf{P}) - f(\mathbf{P}_0) - (\mathbf{P} - \mathbf{P}_0)\cdot\nabla f(\mathbf{P}_0)}{|\mathbf{P} - \mathbf{P}_0|} & \text{if } \mathbf{P} \neq \mathbf{P}_0 \\ 0 & \text{if } \mathbf{P} = \mathbf{P}_0 . \end{cases}$$

Then (7) says that Q is continuous at $\mathbf{P}_0$. Now set $\mathbf{P} = \boldsymbol{\gamma}(t)$ and $\mathbf{P}_0 = \boldsymbol{\gamma}(t_0)$. By simple algebra we have, for every $t \neq t_0$,

$$\frac{f(\boldsymbol{\gamma}(t)) - f(\boldsymbol{\gamma}(t_0))}{t - t_0} = \frac{\boldsymbol{\gamma}(t) - \boldsymbol{\gamma}(t_0)}{t - t_0}\cdot\nabla f(\mathbf{P}_0) + \frac{|\boldsymbol{\gamma}(t) - \boldsymbol{\gamma}(t_0)|}{t - t_0}\, Q(\boldsymbol{\gamma}(t)). \tag{9}$$

The first term on the right-hand side of (9) converges to $\boldsymbol{\gamma}'(t_0)\cdot\nabla f(\mathbf{P}_0)$ as $t \to t_0$, so we have to prove that the remaining term converges to zero, or what is the same, that its absolute value

$$\left|\frac{\boldsymbol{\gamma}(t) - \boldsymbol{\gamma}(t_0)}{t - t_0}\right| |Q(\boldsymbol{\gamma}(t))| \tag{10}$$

converges to zero. But Q, $\boldsymbol{\gamma}$, and the absolute value are all continuous functions, so by Theorem 3 on composite functions

$$\lim_{t\to t_0} |Q(\boldsymbol{\gamma}(t))| = |Q(\boldsymbol{\gamma}(t_0))| = |Q(\mathbf{P}_0)| = 0.$$

Similarly,

$$\lim_{t\to t_0} \left|\frac{\boldsymbol{\gamma}(t) - \boldsymbol{\gamma}(t_0)}{t - t_0}\right| = |\boldsymbol{\gamma}'(t_0)|,$$

so the expression in (10) converges to $|\boldsymbol{\gamma}'(t_0)|\cdot 0 = 0$, and the theorem is proved.

Various special cases of the chain rule formula give some insight into the gradient.

(i) If $\boldsymbol{\gamma}(t) = (x_0 + t, y_0)$, then $\boldsymbol{\gamma}$ traces a straight line $\{(x,y) : y = y_0\}$ parallel to the x axis, with speed 1, and $f\circ\boldsymbol{\gamma}$ gives the values of f along this line. (See Fig. 26.) We find $\boldsymbol{\gamma}'(t) = (1,0)$, hence

$$(f\circ\boldsymbol{\gamma})'(0) = \boldsymbol{\gamma}'(0)\cdot\nabla f(\mathbf{P}_0) = (1,0)\cdot\nabla f(\mathbf{P}_0) = D_1 f(\mathbf{P}_0).$$

Thus, the derivative of f along this curve $\boldsymbol{\gamma}$ equals the partial derivative of f with respect to x.

(ii) If $\mathbf{U}$ is any unit vector and $\boldsymbol{\gamma}(t) = \mathbf{P}_0 + t\mathbf{U}$, then $\boldsymbol{\gamma}$ is the line passing through $\mathbf{P}_0$ with unit speed in the direction $\mathbf{U}$. The composite

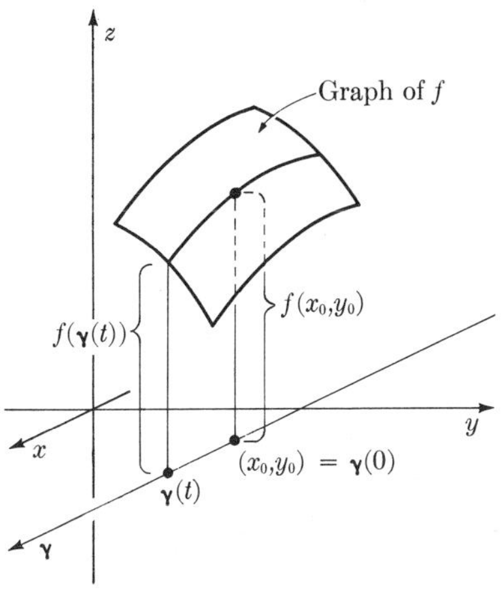

FIGURE 3.26

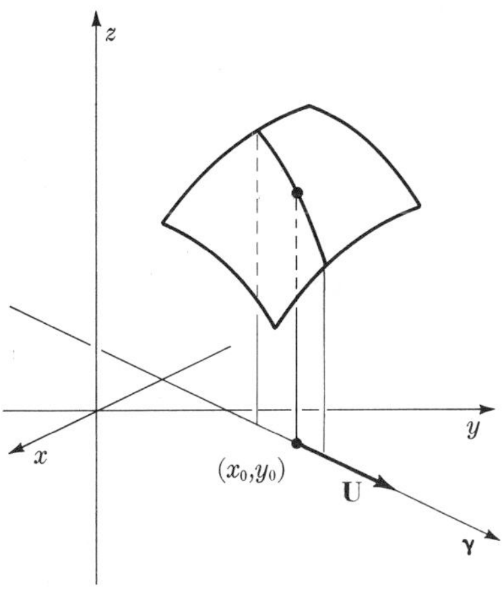

FIGURE 3.27

function $f \circ \boldsymbol{\gamma}$ gives the values of f along this line, and its derivative at $t = 0$,

$$(f \circ \boldsymbol{\gamma})'(0) = \boldsymbol{\gamma}'(0) \cdot \nabla f(\mathbf{P}_0) = \mathbf{U} \cdot \nabla f(\mathbf{P}_0),$$

gives the rate of change of f with respect to distance in the direction $\mathbf{U}$. This is called the *directional derivative of f in the direction* $\mathbf{U}$ (see Fig. 27). When $\mathbf{U} = (1,0)$, the directional derivative is $\mathbf{U} \cdot \nabla f(\mathbf{P}_0) = D_1 f(\mathbf{P}_0) =$ the partial derivative of f with respect to x, as we found in case (i) above; when $\mathbf{U} = (0,1)$, we get the directional derivative $\mathbf{U} \cdot \nabla f(\mathbf{P}_0) = D_2 f(\mathbf{P}_0)$, the partial derivative with respect to y. In general, the derivative in the direction $\mathbf{U}$ is a combination of $D_1 f$ and $D_2 f$.

One sometimes speaks of a directional derivative in a direction $\mathbf{V}$, where $|\mathbf{V}| \neq 1$; in this book, that will be understood as

$$\frac{1}{|\mathbf{V}|} \mathbf{V} \cdot \nabla f.$$

(iii) Suppose $\boldsymbol{\gamma}$ is a curve lying entirely in a contour line $\{\mathbf{P} : f(\mathbf{P}) = c\}$. Then

$$f(\boldsymbol{\gamma}(t)) = c \tag{11}$$

for every t. Differentiating each side of (11) with respect to t yields

$$\nabla f(\boldsymbol{\gamma}(t)) \cdot \boldsymbol{\gamma}'(t) = 0.$$

Thus, for every point $\mathbf{P}_0$ on the curve $\boldsymbol{\gamma}$, $\nabla f(\mathbf{P}_0)$ is orthogonal to the curve at $\mathbf{P}_0$ (see Fig. 28). We describe this situation by saying simply that *the gradient is orthogonal to the contour line.* (This phrase has a fairly clear intuitive meaning (as in Fig. 28); the precise analytic meaning is, of course, that $\nabla f(\mathbf{P}_0)$ is orthogonal at $\mathbf{P}_0$ to every curve lying in the contour line through $\mathbf{P}_0$.)

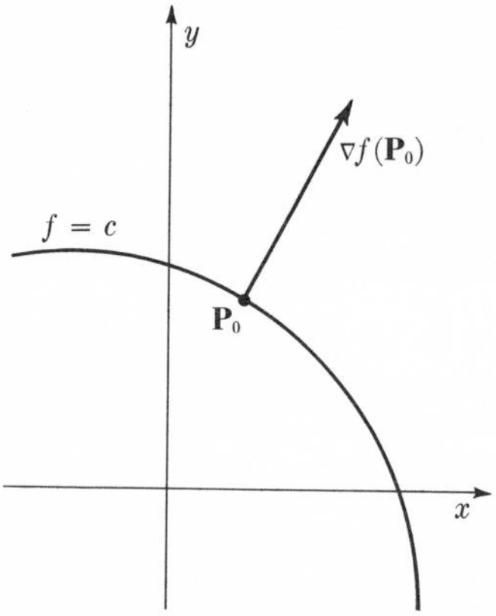

FIGURE 3.28

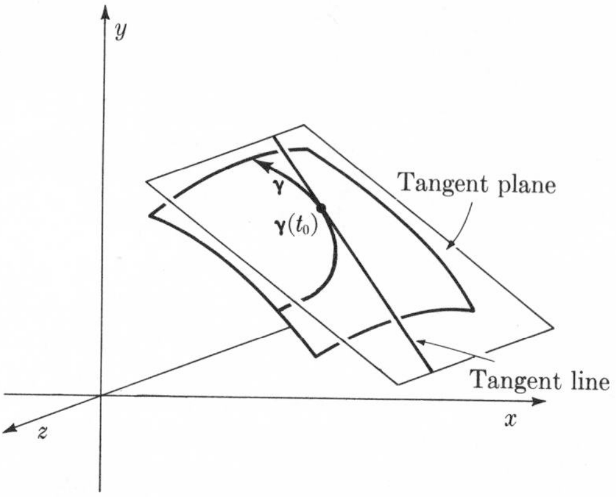

FIGURE 3.29

(iv) Suppose γ is a curve in R^3 lying in the graph of f. Then, as Fig. 29 suggests, *the tangent line to* γ *at* $\gamma(t_0)$ *lies in the tangent plane to* f *at* $\gamma(t_0)$. This fact (whose proof is left as a problem) lends geometric support to the rather abstract definition of tangent plane that we gave, based on Definition 5 and Theorem 5. It shows that our definition of tangent plane is intuitively consistent with the definition of tangent line to a curve.

This whole discussion about tangent planes, the chain rule, and the directional derivative is valid when f is differentiable at the point $\mathbf{P}_0$ in question, in other words, when the limit relation (7) holds. What we need now is an effective way to establish differentiability. Here it is:

Theorem 7. *If $D_1 f$ and $D_2 f$ exist at all points in some disk centered at $\mathbf{P}_0$, and are continuous at $\mathbf{P}_0$, then f is differentiable at $\mathbf{P}_0$.*

Proof. We have to prove that

$$\lim_{\mathbf{P}\to\mathbf{P}_0} \frac{|f(\mathbf{P}) - g(\mathbf{P})|}{|\mathbf{P} - \mathbf{P}_0|} = 0, \tag{12}$$

where

$$g(\mathbf{P}) = f(\mathbf{P}_0) + (\mathbf{P} - \mathbf{P}_0) \cdot \nabla f(\mathbf{P}_0). \tag{13}$$

Referring to Fig. 30, we write

$$\begin{aligned} f(\mathbf{P}) - f(\mathbf{P}_0) &= f(x,y) - f(x_0,y_0) \\ &= f(x,y) - f(x_0,y) + f(x_0,y) - f(x_0,y_0). \end{aligned} \tag{14}$$

If we think of y as fixed, and apply the mean value theorem to f as a function of the one variable x, we get (see Fig. 30)

$$f(x,y) - f(x_0,y) = (x - x_0)f_x(\xi,y) \quad \text{with } \xi \text{ between } x \text{ and } x_0.$$

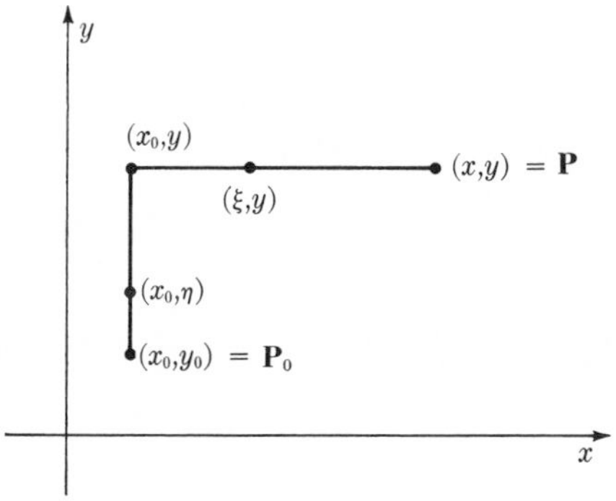

FIGURE 3.30

Similarly, fixing x_0 and considering f as a function only of y,

$$f(x_0,y) - f(x_0,y_0) = (y - y_0)f_y(x_0,\eta) \quad \text{with } \eta \text{ between } y \text{ and } y_0.$$

Hence, from (14),

$$\begin{aligned} f(\mathbf{P}) - f(\mathbf{P}_0) &= (x - x_0)f_x(\xi,y) + (y - y_0)f_y(x_0,\eta) \\ &= (x - x_0)f_x(x_0,y_0) + (y - y_0)f_y(x_0,y_0) + R(\mathbf{P}) \\ &= (\mathbf{P} - \mathbf{P}_0) \cdot \nabla f(\mathbf{P}_0) + R(\mathbf{P}) \end{aligned} \tag{15}$$

where R makes up for changing (ξ,y) and (x_0,η) into (x_0,y_0), i.e.

$$\begin{aligned} R(\mathbf{P}) = (x - x_0)&[f_x(\xi,y) - f_x(x_0,y_0)] \\ &+ (y - y_0)[f_y(x_0,\eta) - f_y(x_0,y_0)]. \end{aligned} \tag{16}$$

From (13), (15), and (16),

$$\frac{|f(\mathbf{P}) - g(\mathbf{P})|}{|\mathbf{P} - \mathbf{P}_0|} = \frac{|R(\mathbf{P})|}{|\mathbf{P} - \mathbf{P}_0|}$$

$$\leq \frac{|x - x_0|}{|\mathbf{P} - \mathbf{P}_0|} \, |f_x(\xi,y) - f_x(x_0\,,y_0)|$$

$$+ \frac{|y - y_0|}{|\mathbf{P} - \mathbf{P}_0|} \, |f_y(x_0\,,\eta) - f_y(x_0\,,y_0)|$$

$$\leq |f_x(\xi,y) - f_x(x_0\,,y_0)| + |f_x(x_0,\eta) - f_y(x_0\,,y_0)|. \tag{17}$$

In arriving at the last line we used $|x - x_0| \leq \sqrt{(x - x_0)^2 + (y - y_0)^2} = |\mathbf{P} - \mathbf{P}_0|$, and similarly $|y - y_0| \leq |\mathbf{P} - \mathbf{P}_0|$. Now the end of the proof is in sight: since f_x and f_y are continuous at $\mathbf{P}_0$, the two terms in the last line of (17) tend to zero as $\mathbf{P} \to \mathbf{P}_0$, so

$$\frac{|f(\mathbf{P}) - g(\mathbf{P})|}{|\mathbf{P} - \mathbf{P}_0|} \quad \text{tends to zero}$$

and (12) is proved.

If you want to complete the argument in all its gory detail, suppose $\epsilon > 0$ is given. Since f_x and f_y are continuous at $\mathbf{P}_0$, there is $\delta > 0$ such that

$$|\mathbf{Q} - \mathbf{P}_0| < \delta \quad \Rightarrow \quad |f_x(\mathbf{Q}) - f_x(\mathbf{P}_0)| < \frac{\epsilon}{2} \text{ and } |f_y(\mathbf{Q}) - f_y(\mathbf{P}_0)| < \frac{\epsilon}{2}. \tag{18}$$

Further, if $\mathbf{Q}_1 = (\xi,y)$ and $\mathbf{Q}_2 = (x_0\,,n)$ then

$$|\mathbf{Q}_1 - \mathbf{P}_0| = \sqrt{(\xi - x_0)^2 + (y - y_0)^2} \leq \sqrt{(x - x_0)^2 + (y - y_0)^2}$$
$$\leq |\mathbf{P} - \mathbf{P}_0|$$

since ξ is between x and x_0; and similarly $|\mathbf{Q}_2 - \mathbf{P}_0| \leq |\mathbf{P} - \mathbf{P}_0|$. Hence from (18)

$$|\mathbf{P} - \mathbf{P}_0| < \delta \quad \Rightarrow \quad |\mathbf{Q}_1 - \mathbf{P}_0| < \delta \quad \Rightarrow \quad |f_x(\mathbf{Q}_1) - f_x(\mathbf{P}_0)| < \frac{\epsilon}{2}$$

and

$$|\mathbf{P} - \mathbf{P}_0| < \delta \quad \Rightarrow \quad |\mathbf{Q}_2 - \mathbf{P}_0| < \delta \quad \Rightarrow \quad |f_y(\mathbf{Q}_2) - f_y(\mathbf{P}_0)| < \frac{\epsilon}{2}.$$

Combining this with (17) and recalling the definitions of $\mathbf{Q}_1$ and $\mathbf{Q}_2$, we obtain

$$|\mathbf{P} - \mathbf{P}_0| < \delta \quad \Rightarrow \quad \frac{|f(\mathbf{P}) - g(\mathbf{P})|}{|\mathbf{P} - \mathbf{P}_0|} < \frac{\epsilon}{2} + \frac{\epsilon}{2} = \epsilon,$$

and the proof of (12) is complete.

Summary. This has been a long section with some difficult proofs, but the end results can be summed up rather briefly. If the first partials $D_1 f$ and $D_2 f$ exist throughout a disk centered at $\mathbf{P}_0$ and are continuous at $\mathbf{P}_0$, then f is *differentiable at* $\mathbf{P}_0$, that is, f satisfies the condition

$$\lim_{\mathbf{P}\to\mathbf{P}_0} \frac{f(\mathbf{P}) - f(\mathbf{P}_0) - (\mathbf{P} - \mathbf{P}_0)\cdot\nabla f(\mathbf{P}_0)}{|\mathbf{P} - \mathbf{P}_0|} = 0,$$

where $\nabla f(\mathbf{P}_0) = (D_1 f(\mathbf{P}_0), D_2 f(\mathbf{P}_0))$ is the *gradient* of f at $\mathbf{P}_0$. The gradient is orthogonal to the contour lines, and gives the slope of the tangent plane. The equation of the tangent plane at a point (x_0, y_0, z_0) on the graph of f is

$$z = z_0 + (\mathbf{P} - \mathbf{P}_0)\cdot\nabla f(\mathbf{P}_0),$$

where $\mathbf{P} = (x,y)$, $\mathbf{P}_0 = (x_0, y_0)$, and $z_0 = f(\mathbf{P}_0)$.

If $\boldsymbol{\gamma}$ is any differentiable curve such that $\boldsymbol{\gamma}(t_0) = \mathbf{P}_0$, then the *chain rule* holds,

$$(f\circ\boldsymbol{\gamma})'(t_0) = \boldsymbol{\gamma}'(t_0)\cdot\nabla f(\mathbf{P}_0).$$

The directional derivative of f in the direction $\mathbf{U}$ is $\nabla f\cdot\mathbf{U}$, where $\mathbf{U}$ is any unit vector.

Example 1. Consider the function $f(x,y) = x^2 + 2y^2 - 1$. The partial derivatives $f_x = 2x$ and $f_y = 4y$ are continuous everywhere, so the general theory applies. Figure 31 shows the contour lines and the gradient $(2x,4y)$ at several points; notice that the gradient $\nabla f(\mathbf{P}_0)$ really is orthogonal to the contour line through $\mathbf{P}_0$. At the origin we find $\nabla f = (0,0)$, so the directional derivative $\nabla f\cdot\mathbf{U}$ is zero in every direction $\mathbf{U}$. At the point $(1,1)$ we have $\nabla f = (2,4)$. The directional derivative at $(1,1)$ in the direction $(1/\sqrt{2}, 1/\sqrt{2})$ is $(2,4)\cdot(1/\sqrt{2}, 1/\sqrt{2}) = 3\sqrt{2}$.

The point $(0,0,-1)$ is on the graph of f, and the tangent plane at this point has slope $\nabla f(0,0) = (0,0)$, so its equation is

$$z = -1 + [\mathbf{P} - (0,0)]\cdot\nabla f(0,0), \qquad \text{or} \qquad z = -1.$$

This is a horizontal plane, as shown in Fig. 31. The tangent plane at $(1,1,2)$ has slope $\nabla f(1,1) = (2,4)$, so its equation is

$$z = 2 + [\mathbf{P} - (1,1)]\cdot(2,4).$$

Setting $\mathbf{P} = (x,y)$ and multiplying out the dot product, we get the equation of the tangent plane in the form

$$z = 2 + (2x + 4y) - 2 - 4 = -4 + 2x + 4y.$$

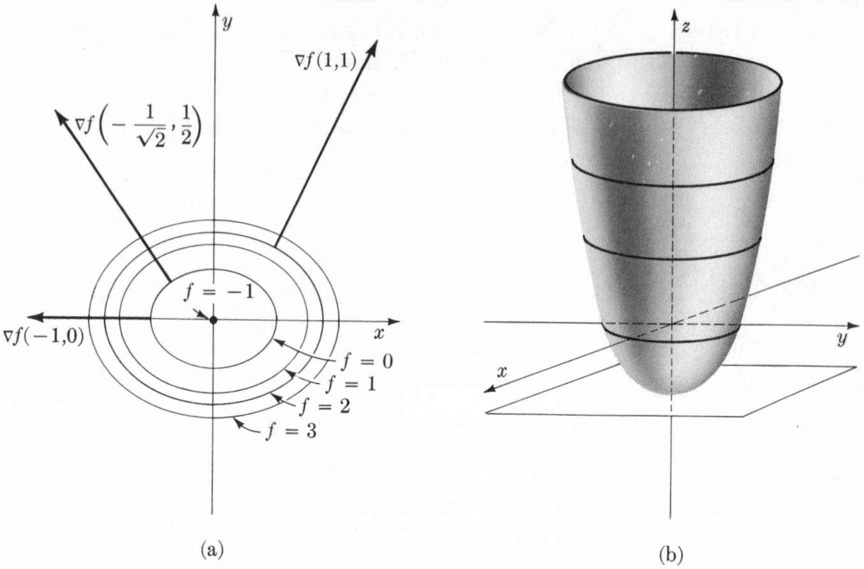

FIGURE 3.31

Example 2. Consider the function $f(x,y) = xy$. The partial derivatives $f_x = y$ and $f_y = x$ are continuous everywhere, so the general theory applies. Figure 32 shows the contour lines and the gradient $\nabla f(x,y) = (y,x)$ at several points. At the point $(-2,3)$, for example, we have $\nabla f(-2,3) = (3,-2)$. Starting at $(-2,3)$, the unit vector $\left(\frac{2}{\sqrt{13}}, \frac{-3}{\sqrt{13}}\right)$ points toward the origin. Thus the directional derivative "toward the origin" at this point is

$$\nabla f(-2,3)\cdot\left(\frac{2}{\sqrt{13}}, \frac{-3}{\sqrt{13}}\right) = (3,-2)\cdot\left(\frac{2}{\sqrt{13}}, \frac{-3}{\sqrt{13}}\right) = \frac{12}{\sqrt{13}}$$

and the directional derivative "away from the origin" is

$$\nabla f(-2,3)\cdot\left(\frac{-2}{\sqrt{13}}, \frac{3}{\sqrt{13}}\right) = \frac{-12}{\sqrt{13}}.$$

Thus f increases as you move from $(-2,3)$ toward the origin, and decreases as you move away; this is consistent with Fig. 32. The equation of the tangent plane to the graph at $(-2,3,-6)$ is

$$z = -6 + (\mathbf{P} - (-2,3))\cdot\nabla f(-2,3),$$

or

$$\begin{aligned} z &= -6 + ((x,y) - (-2,3))\cdot(3,-2) \\ &= -6 + 3x - 2y + 6 + 6 = 6 + 3x - 2y. \end{aligned}$$

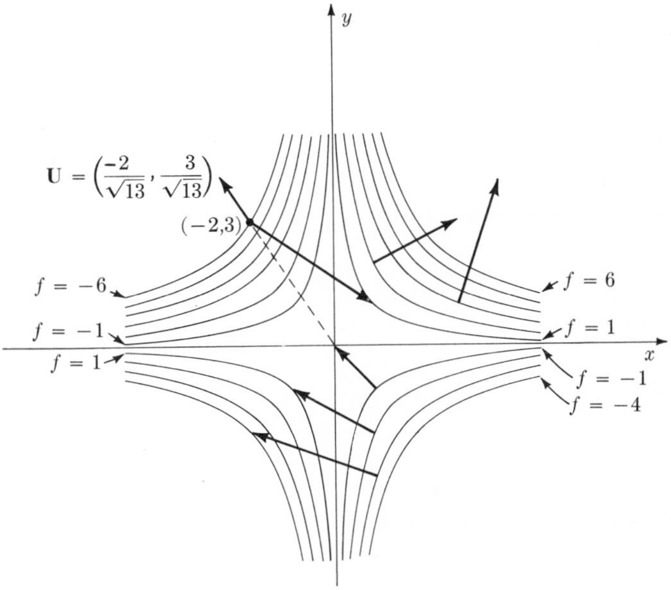

U is a unit vector pointing away from the origin, *not* a gradient; all other arrows represent gradients

FIGURE 3.32

Example 3. Find a line orthogonal to the graph of $f(x,y) = xy$ at the point $(-2,3,-6)$. *Solution.* "Orthogonal to the graph" means "orthogonal to the tangent plane to the graph." Since the equation of the tangent plane is

$$z = 6 + 3x - 2y,$$

or

$$3x - 2y - z = -6,$$

a vector normal to this plane is $\mathbf{N} = (3,-2,-1)$. Thus the line orthogonal to the plane (and hence to the graph) at $(-2,3,-6)$ is given parametrically by

$$\mathbf{Q} = (-2,3,-6) + t\mathbf{N} = (-2,3,-6) + t(3,-2,-1),$$

or

$$x = -2 + 3t, \qquad y = 3 - 2t, \qquad z = -6 - t.$$

PROBLEMS

The first nine problems give routine practice with gradients, directional derivatives, tangent planes, and normals. Problems 10–14 concern the theory developed above. The final five problems develop the concept of an *open connected set.*

1. Find the gradients of the following functions. At what points are the partial derivatives continuous?

(a) e^{xy}

(b) $\sqrt{x^2 + y^2}$

(c) $\cos(\sqrt{x^2 + y^2})$

(d) y/x

(e) $x \int_0^y e^{t^2}\,dt$

(f) $\arctan(x/y)$

2. For the following functions, sketch the contour line that passes through the point (1,2), and sketch the gradient at that point.

(a) $f(x,y) = x^2 + y^2$ (Since $f(1,2) = 5$, the required contour line is $\{(x,y) : f(x,y) = 5\}$.)

(b) $f(x,y) = xy$

(c) $f(x,y) = 4x^2 - y^2$

(d) $f(x,y) = x^2 + y$

3. For each of the functions in Problem 2, find the equation of the tangent plane at $(1,1,f(1,1))$.

4. Find the directional derivative of the given function at the given point in the given direction.

(a) $x \arctan(x/y)$ at (1,1) in the direction $(0,-1)$

(b) $x \arctan(x/y)$ at (1,1) in the direction (1,0)

(c) $e^{-x^2-y^2}$ at (0,0) in the direction $(\frac{3}{5}, \frac{4}{5})$

(d) $e^{-x^2-y^2}$ at $(1,-1)$ in the direction $(\frac{3}{5}, \frac{4}{5})$

5. If two surfaces intersect at a point (x_0,y_0,z_0), their *angle of intersection* at (x_0, y_0, z_0) is the angle between the normals to their tangent planes at that point. Find the angle of intersection of the graphs of $f(x,y) = xy$ and $g(x,y) = 1 - x^2 - 2y^2$ at the point (1,0,0). (You should find the angle $\arccos(1/\sqrt{10})$.)

6. (a) Find all points at which the graph of $f(x,y) = 1 - x^2 - y^2$ intersects the xy plane.

(b) Show that at each of these points the angle of intersection is $\arccos(-1/\sqrt{5})$. (See Problem 5. The answer $\arccos(1/\sqrt{5})$ is equally good; it corresponds to a different choice of normals.)

7. Let $f(x,y) = x^2 + y^2$ and $\gamma(t) = (\cos t, \sin t)$.

(a) Check that $\gamma(t)$ lies in the contour line $\{(x,y) : f(x,y) = 1\}$.

(b) Show that the velocity vector $\gamma'(0)$ is orthogonal to the gradient ∇f at the point $\gamma(0) = (1,0)$. Sketch the curve γ, the velocity $\gamma'(0)$, and the gradient $\nabla f(1,0)$.

(c) Check that for every t, $\gamma'(t)$ is orthogonal to the gradient ∇f at the point $\gamma(t)$.

8. Let $f(x,y) = y - x^2$ and $\gamma(t) = (t,t^2)$.
(a) Check that $\gamma(t)$ lies in the contour line $\{(x,y): f(x,y) = 0\}$.
(b) Show that the velocity vector $\gamma'(1)$ is orthogonal to the gradient ∇f at the point $\gamma(1) = (1,1)$. Sketch the curve γ, the velocity $\gamma'(1)$, and the gradient $\nabla f(0,0)$.
(c) Check that, for every t, $\gamma'(t)$ is orthogonal to the gradient ∇f at the point $\gamma(t)$.

9. Let $f(x,y) = x^2y^3$.
(a) Find the equation of the tangent plane at the point $(1,1,1)$.
(b) Show that the vector $(2,3,-1)$ is a normal to the tangent plane at the point $(1,1,1)$.
(c) Show that the curve $\gamma(t) = (\sqrt{2}\cos t, \sqrt{2}\sin t, 4\sqrt{2}\cos^2 t \sin^3 t)$ lies entirely in the graph of f.
(d) Show that the curve in part (c) passes through the point $(1,1,1)$, and that its velocity vector at that point is $(-1,1,1)$.
(e) Prove that the line tangent to the curve γ at the point $(1,1,1)$ lies in the tangent plane to the graph of f at that point.

10. Suppose $\gamma(t) = (g_1(t),g_2(t),g_3(t))$ is a curve lying entirely in the graph of f.
(a) Show that $g_3(t) = f(g_1(t),g_2(t))$.
(b) Show that $g_3'(t) = D_1f(g_1(t),g_2(t))g_1'(t) + D_2f(g_1(t),g_2(t))g_2'(t)$.
(c) Show that at any point $(x_0,y_0,z_0) = \gamma(t_0)$, the tangent vector $\gamma'(t_0)$ is orthogonal to $\mathbf{N}$, the normal of the tangent plane to the graph of f at (x_0,y_0,z_0). (Hence, the line tangent to γ lies in the plane tangent to the graph.)

11. (a) Let f and g be any functions. Prove that if

$$\lim_{\mathbf{P}\to\mathbf{P}_0} |\mathbf{P} - \mathbf{P}_0|^{-1} |f(\mathbf{P}) - g(\mathbf{P})| = 0,$$

then $\lim_{\mathbf{P}\to\mathbf{P}_0} |f(\mathbf{P}) - g(\mathbf{P})| = 0$.

(b) If $f(\mathbf{P})$ is defined for all $\mathbf{P}$ near $\mathbf{P}_0$, and is continuous at $\mathbf{P}_0$, and if g is *any* polynomial of degree 1 such that $g(\mathbf{P}_0) = f(\mathbf{P}_0)$, prove that

$$\lim_{\mathbf{P}\to\mathbf{P}_0} |g(\mathbf{P}) - f(\mathbf{P})| = 0. \tag{19}$$

(c) Suppose that g is a first degree polynomial with $g(\mathbf{P}_0) = f(\mathbf{P}_0)$, and suppose that $\lim_{\mathbf{P}\to\mathbf{P}_0} |g(\mathbf{P}) - f(\mathbf{P})| = 0$. Prove that f is continuous at $\mathbf{P}_0$. (This problem should be compared to the definition of differentiability. Part (a) shows that condition (19) is weaker than the condition for differentiability. Parts (b) and (c) show that (19) corresponds closely to the continuity of f at $\mathbf{P}_0$, whereas in the text we showed that the stronger condition

$$\lim_{\mathbf{P}\to\mathbf{P}_0} |\mathbf{P} - \mathbf{P}_0|^{-1}\, |f(\mathbf{P}) - g(\mathbf{P})| = 0$$

corresponds closely to the behavior of the partial derivatives of f at $\mathbf{P}_0$.)

12. Suppose that $f(\mathbf{P}_0) \geq f(\mathbf{P})$ for all $\mathbf{P}$, and that the partial derivatives of f exist at $\mathbf{P}_0$. Prove that $D_1 f(\mathbf{P}_0) = 0$ and $D_2 f(\mathbf{P}_0) = 0$. (Hint: Look at the functions $f_1(x) = f(x,y_0)$ and $f_2(y) = f(x_0,y)$, and apply a familiar theorem about functions of one variable.)

13. This problem concerns the geometric meaning of the condition

$$\lim_{\mathbf{P}\to\mathbf{P}_0} \frac{f(\mathbf{P}) - f(\mathbf{P}_0) - (\mathbf{P} - \mathbf{P}_0)\cdot\nabla f(\mathbf{P}_0)}{|\mathbf{P} - \mathbf{P}_0|} = 0. \qquad (*)$$

Referring to Fig. 33, let $\mathbf{P} = (x,y)$, $\mathbf{P}_0 = (x_0,y_0)$, $\mathbf{Q} = (x,y,f(x,y))$, $\mathbf{Q}_0 = (x_0,y_0,f(x_0,y_0))$, $\nabla f(\mathbf{P}_0) = (a,b)$, $\mathbf{N} = (-a,-b,1)$, and let θ be the angle between $\mathbf{Q} - \mathbf{Q}_0$ and $\mathbf{N}$. You will show that $\mathbf{N}$ is normal to the tangent plane at $\mathbf{Q}_0$, and that $\theta \to \pi/2$ as $\mathbf{P} \to \mathbf{P}_0$.

(a) Prove that $\mathbf{N}$ is normal to the tangent plane at $\mathbf{Q}_0$.

(b) Prove that

$$\cos\theta = \frac{f(\mathbf{P}_0) + (\mathbf{P} - \mathbf{P}_0)\cdot\nabla f(\mathbf{P}_0) - f(\mathbf{P})}{|\mathbf{Q} - \mathbf{Q}_0|\cdot|\mathbf{N}|}.$$

(c) Prove that $|\mathbf{N}| \geq 1$ and $|\mathbf{Q} - \mathbf{Q}_0| \geq |\mathbf{P} - \mathbf{P}_0|$.

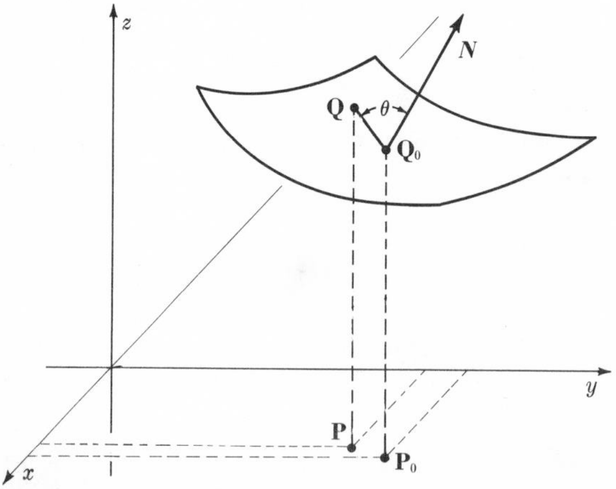

FIGURE 3.33

(d) Prove that if (*) holds, then $\lim_{P \to P_0} \cos \theta = 0$.

(e) Prove that if (*) holds, then $\lim_{P \to P_0} \theta = \pi/2$. (Hint: arccos is a continuous function.)

14. Suppose that f and h are differentiable at $\mathbf{P}_0$. Prove that $f + h$ is differentiable at $\mathbf{P}_0$, and $(\nabla(f + h))(\mathbf{P}_0) = \nabla f(\mathbf{P}_0) + \nabla h(\mathbf{P}_0)$.

Problems 15–19 concern *connected open sets.* An open set S in which every pair of points $\mathbf{P}_1$ and $\mathbf{P}_2$ can be joined by a differentiable curve γ lying in S is called *connected.* Figure 34(a) shows a connected open set, and Fig. 34(b) shows a disconnected one. Every open disk D is connected, since any two points in D can be joined by the line segment between them. For exactly the same reason, every open rectangle is connected.

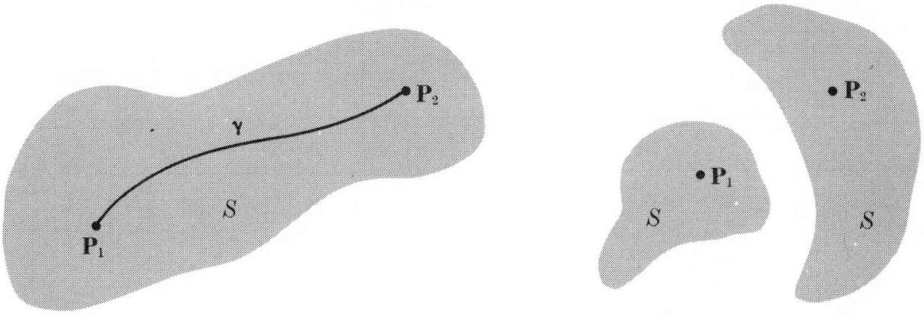

(a) S connected (b) S not connected

FIGURE 3.34

15. Suppose that S is a connected open set, that f is differentiable on S, and that $\nabla f \equiv \mathbf{0}$. Prove that f is constant on S. (Hint: Take any fixed point $\mathbf{P}_0$ in S. For every $\mathbf{P}_1$ in S there is a curve $\boldsymbol{\gamma}: [a,b] \to S$ such that $\boldsymbol{\gamma}(a) = \mathbf{P}_0$ and $\boldsymbol{\gamma}(b) = \mathbf{P}_1$. Use the chain rule (8) to prove that $f(\boldsymbol{\gamma}(b)) = f(\boldsymbol{\gamma}(a))$.)

16. Suppose S is a connected open set, f and g are differentiable, and $\nabla f \equiv \nabla g$ on S. What can you conclude about the difference between f and g? (See the two preceding problems.)

17. Suppose that S is a connected open set, that f is continuous on S, that $\mathbf{P}_1$ and $\mathbf{P}_2$ are two points in S. Prove the *Intermediate Value theorem:* If v is any number between $f(\mathbf{P}_1)$ and $f(\mathbf{P}_2)$, then there is a point $\mathbf{P}$ in S such that $f(\mathbf{P}) = v$. (Hint: Use the definition of connectedness given above, and apply the intermediate value theorem for functions of one variable; see Fig. 35.)

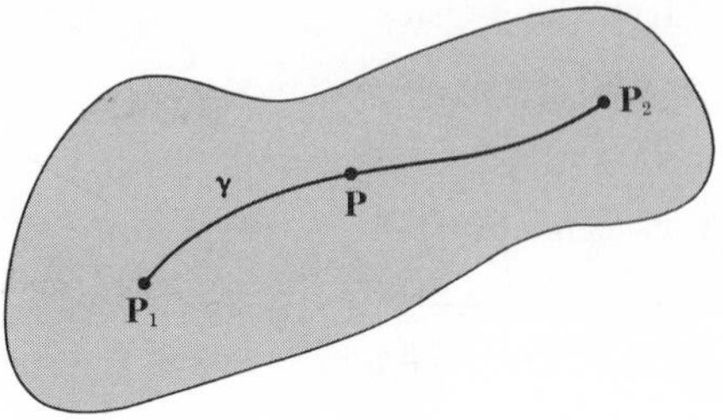

FIGURE 3.35

18. Prove that the following sets are connected.

(a) R^2

(b) $U = \{(x,y): y > 0\}$ (Hint: Given $\mathbf{P}_1$ and $\mathbf{P}_2$ in U, prove that the line segment given by $\boldsymbol{\gamma}(t) = (1 - t)\mathbf{P}_1 + t\mathbf{P}_2$ lies in U for $0 \leq t \leq 1$, while $\boldsymbol{\gamma}(0) = \mathbf{P}_1$ and $\boldsymbol{\gamma}(1) = \mathbf{P}_2$.)

(c) $\{(x,y): x > 0\}$

(d) $R = \{(x,y): a < x < b \text{ and } c < y < d\}$

(e) $D = \{(x,y): x^2 + y^2 < 1\}$
(Hint: Use the same definition of $\boldsymbol{\gamma}$ as in part (b).)

(f) $\{\mathbf{P}: |\mathbf{P}| > 0\}$
(Hint: If $\mathbf{P}_1 = (r_1 \cos\theta_1, r_1 \sin\theta_1)$ and $\mathbf{P}_2 = (r_2 \cos\theta_2, r_2 \sin\theta_2)$, let $r(t) = (1 - t)r_1 + tr_2$, $\theta(t) = (1 - t)\theta_1 + t\theta_2$, and $\boldsymbol{\gamma}(t) = (r(t)\cos\theta(t), r(t)\sin\theta(t))$. See Fig. 36.)

(g) $\{\mathbf{P}: 1 < |\mathbf{P}| < 2\}$

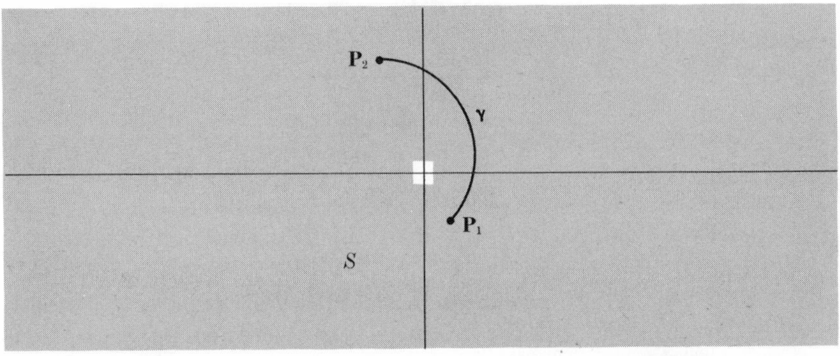

FIGURE 3.36

19. Prove that the following sets are *not* connected.
(a) $\{(x,y): y \neq 0\}$ (Hint: Apply Problem 17 with $\mathbf{P}_1 = (0,-1)$, $\mathbf{P}_2 = (0,1)$, $f(x,y) = y$, and $v = 0$.)
(b) $\{(x,y): x \neq 0\}$
(c) $\{\mathbf{P}: |\mathbf{P}| < 1 \text{ or } |\mathbf{P}| > 2\}$
(Hint: Apply Problem 17 with $f(\mathbf{P}) = |\mathbf{P}|^2$.)

3.4 COMPUTATIONS WITH THE CHAIN RULE

In geometric questions about contour lines, directional derivatives, and tangent planes, the chain rule can be applied best in the form that we have given,

$$(f\circ\boldsymbol{\gamma})'(t) = \nabla f(\boldsymbol{\gamma}(t))\cdot\boldsymbol{\gamma}'(t). \tag{1}$$

However, in many computational problems Leibniz notation is more convenient. To convert (1) into this notation we write

$$z = f(x,y), \qquad \text{so} \qquad \nabla f = \left(\frac{\partial z}{\partial x}, \frac{\partial z}{\partial y}\right),$$

and we set

$$x = \gamma_1(t), \qquad y = \gamma_2(t), \qquad \text{so} \qquad \boldsymbol{\gamma}'(t) = \left(\frac{dx}{dt}, \frac{dy}{dt}\right).$$

Then the chain rule (1) takes the form

$$\frac{dz}{dt} = \frac{\partial z}{\partial x}\frac{dx}{dt} + \frac{\partial z}{\partial y}\frac{dy}{dt}. \tag{2}$$

Notice that dx does *not* cancel ∂x, and dy does not cancel ∂y; with two or more variables, Leibniz notation no longer makes the chain rule look like simple algebra.

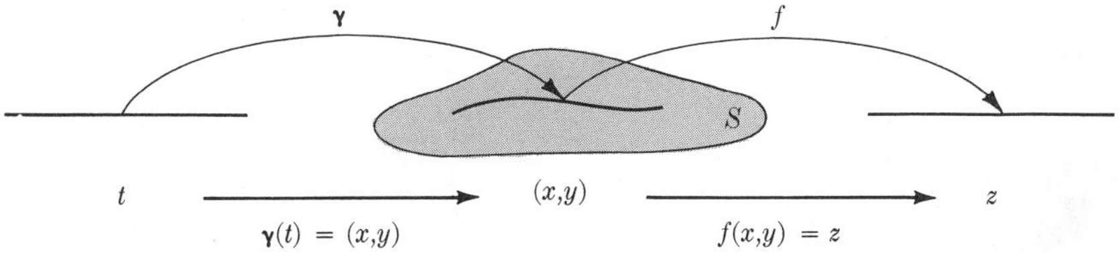

FIGURE 3.37

Figure 37 shows the situation schematically. The function $\boldsymbol{\gamma}$ carries a real number t into a point $(x,y) = \boldsymbol{\gamma}(t)$ in the domain of f, and f carries (x,y) into a real number $z = f(x,y)$. The composite function thus carries t into z, and its derivative is given by (2). In Fig. 37, z is called the "dependent variable," t is the "independent variable," and x and y are the "intermediate variables."

The chain rule computes the derivative of the dependent variable z with respect to the independent variable t; the formula involves the derivative of z with respect to each intermediate variable, multiplied by the derivative of the intermediate variable with respect to the independent variable (Fig. 38).

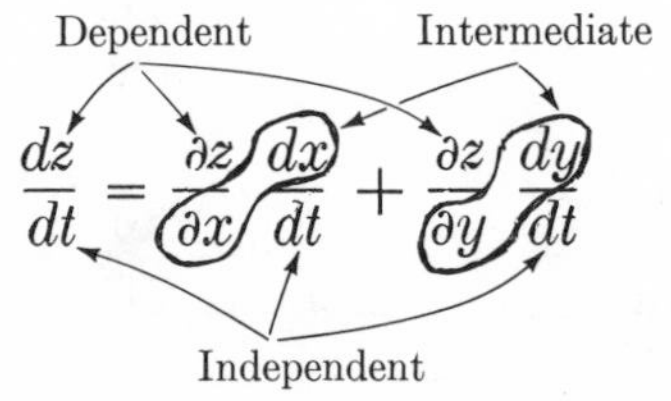

FIGURE 3.38

Example 1. If $z = f(x,y) = e^{xy}$, $x = t^2$, $y = 1/t$, we get $\partial z/\partial x = ye^{xy}$, $\partial z/\partial y = xe^{xy}$, hence from (2)

$$\frac{dz}{dt} = ye^{xy}2t + xe^{xy}(-1/t^2).$$

Substituting for x and y their expressions in terms of t, we find

$$\frac{dz}{dt} = \frac{1}{t}\,e^t \cdot 2t + t^2e^t\left(-\frac{1}{t^2}\right) = e^t.$$

You can easily check this computation by noting that $z = f(t^2,1/t) = e^t$, hence $dz/dt = e^t$.

Figure 39 shows another important version of the chain rule. Here $z = f(x,y)$ as before, but x and y are given as functions of *two* independent variables s and t, say $x = \varphi(s,t)$ and $y = \psi(s,t)$. Thus z can be considered as a function of the two variables s and t. In this case the partial derivatives $\partial z/\partial s$ and $\partial z/\partial t$ are given by formulas similar to (2),

$$\frac{\partial z}{\partial s} = \frac{\partial z}{\partial x}\frac{\partial x}{\partial s} + \frac{\partial z}{\partial y}\frac{\partial y}{\partial s} \tag{3}$$

$$\frac{\partial z}{\partial t} = \frac{\partial z}{\partial x}\frac{\partial x}{\partial t} + \frac{\partial z}{\partial y}\frac{\partial y}{\partial t}, \tag{4}$$

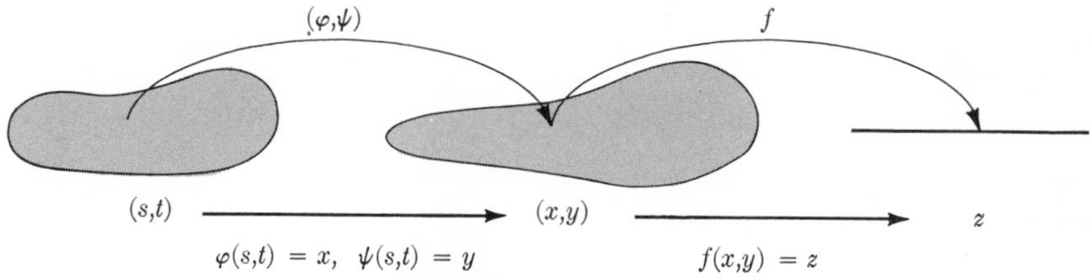

FIGURE 3.39

and for a very simple reason. To compute $\partial z/\partial t$, $\partial x/\partial t$, and $\partial y/\partial t$ we hold s fixed and differentiate as if we had functions of the one variable t; thus formula (2) implies (4). Similarly, to compute $\partial z/\partial s$ we hold t constant, so the rule (2) for ordinary derivatives implies (3).

Notice in (3) and (4) that cancellation of ∂x and ∂y from numerator and denominator in each term leads to complete nonsense.

Example 2. Let $z = xe^y$, $x = s + t$, $y = s^2 - t$. Then

$$\frac{\partial z}{\partial s} = \frac{\partial z}{\partial x}\frac{\partial x}{\partial s} + \frac{\partial z}{\partial y}\frac{\partial y}{\partial s} = e^y \cdot 1 + xe^y \cdot 2s = e^{s^2-t}(1 + (s+t)2s)$$

$$\frac{\partial z}{\partial t} = \frac{\partial z}{\partial x}\frac{\partial x}{\partial t} + \frac{\partial z}{\partial y}\frac{\partial y}{\partial t} = e^y \cdot 1 + xe^y(-1) = e^{s^2-t}(1 - s - t).$$

You can check these results by differentiating $(s + t)e^{s^2-t}$ directly.

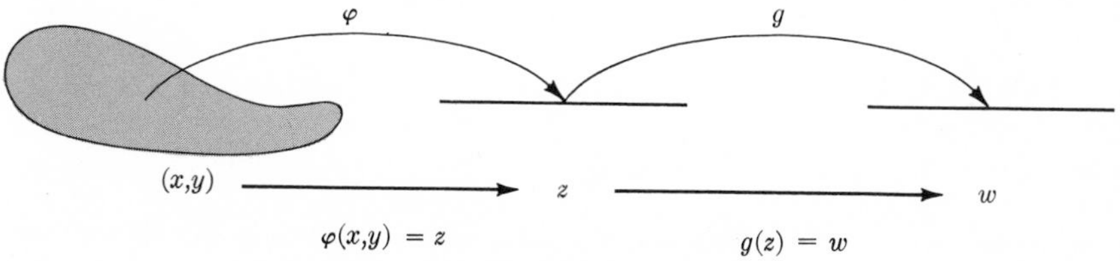

FIGURE 3.40

Figure 40 shows yet another version of the chain rule:

$$\frac{\partial w}{\partial x} = \frac{dw}{dz}\frac{\partial z}{\partial x} \tag{5}$$

$$\frac{\partial w}{\partial y} = \frac{dw}{dz}\frac{\partial z}{\partial y} \tag{6}$$

or

$$\nabla(g \circ \varphi) = (g' \circ \varphi)\nabla\varphi. \tag{7}$$

Since y is held constant in taking $\partial/\partial x$, formula (5) follows from the one-variable chain rule, and (6) follows analogously. Finally, (7) is simply a different notation for (5) and (6) together.

Example 3. Suppose g is a differentiable function of one variable, and let $f(\mathbf{P}) = g(|\mathbf{P}|)$, i.e., $f(x,y) = g(\sqrt{x^2+y^2})$. Find ∇f. *Solution.* We have the situation in Fig. 40 with $\varphi(x,y) = \sqrt{x^2+y^2}$, and $f = g \circ \varphi$. Here

$$\nabla\varphi(x,y) = \left(\frac{x}{\sqrt{x^2+y^2}}, \frac{y}{\sqrt{x^2+y^2}}\right),$$

so by (7)

$$\begin{aligned}(\nabla f)(x,y) &= g'(\varphi(x,y))\nabla\varphi(x,y)\\ &= g'(\sqrt{x^2+y^2})\left(\frac{x}{\sqrt{x^2+y^2}}, \frac{y}{\sqrt{x^2+y^2}}\right).\end{aligned} \tag{8}$$

Setting $\mathbf{P} = (x,y)$ gives $|\mathbf{P}| = \sqrt{x^2+y^2}$, hence from (8)

$$\nabla f(\mathbf{P}) = \frac{1}{|\mathbf{P}|}g'(|\mathbf{P}|)\mathbf{P}.$$

In applying the chain rule it is essential to know which variables are respectively independent, intermediate, and dependent. There is no standard convention governing which letters play which roles, but you can easily keep the given situation in mind with a diagram such as, for example, the one in Fig. 40,

$$(x,y) \rightarrow z \rightarrow w.$$

Example 4. Let $u = f(x+y)$, where f is any differentiable function of one variable. Show that $\partial u/\partial x = \partial u/\partial y$. *Solution.* We have the situation

$$(x,y) \rightarrow z \rightarrow u$$

where

$$z = x + y, \qquad u = f(z).$$

Hence, as in (5) and (6),

$$\frac{\partial u}{\partial x} = \frac{du}{dz}\frac{\partial z}{\partial x} = f'(z)\cdot 1 = f'(x+y)$$

$$\frac{\partial u}{\partial y} = \frac{du}{dz}\frac{\partial z}{\partial y} = f'(z)\cdot 1 = f'(x+y),$$

so $\partial u/\partial x = \partial u/\partial y$.

Example 5. Show that if F is a function defined on R^2 and has continuous derivatives satisfying $\partial F/\partial x = \partial F/\partial y$, then $F(x,y) = f(x+y)$ for some differentiable function f of one variable. (Notice that this is the converse of Example 4.) *Solution.* We use a tricky substitution. Set

$$s = x + y, \qquad t = x - y, \tag{9}$$

so

$$x = \tfrac{1}{2}(s+t), \qquad y = \tfrac{1}{2}(s-t). \tag{10}$$

Thus we are in the situation $(s,t) \to (x,y) \to u$ where x and y are given by (10), and $u = F(x,y)$. Then the hypothesis that $\partial F/\partial x = \partial F/\partial y$ becomes $\partial u/\partial x = \partial u/\partial y$. Hence

$$\begin{aligned}\frac{\partial u}{\partial t} &= \frac{\partial u}{\partial x}\frac{\partial x}{\partial t} + \frac{\partial u}{\partial y}\frac{\partial y}{\partial t}\\ &= \frac{\partial u}{\partial x}\cdot\frac{1}{2} + \frac{\partial u}{\partial y}\cdot\left(-\frac{1}{2}\right) \qquad \text{(by (10))}\\ &= 0.\end{aligned}$$

Since $\partial u/\partial t = 0$, it follows that for any fixed s, u is a constant independent of t. Call this constant $f(s)$; then $f(s) = u = F(x,y)$. Thus, by (9), $F(x,y) = f(x+y)$, and it remains only to show that f is differentiable. But, setting $y = 0$, we get $f(x) = F(x,0)$, so the existence of $\partial F/\partial x$ implies the existence of $f'(x)$, and the problem is solved.

PROBLEMS

The first six problems are for practice in computations. The others concern *homogeneous functions* (defined in Problem 7) and *thermodynamics* (Problem 10).

1. Find the required derivatives in two ways: (i) by the chain rule, (ii) by substituting and computing directly. Reconcile the two results, as in Example 1.

(a) $w = x^2 + 2y$, $x = e^r$, $y = e^s \cos r$; find $\partial w/\partial r$ and $\partial w/\partial s$. (The scheme here is $(r, s) \to (x, y) \to w$.)

(b) $z = \log(x^2 + y^2)$, $x = r\cos\theta$, $y = r\sin\theta$; find $\partial z/\partial r$ and $\partial z/\partial\theta$.
(c) $z = r^2\cos 2\theta$, $r = \sqrt{x^2 + y^2}$, $\theta = \arctan(y/x)$; find $\partial z/\partial x$ and $\partial z/\partial y$.
(d) $w = u^3 + \sin u$, $u = ax + y$; find $\partial w/\partial x$ and $\partial w/\partial y$.
(e) $u = z^2 + e^z$, $z = ax - y$; find $\partial u/\partial x$ and $\partial u/\partial y$.

2. Suppose $F(x,t) = f(x + ct)$, where f is a differentiable function of one variable. Prove that

$$c\frac{\partial F}{\partial x} = \frac{\partial F}{\partial t}.$$

3. Suppose that F is differentiable at every point of R^2, and $cD_1F = D_2F$, where $c \neq 0$. Prove that $F(x,t) = f(x + ct)$ for some differentiable function of one variable. (Hint: Let $z = F(x,t)$, $x = (u + v)/2$, $t = (u - v)/2c$, and show that $\partial z/\partial v = 0$.)

4. Let $f(\mathbf{P}) = |\mathbf{P}|^a$, where a is a real constant. Show that $\nabla f(\mathbf{P}) = a|\mathbf{P}|^{a-2}\mathbf{P}$.

5. Suppose $f(u,v)$ has continuous partial derivatives, and let

$$z = f(x + y, x - y).$$

Prove that

$$\frac{\partial z}{\partial x}\frac{\partial z}{\partial y} = \left(\frac{\partial f}{\partial u}\right)^2 - \left(\frac{\partial f}{\partial v}\right)^2.$$

6. Let $z = f(x,y)$, $x = r\cos\theta$, $y = r\sin\theta$. Show that

(a) $\dfrac{\partial z}{\partial r} = f_x\cos\theta + f_y\sin\theta$ and $\dfrac{\partial z}{\partial\theta} = -rf_x\sin\theta + rf_y\cos\theta$.

(b) $(f_x)^2 + (f_y)^2 = \left(\dfrac{\partial z}{\partial r}\right)^2 + \dfrac{1}{r^2}\left(\dfrac{\partial z}{\partial\theta}\right)^2$. (This gives the formula for $|\nabla f|^2$ in polar coordinates.)

7. A function $f(\mathbf{P})$ defined for $|\mathbf{P}| \neq 0$ is called *homogeneous of degree n* if $f(t\mathbf{P}) = t^nf(\mathbf{P})$ for every $\mathbf{P} \neq \mathbf{0}$ and every $t > 0$.
(a) Prove that every polynomial of the form

$$f(x,y) = a_0x^n + a_1x^{n-1}y + \cdots + a_ny^n$$

is homogeneous of degree n.
(b) Prove that $h(x,y) = xy/(x^2 + y^2)$ is homogeneous of degree zero, and that $f(\mathbf{P}) = |\mathbf{P}|^n$ is homogeneous of degree n.
(c) Prove that if f is homogeneous of degree zero, and f is continuous at $(0,0)$, then f is constant. (Hint: $f(0,0) = \lim_{t\to 0+} f(t\mathbf{P})$ for every $\mathbf{P} \neq (0,0)$.)

8. Suppose that f is homogeneous of degree n in the sense of Problem 7, and that f is differentiable at every point $\mathbf{P}_0 \neq (0,0)$. Prove that $\mathbf{P}_0 \cdot \nabla f(\mathbf{P}_0) = nf(\mathbf{P}_0)$, i.e. $xf_x + yf_y = nf$. (Hint: Differentiate the identity $f(tx_0, ty_0) = t^n f(x_0, y_0)$ with respect to t. The scheme here is $t \rightarrow (x,y) \rightarrow z$, where $x = tx_0$, $y = ty_0$, and $z = f(x,y)$. In more geometric notation, you are differentiating $f(\boldsymbol{\gamma}(t)) = t^n f(\mathbf{P}_0)$, where $\boldsymbol{\gamma}(t) = t\mathbf{P}_0$.)

9. Prove that if f is homogeneous of degree n and has continuous partial derivatives, then $D_1 f$ and $D_2 f$ are homogeneous of degree $n - 1$. (Hint: For $t > 0$,

$$D_1 f(x,y) = \lim_{h \to 0} \frac{f(x + th, y) - f(x,y)}{th}.)$$

10. In *thermodynamics* there are five basic quantities: T (temperature), V (volume), P (pressure), E (energy), and S (an esoteric quantity called *entropy*). It is generally assumed that *any two* of these may be considered as independent variables; the other three are then functions of those two. A symbol such as $\partial S/\partial T$ would imply that T is considered an independent variable, but it would not tell which is the *other* independent variable. This ambiguity is eliminated by writing $(\partial S/\partial T)_V$ for the derivative of S with respect to T when T and V are considered independent, and $(\partial S/\partial T)_P$ for the derivative of S with respect to T when T and P are independent, and so on. With this convention, certain identities are obvious; for example, when T and V are independent we have

$$\left(\frac{\partial T}{\partial T}\right)_V = 1, \qquad \left(\frac{\partial T}{\partial V}\right)_T = 0$$

$$\left(\frac{\partial V}{\partial T}\right)_V = 0, \qquad \left(\frac{\partial V}{\partial V}\right)_T = 1.$$

Beyond these formal identities, the theory of thermodynamics assumes two basic equations:

$$T\left(\frac{\partial S}{\partial T}\right)_V = \left(\frac{\partial E}{\partial T}\right)_V \tag{*}$$

and

$$T\left(\frac{\partial S}{\partial V}\right)_T = \left(\frac{\partial E}{\partial V}\right)_T + P. \tag{**}$$

Corresponding relations when other independent variables are chosen can then be deduced by the chain rule, as outlined below.†

† Part (a) requires §3.6. Assume the formula in (a) and do (b)–(g). Sorry!

(a) Considering T and V as independent variables, differentiate (*) with respect to V and (**) with respect to T, and conclude that

$$\left(\frac{\partial P}{\partial T}\right)_V = \left(\frac{\partial S}{\partial V}\right)_T.$$

(Assume that all first and second derivatives are continuous.)

(b) Suppose that T and P are chosen as independent. Using the scheme $(T,P) \to (T,V) \to P$, explain why

$$\left(\frac{\partial P}{\partial P}\right)_T = \left(\frac{\partial P}{\partial T}\right)_V \left(\frac{\partial T}{\partial P}\right)_T + \left(\frac{\partial P}{\partial V}\right)_T \left(\frac{\partial V}{\partial P}\right)_T.$$

(c) From part (b), deduce that

$$1 = \left(\frac{\partial P}{\partial V}\right)_T \left(\frac{\partial V}{\partial P}\right)_T.$$

(d) Compute $(\partial P/\partial T)_P$ by the scheme in part (b), and deduce that

$$\left(\frac{\partial P}{\partial T}\right)_V = -\left(\frac{\partial P}{\partial V}\right)_T \left(\frac{\partial V}{\partial T}\right)_P.$$

(e) Compute $(\partial S/\partial P)_T$ by the scheme $(T,P) \to (T,V) \to S$. Using parts (a), (c), and (d), show that

$$\left(\frac{\partial S}{\partial P}\right)_T = -\left(\frac{\partial V}{\partial T}\right)_P.$$

(f) Prove that

$$\left(\frac{\partial E}{\partial P}\right)_T = -T\left(\frac{\partial V}{\partial T}\right)_P - P\left(\frac{\partial V}{\partial P}\right)_T,$$

using (*) or (**) and any methods or results from parts (a)–(e).

(g) Show that $T = \left(\frac{\partial E}{\partial S}\right)_V$.

3.5 THE IMPLICIT FUNCTION THEOREM*

For the mathematician (like the philosopher) existence is a fundamental question. Does there exist a square root of 2? Does a function have a maximum value? Does a system of simultaneous linear equations have a nonzero solution? Given f, is there a function F satisfying the equation $F'(x) = f(x)$?

* This section is not required in the rest of the text.

The implicit function theorem concerns another existence question: When does an equation $f(x,y) = c$ define y as a function of x? The answer is a little complicated, and has to be digested slowly.

Theorem 8. Implicit Function Theorem. *Suppose that* $f(x_0,y_0) = c$, $f_y(x_0,y_0) \neq 0$, *and that* f *has continuous first derivatives in an open set containing* (x_0,y_0). *Then there is a rectangle*

$$R = \{(x,y): |x - x_0| < \delta, |y - y_0| < \epsilon\}, \qquad \delta > 0, \epsilon > 0,$$

and there is a differentiable function φ *defined on the open interval* $(x_0 - \delta, x_0 + \delta)$ *such that*

$$\text{for } (x,y) \text{ in } R, \quad f(x,y) = c \quad \Leftrightarrow \quad y = \varphi(x).$$

differentiable f.

In other words, if we start at a point (x_0,y_0) on the contour line

$$\{(x,y): f(x,y) = c\}, \tag{1}$$

and if $f_y \neq 0$ at that point, then near (x_0,y_0) the contour line (1) is precisely the graph of φ (see Fig. 41). The theorem guarantees that such a function φ exists, even though it might be impossible to write an explicit formula for it. The equation $f(x,y) = c$ is said to determine y *implicitly* as a function $\varphi(x)$, hence the name of the theorem.

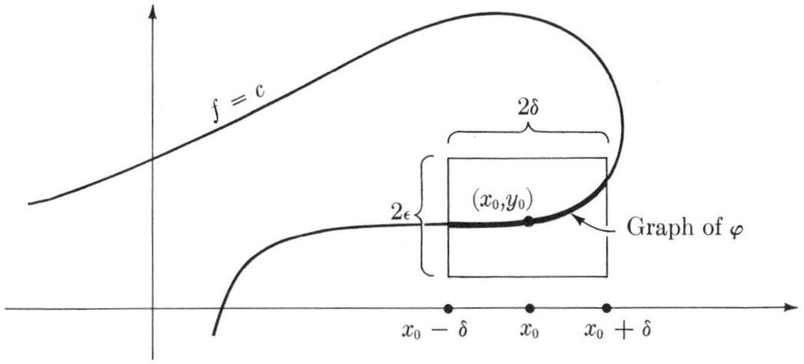

FIGURE 3.41

This is a *local* existence theorem; we assume things about f only near the point (x_0,y_0) and the resulting function φ is guaranteed to exist only near x_0 (precisely, for $x_0 - \delta < x < x_0 + \delta$), and its graph gives only that part of the contour line $f = c$ which is near x_0 (precisely, in the rectangle R).

The simple equation

$$x^2 + y^2 = 1 \tag{2}$$

shows why it is important that $f_y(x_0,y_0) \neq 0$, and why φ may be defined only in a small interval about x_0. If we take $f(x,y) = x^2 + y^2$, $c = 1$, and $(x_0,y_0) = (0,1)$, then the implicit function theorem applies; for f has continuous derivatives everywhere, $f(x_0,y_0) = 1$, and $f_y(x_0,y_0) = 2 \neq 0$.

Hence there is a rectangle R such that the part of the contour line (2) lying in R is the graph of a function φ. In fact, as Fig. 42(a) shows, we can take

$$R = \{(x,y): |x - 0| < 1, |y - 1| < 1\}, \qquad \varphi(x) = \sqrt{1 - x^2}\,.$$

Taking another point $(x_0, y_0) = (3/5, -4/5)$, Fig. 42(b), we find the rectangle

$$R = \{(x,y): |x - \tfrac{3}{5}| < \tfrac{2}{5}, |y + \tfrac{4}{5}| < \tfrac{4}{5}\}$$

and the implicit function $\varphi(x) = -\sqrt{1 - x^2}$ (note the minus sign); φ is defined for $|x - 3/5| < 2/5$, but it does not give *all* of the contour line (1) lying over that interval, only the part near $(3/5, -4/5)$. Generally, if (x_0, y_0) lies on the unit circle, then equation (2) defines y as a function of x on the interval $(x_0 - \delta, x_0 + \delta)$ with $\delta = 1 - |x_0|$ (Fig. 42(c)); when x_0 is near ± 1, this interval is very small, and when $x_0 = \pm 1$ (the points where $f_y = 0$), it disappears completely.

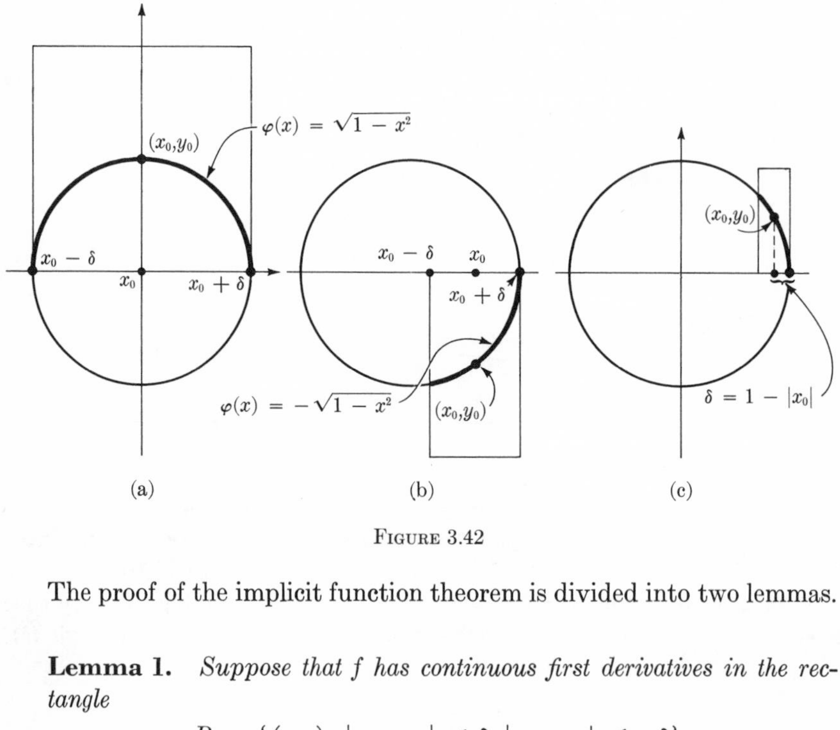

FIGURE 3.42

The proof of the implicit function theorem is divided into two lemmas.

Lemma 1. *Suppose that f has continuous first derivatives in the rectangle*

$$R = \{(x,y): |x - x_0| < \delta, |y - y_0| < m\delta\},$$

and $f_y > 0$, $|f_x/f_y| \leq m$, $f(x_0, y_0) = c$. Then there is a unique function φ defined on the interval $(x_0 - \delta, x_0 + \delta)$ such that

$$\textit{for } (x,y) \textit{ in } R, \quad f(x,y) = c \iff y = \varphi(x).$$

Further,

$$\varphi'(x_0) = \frac{-f_x(x_0, y_0)}{f_y(x_0, y_0)}.$$

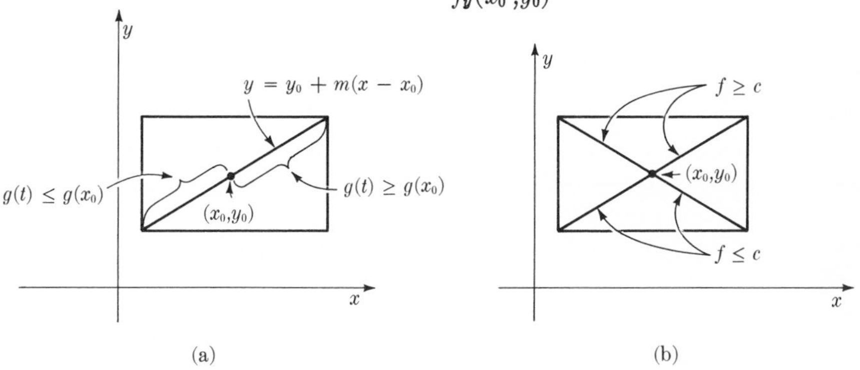

FIGURE 3.43

Proof. The values of f along the line of slope m in Fig. 43(a) are given by $g(t) = f(t, y_0 + m(t - x_0))$. By the chain rule,

$$g'(t) = f_x(t, y_0 + m(t - x_0)) + mf_y(t, y_0 + m(t - x_0)).$$

By assumption, $mf_y \geq |f_x|$, so $g' \geq 0$. Hence for $t \geq x_0$, we have $g(t) \geq g(x_0) = c$, and for $t \leq x_0$, we have $g(t) \leq g(x_0) = c$.

In other words, along the line of slope m, $f \geq c$ for $x \geq x_0$ and $f \leq c$ for $x \leq x_0$, as shown in Fig. 43(b). Similarly, along the line of slope $-m$, $f \leq c$ for $x \geq x_0$ and $f \geq c$ for $x \leq x_0$.

Now fix x in the interval $[x_0, x_0 + \delta)$, and look at the function

$$h(y) = f(x,y)$$

which gives the values of f along the vertical line in Fig. 44(a). We have just shown that

$$h(y_0 + m(x - x_0)) \geq c \qquad \text{and} \qquad h(y_0 - m(x - x_0)) \leq c;$$

by the Intermediate Value theorem, there is a number y_1 such that

$$y_0 - m(x - x_0) \leq y_1 \leq y_0 + m(x - x_0) \qquad \text{and} \qquad h(y_1) = c. \tag{3}$$

Moreover, $h'(y) = f_y(x,y) > 0$, so h is strictly increasing on the interval $(y_0 - m\epsilon, y_0 + m\epsilon)$; thus there is *only one* y_1 in that interval for which $h(y_1) = c$. Denote this unique value of y_1 by $\varphi(x)$. From (3),

$$y_0 - m(x - x_0) \leq \varphi(x) \leq y_0 + m(x - x_0) \tag{4}$$

(see Fig. 44(b)).

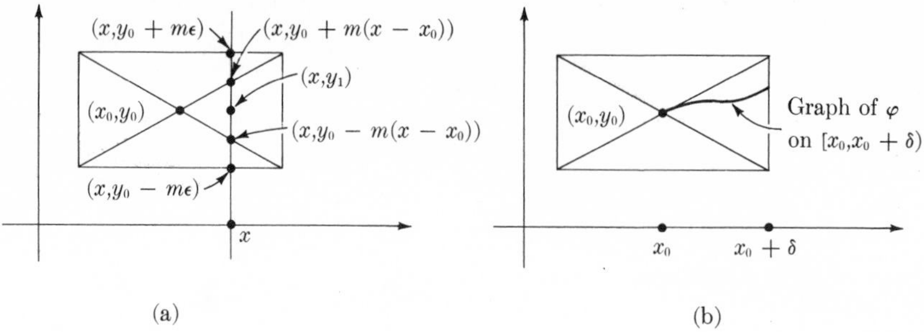

FIGURE 3.44

We have shown that $f(x,y) = c$ determines a unique function φ on the interval $[x_0, y_0 + \delta)$; φ is similarly determined on $(x_0 - \delta, x_0]$ and

$$y_0 + m(x - x_0) \le \varphi(x) \le y_0 - m(x - x_0), \qquad x \le x_0. \tag{4'}$$

Hence φ is uniquely defined on $(x_0 - \delta, x_0 + \delta)$, and we see from (4) and (4′) that

$$|\varphi(x) - y_0| \le m|x - x_0|. \tag{5}$$

It remains to take the derivative $\varphi'(x_0)$. Because f has continuous derivatives, it is differentiable at (x_0, y_0); thus (as in the proof of Theorem 6)

$$f(x,y) = f(x_0,y_0) + (x - x_0)f_x(x_0,y_0) + (y - y_0)f_y(x_0,y_0) + \sqrt{(x - x_0)^2 + (y - y_0)^2}\,Q(x,y),$$

where Q is continuous and $Q(x_0,y_0) = 0$. Setting $y = \varphi(x)$, we have $f(x,\varphi(x)) = c$, so

$$c = c + (x - x_0)f_x(x_0,y_0) + (\varphi(x) - y_0)f_y(x_0,y_0) + \sqrt{(x - x_0)^2 + (\varphi(x) - y_0)^2}\,Q(x,\varphi(x)),$$

hence

$$\frac{\varphi(x) - y_0}{x - x_0} = -\frac{f_x(x_0,y_0)}{f_y(x_0,y_0)} - \frac{\sqrt{(x - x_0)^2 + (\varphi(x) - y_0)^2}}{x - x_0}\,\frac{Q(x,\varphi(x))}{f_y(x_0,y_0)}. \tag{6}$$

We complete the proof by using (5) to show that

$$\lim_{x \to x_0}\left(\frac{\sqrt{(x - x_0)^2 + (\varphi(x) - y_0)^2}}{|x - x_0|}\,\frac{Q(x,\varphi(x))}{f_y(x_0,y_0)}\right) = 0. \tag{7}$$

First of all, (5) shows that φ is continuous at x_0 and $\varphi(x_0) = y_0$, so by composition $Q(x,\varphi(x))$ is continuous at x_0 and

$$\lim_{x \to x_0} Q(x,\varphi(x)) = Q(x_0,\varphi(x_0)) = 0. \tag{8}$$

Again by (5),

$$\frac{\sqrt{(x - x_0)^2 + (\varphi(x) - y_0)^2}}{|x - x_0|} \le \frac{\sqrt{(x - x_0)^2 + m^2(x - x_0)^2}}{|x - x_0|}$$

$$\le \sqrt{1 + m^2}\,; \tag{9}$$

and (8) and (9) imply (7). Since $\varphi(x_0) = y_0$, (7) and (6) imply $\varphi'(x_0) = -f_x(x_0, y_0)/f_y(x_0, y_0)$, and Lemma 1 is proved.

Lemma 1 looks a lot like the implicit function theorem itself, but it makes more specific hypotheses about f. Lemma 2 bridges this gap.

Lemma 2. *If f has continuous derivatives in a disk of radius r about $\mathbf{P}_0 = (x_0, y_0)$, and $f_y(\mathbf{P}_0) > 0$, then there are positive numbers m and δ such that*

$$f_y > 0 \qquad \textit{and} \qquad \left|\frac{f_x}{f_y}\right| \le m \tag{10}$$

in the rectangle

$$R = \{(x,y) : |x - x_0| < \delta,\ |y - y_0| < m\delta\}. \tag{11}$$

Proof. Since f_y is continuous, there is a number $\delta_1 > 0$ such that $\delta_1 \le r$ and

$$|\mathbf{P} - \mathbf{P}_0| < \delta_1 \ \Rightarrow\ |f_y(\mathbf{P}) - f_y(\mathbf{P}_0)| < f_y(\mathbf{P}_0);$$

hence

$$f_y(\mathbf{P}) > 0 \quad \text{for } |\mathbf{P} - \mathbf{P}_0| < \delta_1. \tag{12}$$

It follows that $|f_x/f_y|$ is continuous for $|\mathbf{P} - \mathbf{P}_0| < \delta_1$, so there is a number $\delta_2 \le \delta_1$ such that

$$|\mathbf{P} - \mathbf{P}_0| < \delta_2 \ \Rightarrow\ \left|\frac{f_x(\mathbf{P})}{f_y(\mathbf{P})}\right| < \left|\frac{f_x(\mathbf{P}_0)}{f_y(\mathbf{P}_0)}\right| + 1. \tag{13}$$

Now define the numbers m and δ of the lemma by

$$m = \left|\frac{f_x(\mathbf{P}_0)}{f_y(\mathbf{P}_0)}\right| + 1, \qquad (1 + m^2)\delta^2 = \delta_2{}^2.$$

Then the rectangle (11) lies in the disk of radius δ_2 about $\mathbf{P}_0$ (see Fig. 45); hence (10) follows from (12) and (13), and Lemma 2 is proved.

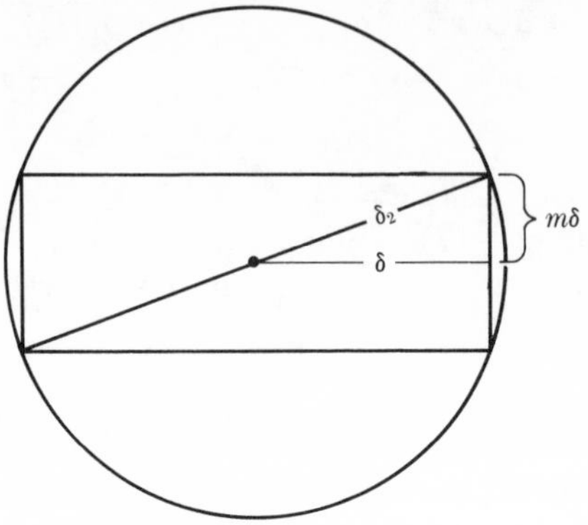

FIGURE 3.45 $\delta^2 + (m\delta)^2 = \delta_2^{\,2}$

Returning at last to Theorem 8 itself, we can suppose that $f_y(x_0, y_0) > 0$; for if $f_y(x_0, y_0) < 0$, simply replace f by $-f$ and c by $-c$, and all the hypotheses will still be satisfied. Supposing $f_y(x_0, y_0) > 0$, Lemma 2 provides a rectangle R in which Lemma 1 applies; then Lemma 1 provides a function φ such that

$$\text{for } (x,y) \text{ in } R, \quad f(x,y) = c \quad \Leftrightarrow \quad y = \varphi(x),$$

and φ is differentiable *at* x_0. But the hypotheses of Theorem 8 apply at *every* point of the graph of φ, so by what we have already shown φ is differentiable everywhere. *Q.E.D.*

We can, of course, interchange the roles of x and y. If $f_x(x_0, y_0) \neq 0$, then $f(x,y) = c$ determines x as a function ψ of y; i.e. near (x_0, y_0) the contour line $f = c$ is the set $\{(x,y): |y - y_0| < \delta, x = \psi(y)\}$.

Example 1. Represent the contour line

$$y - xe^y = 1 \tag{14}$$

near the point $(-1,0)$ as a function. *Solution.* Here $f(x,y) = y - xe^y$, so $\nabla f(x,y) = (-e^y, 1 - xe^y)$, and $\nabla f(-1,0) = (-1,2)$. Since $f_x \neq 0$ and $f_y \neq 0$, we can represent the contour line either as $y = \varphi(x)$, or as $x = \psi(y)$. In fact, in the second case you can see easily that $\psi(y) = (y - 1)e^{-y}$ (simply solve (14) for x). The function φ, on the other hand, cannot be given explicitly; we only know that it exists by Theorem 8.

Example 2. Let φ be the function in Example 1. Compute $\varphi'(-1)$, and $\varphi'(x)$ for x near -1. *Solution.* By Theorem 8, φ is differentiable. Since

$$\varphi(x) - xe^{\varphi(x)} = 1,$$

we find

$$\varphi'(x) - e^{\varphi(x)} - x\varphi'(x)e^{\varphi(x)} = 0;$$

hence

$$\varphi'(x) = \frac{e^{\varphi(x)}}{1 - xe^{\varphi(x)}}. \tag{15}$$

In particular, since $(-1,0)$ is on the graph of φ (see Example 1), we have $\varphi(-1) = 0$; hence

$$\varphi'(-1) = \frac{1}{1-(-1)} = \frac{1}{2}.$$

The next example illustrates how to find a specific interval in which φ is defined, even though φ cannot be found explicitly.

Example 3. Find a rectangle R as guaranteed by Theorem 8 for the equation $y - xe^y = 1$, taking $(x_0,y_0) = (-1,0)$. (This is the equation considered in Example 1.) *Solution.* From the proof of Theorem 8, we only need to find a rectangle R satisfying the hypotheses in Lemma 1 for some number m. We have

$$\frac{f_x(x,y)}{f_y(x,y)} = \frac{-e^y}{1 - xe^y} = \frac{-1}{e^{-y} - x}.$$

If $|x - (-1)| < \frac{1}{2}$ and $|y| < 1$, then $-x > \frac{1}{2}$, so $e^{-y} - x > \frac{1}{2}$; hence

$$\left|\frac{f_x(x,y)}{f_y(x,y)}\right| = \frac{1}{e^{-y} - x} < 2.$$

Thus Lemma 1 is satisfied with $\delta = \frac{1}{2}$ and $m = 2$. It follows that φ is defined for $|x - (-1)| < \frac{1}{2}$.

The implicit function theorem justifies the technique of "implicit differentiation," as exemplified by the following calculation:

$$x \cos xy = 1 \tag{16}$$

$$\cos xy - xy \sin xy - x^2 \sin xy \frac{dy}{dx} = 0$$

$$\frac{dy}{dx} = \frac{\cos xy - xy \sin xy}{x^2 \sin xy}.$$

Here we differentiated (16) *as if* y were a function of x, then solved for dy/dx. The general scheme is

$$f(x,y) = c, \tag{17}$$

$$f_x + f_y \frac{dy}{dx} = 0 \tag{18}$$

$$\frac{dy}{dx} = -\frac{f_x}{f_y}. \tag{19}$$

Here (18) follow from (17) by the chain rule, *if* y is a function of x. However, in (19) we see that the final calculation works only when $f_y \neq 0$; and in precisely this case, the implicit function theorem guarantees that y *is* a function of x. Thus, whenever (19) is algebraically legitimate (i.e. does not require division by zero), the whole calculation is legitimate (i.e. y really is a differentiable function of x).

Our final application of the implicit function theorem concerns the "Lagrange multiplier" condition for finding maxima and minima of one function g along the contour line of another function f.

Theorem 9. *Suppose that f and g have continuous derivatives throughout a disk centered at $\mathbf{P}_0$, that $f(\mathbf{P}_0) = c$, and that $g(\mathbf{P}_0) \geq g(\mathbf{P})$ for every $\mathbf{P}$ on the contour line $\{\mathbf{P}: f(\mathbf{P}) = c\}$. If $\nabla f(\mathbf{P}_0) \neq \mathbf{0}$, then $\nabla g(\mathbf{P}_0)$ is a multiple of $\nabla f(\mathbf{P}_0)$,*

$$\nabla g(\mathbf{P}_0) = \lambda \nabla f(\mathbf{P}_0).$$

(The number λ is the "Lagrange multiplier" referred to above. Since ∇f is orthogonal to the contour line $f = c$, the criterion $\nabla g = \lambda \nabla f$ says that ∇g is orthogonal to the contour line; see Fig. 46, and compare §3.2.)

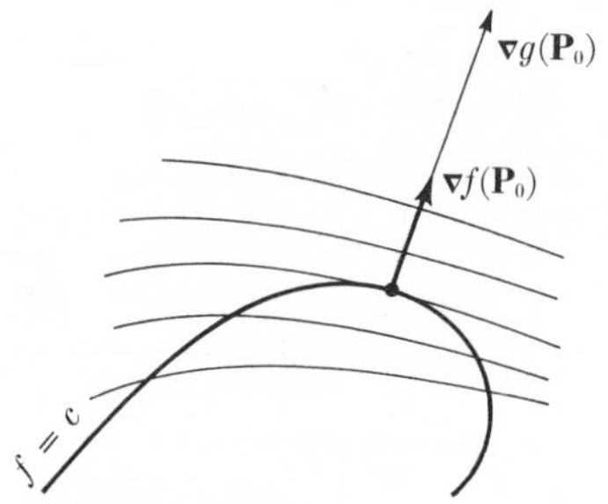

FIGURE 3.46

Proof. Since the vector $\nabla f(\mathbf{P}_0) \neq \mathbf{0}$, at least one of its components is not zero; say $f_x(\mathbf{P}_0) \neq 0$. By the implicit function theorem, the contour line near $\mathbf{P}_0 = (x_0, y_0)$ has the form

$$\{(x,y): x = \psi(y)\}$$

where ψ is differentiable on an open interval about y_0, and $\psi(y_0) = x_0$. By assumption, the function

$$h(y) = g(\psi(y), y))$$

has a maximum at $y = y_0$, hence

$$0 = h'(y_0) = g_x(\mathbf{P}_0)\psi'(y_0) + g_y(\mathbf{P}_0). \tag{20}$$

To eliminate $\psi'(y_0)$, differentiate the identity $f(\psi(y),y) \equiv c$ by the chain rule, obtaining

$$f_x(\mathbf{P}_0)\psi'(y_0) + f_y(\mathbf{P}_0) = 0;$$

solve for ψ' and substitute in (20), obtaining

$$0 = -g_x(\mathbf{P}_0)\frac{f_y(\mathbf{P}_0)}{f_x(\mathbf{P}_0)} + g_y(\mathbf{P}_0). \tag{21}$$

If we set $\lambda = g_x(\mathbf{P}_0)/f_x(\mathbf{P}_0)$, then obviously

$$g_x(\mathbf{P}_0) = \lambda f_x(\mathbf{P}_0),$$

and from (21)

$$g_y(\mathbf{P}_0) = \lambda f_y(\mathbf{P}_0),$$

so $\nabla g(\mathbf{P}_0) = \lambda\nabla f(\mathbf{P}_0)$. *Q.E.D.*

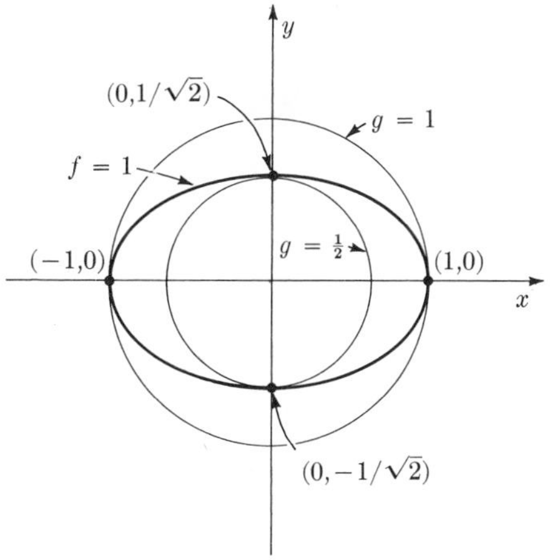

FIGURE 3.47

Example 4. Find the maxima and minima of $g(x,y) = x^2 + y^2$ on the ellipse $f(x,y) = x^2 + 2y^2 = 1$ in Fig. 47. *Solution.* Here

$$\nabla g = (2x,2y), \qquad \nabla f = (2x,4y).$$

If $\nabla g = \lambda\nabla f$, then $2x = \lambda\cdot 2x$ and $2y = \lambda\cdot 4y$, so either

$$x = 0, \qquad \lambda = \tfrac{1}{2}$$

or

$$y = 0, \qquad \lambda = 1.$$

Since we consider only the points on $x^2 + 2y^2 = 1$, we find for $x = 0$ that $y = \pm 1/\sqrt{2}$, and for $y = 0$ that $x = \pm 1$. Since $g(0, \pm 1/\sqrt{2}) = \frac{1}{2}$, and $g(\pm 1,0) = 1$, we conclude that *if* there is any maximum it occurs at $(\pm 1,0)$, and *if* there is a minimum it occurs at $(0,\pm 1/\sqrt{2})$. (In fact, since $x^2 + y^2$ is the square of the distance from (x,y) to the origin, it is intuitively obvious that 1 really is the maximum and $\frac{1}{2}$ really is the minimum.)

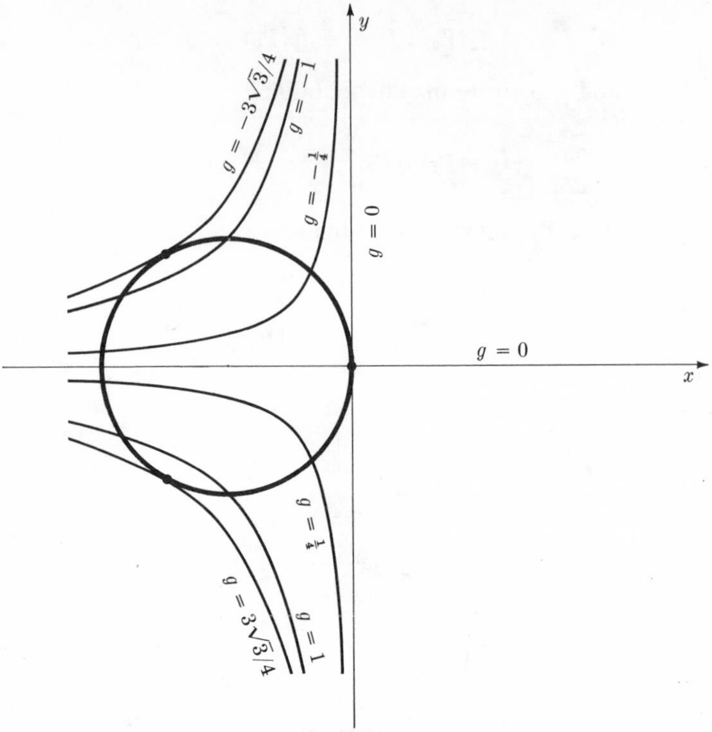

FIGURE 3.48

Example 5. Find the maximum of $g(x,y) = xy$ on the curve $f(x,y) = (x+1)^2 + y^2 = 1$, *assuming* that such a maximum exists. *Solution.* $\nabla f(x,y) = (2x+2,2y)$. Thus $\nabla f(\mathbf{P}) = \mathbf{0}$ only at $\mathbf{P} = (-1,0)$. Since $f(-1,0) = 0$, it follows that $\nabla f(\mathbf{P}) \neq \mathbf{0}$ at every point on the contour $f = 1$, so the Lagrange condition $\nabla g = \lambda \nabla f$ must be satisfied at the maximum point. Since $\nabla g(x,y) = (y,x)$, the two conditions $\nabla g = \lambda \nabla f$, $f = 1$ become

$$\begin{aligned} y &= \lambda \cdot (2x+2) \\ x &= \lambda \cdot (2y) \\ (x+1)^2 + y^2 &= 1. \end{aligned} \tag{22}$$

In these equations, $y = 0 \Rightarrow x = 0 \Rightarrow \lambda = 0$; we thus find that the point $(0,0)$ satisfies the Lagrange condition. For any other solution of (22), $y \neq 0$; thus $\lambda = x/2y$, and

$$y = \frac{x}{2y}(2x+2), \qquad \text{or} \qquad y^2 = x^2 + x.$$

Solving this simultaneously with $(x+1)^2+y^2=1$ gives

$$(x+1)^2+x^2+x=1 \qquad \text{or} \qquad 2x^2+3x=0,$$

$$x=0 \qquad \text{or} \qquad x=-3/2.$$

For $x=0$ we get the point $(0,0)$ on the given curve $f=1$, and for $x=1$, and for $x=-3/2$ we get the two points $(-3/2,\pm\sqrt{3}/2)$. From the contour lines of g given in Fig. 48 it is clear that $(-3/2,-\sqrt{3}/2)$ gives a maximum, $(-3/2,\sqrt{3}/2)$ gives a minimum, and $(0,0)$ gives neither.

PROBLEMS

1. Find a function φ as guaranteed by the implicit function theorem, in the following cases:

(a) $xy=1,\qquad (x_0,y_0)=(1,1)$
(b) $x^2+2y^2=3,\qquad (x_0,y_0)=(-1,1)$
(c) $x-y^2=0,\qquad (x_0,y_0)=(1,-1)$
(d) $xe^{xy}=2,\qquad (x_0,y_0)=(1,\log 2)$

2. For each part of Problem 1, find a rectangle R as guaranteed by the implicit function theorem. (Hint: Sketch the contour line first.)

3. In each of the following problems, find dy/dx in general, and evaluate dy/dx as an explicit number when $x=x_0$.

(a) $(x+y)e^{xy}=2e,\qquad (x_0,y_0)=(1,1)$
(b) $x^3+5y^5+7xy+y=1,\qquad (x_0,y_0)=(1,0)$
(c) $x^2-xy+y^2=3,\qquad (x_0,y_0)=(1,2)$
(d) $x\cos xy=0,\qquad (x_0,y_0)=(1,\pi/2)$
(e) $x^5+y^5+xy=-4,\qquad (x_0,y_0)=(2,-2)$

4. Find a rectangle R as guaranteed by Theorem 8 for the equation in Problem 3(a). (Hint: Show that $|f_x/f_y|\le 8$ when $|x-1|<1/8$ and $|y-1|<1$, and apply Lemma 1.)

5. Find a rectangle R as guaranteed by Theorem 8 for the equation in Problem 3(b). (Hint: You can show that $|f_x/f_y|\le 20$ when $|x-1|<1$ and $|y|<1$.)

6. Show that in the following cases there is *no* rectangle about the origin

$$R=\{(x,y):|x|<\delta,\ |y|<m\delta\} \quad (\text{with } \delta>0)$$

such that the part of the contour line $f=0$ lying in R is the graph of a function of x on $(-\delta,\delta)$, or the graph of a function of y on $(-m\delta,m\delta)$.

(a) $f(x,y)=xy$
(b) $f(x,y)=x^2+y^2$

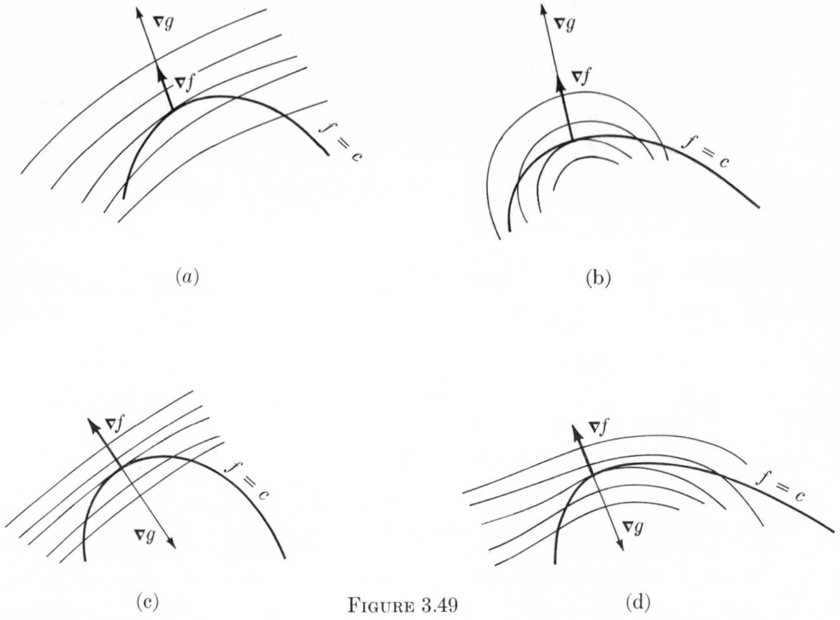

FIGURE 3.49

7. Suppose that $\nabla f(\mathbf{P}_0) \neq \mathbf{0}$ and $f(\mathbf{P}_0) = c$; thus, near $\mathbf{P}_0$, the contour line $f = c$ is the graph of a function $\varphi(x)$ or a function $\psi(y)$. Show that in either case the tangent line to the graph at (x_0, y_0) is orthogonal to $\nabla f(\mathbf{P}_0)$. (Thus, the gradient is orthogonal to the tangent line.)

8. Let g be a function of one variable. Show that near any point $x_0 = g(y_0)$ where $g'(y_0) \neq 0$ there is an inverse function φ such that $g(\varphi(x)) = x$, and $\varphi'(x) = 1/g(\varphi(x))$. (Hint: Let $f(x,y) = x - g(y)$. *Remark:* In this problem you are deducing part of the *inverse function* theorem for one variable from the *implicit function* theorem for two variables.)

9. Use Lagrange multipliers to find maxima of the function g on the given contour line of f. (Assume in each case that a maximum exists.)

(a) $g(x,y) = 3x^2 + 2\sqrt{2}\,xy + 4y^2$ on $x^2 + y^2 = 9$

(b) $g(x,y) = x^2 + y^2$ on $5x^2 + 6xy + 5y^2 = 16$

(c) $g(x,y) = xy$ on $x + y = 1$

(Notice that in part (b) you are finding the points on the given contour line which are farthest from the origin.)

10. Let F be a differentiable function of one variable, and set

$$f(x,y) = F(x) - y \quad \text{and} \quad g(x,y) = y.$$

Show that the Lagrange condition

$$\nabla g(x,y) = \lambda \nabla f(x,y)$$

is equivalent to $F'(x) = 0$. (Thus the familiar necessary condition for a local maximum or minimum of a function of one variable is a special case of the Lagrange multiplier condition.)

11. Figure 49 shows a variety of points where the Lagrange condition $\nabla g = \lambda \nabla f$ is satisfied. Which (if any) are maxima of g on $f = c$, which are minima, and which are neither? (The light lines are contour lines of g.)

3.6 DERIVATIVES OF HIGHER ORDER

Our study of a function f, based up to now on the first derivatives $D_1 f$ and $D_2 f$, can be extended by taking derivatives of higher order. The first derivative

$$D_1 f(a,b) = \lim_{h \to 0} \frac{f(a+h,b) - f(a,b)}{h} \tag{1}$$

defines a function $D_1 f$ whose domain is the set of points (a,b) where the limit (1) exists. The derivatives of this function $D_1 f$ are denoted $D_1D_1 f$ and $D_2D_1 f$, and by a variety of other notations as well:

$$D_1D_1 f = D_1^2 f = \frac{\partial}{\partial x}\left(\frac{\partial f}{\partial x}\right) = \frac{\partial^2 f}{\partial x^2} = f_{xx}\,,$$

$$D_2D_1 f = \frac{\partial}{\partial y}\left(\frac{\partial f}{\partial x}\right) = \frac{\partial^2 f}{\partial y \partial x} = f_{xy}\,.$$

Similarly, we can differentiate $D_2 f$, obtaining

$$D_1D_2 f = \frac{\partial^2 f}{\partial x \partial y} = f_{yx}$$

and

$$D_2D_2 f = D_2^2 f = \frac{\partial^2 f}{\partial y^2} = f_{yy}\,.$$

These are the *second order* partial derivatives of f. For example, if $f(x,y) = e^{xy}$, we find

$$f_x = ye^{xy}, \qquad f_y = xe^{xy},$$

so the derivatives of f_x are

$$f_{xx} = y^2 e^{xy}, \qquad f_{xy} = e^{xy} + xye^{xy},$$

and the derivatives of f_y are

$$f_{yx} = e^{xy} + xye^{xy}, \qquad f_{yy} = x^2 e^{xy}.$$

If $g(x,y) = x \cos y$, then

$$\begin{aligned} g_x &= \cos y, & g_y &= -x \sin y \\ g_{xx} &= 0, & g_{yx} &= -\sin y \\ g_{xy} &= -\sin y, & g_{yy} &= -x \cos y \\ g_{xyx} &= 0, & g_{yxx} &= 0. \end{aligned}$$

Notice that $f_{xy} = f_{yx}$, and $g_{xy} = g_{yx}$. This is not just a coincidence.

Theorem 10. *If f_x, f_y, f_{xy}, and f_{yx} all exist in an open set containing $\mathbf{P}_0$, and if f_{xy} and f_{yx} are continuous at $\mathbf{P}_0$, then $f_{xy}(\mathbf{P}_0) = f_{yx}(\mathbf{P}_0)$.*

The proof depends on obtaining f_{xy} and f_{yx} as limits of difference quotients; it turns out that both are limits of the *same* quotient, hence they are equal. We begin by investigating f_{yx}.

By definition (1), $f_{yx}(a,b)$ is approximated by the difference quotient

$$\frac{f_y(a+h,b) - f_y(a,b)}{h}. \tag{2}$$

Going further, in (2) we can approximate $f_y(a,b)$ by

$$\frac{f(a,b+h) - f(a,b)}{h}$$

and $f_y(a+h,b)$ by

$$\frac{f(a+h,b+h) - f(a+h,b)}{h}.$$

Putting these approximations in (2), we get the "mixed second difference quotient"

$$Q(h) = \frac{f(a+h,b+h) - f(a+h,b) - f(a,b+h) + f(a,b)}{h^2}. \tag{3}$$

After all these approximations, it is not entirely clear that Q bears any relation to the second derivative $f_{yx}(a,b)$. However:

Lemma 1. *If f_y and f_{yx} exist in a disk centered at (a,b), and f_{yx} is continuous at (a,b), then*

$$\lim_{h \to 0} Q(h) = f_{yx}(a,b).$$

Proof. If we define the function of one variable

$$F(y) = f(a + h,y) - f(a,y),$$

then

$$Q(h) = \frac{F(b + h) - F(b)}{h^2}.$$

By the mean value theorem,

$$\begin{aligned} F(b + h) - F(b) &= hF'(b + \theta h) \qquad 0 < \theta < 1 \\ &= h[f_y(a + h,b + \theta h) - f_y(a,b + \theta h)]; \end{aligned}$$

hence

$$Q(h) = \frac{f_y(a + h,b + \theta h) - f_y(a,b + \theta h)}{h}.$$

Applying the Mean Value theorem now to the function $G(x) = f_y(x,b + \theta h)$, we get $G(a + h) - G(a) = hG'(a + \theta' h)$, $0 < \theta' < 1$; hence

$$Q(h) = f_{yx}(a + \theta' h,b + \theta h), \qquad 0 < \theta < 1, \quad 0 < \theta' < 1.$$

Since f_{yx} is continuous at (a,b) we get $\lim_{h \to 0} Q(h) = f_{yx}(a,b)$. *Q.E.D.*

Now if you construct a mixed second difference quotient to approximate f_{xy} instead of f_{yx}, you will get exactly the same expression Q as in (3). Hence, reversing the roles of x and y, you can prove:

Lemma 2. *If f_x and f_{xy} exist in a disk centered at (a,b), and f_{xy} is continuous at (a,b), then*

$$\lim_{h \to 0} Q(h) = f_{xy}(a,b).$$

Returning to Theorem 10, the hypotheses there guarantee that Lemmas 1 and 2 are both valid; hence $f_{yx}(a,b) = \lim_{h \to 0} Q(h) = f_{xy}(a,b)$. *Q.E.D.*

Problem 18(b) below shows that $f_{xy}(a,b)$ may actually be different from $f_{yx}(a,b)$ if these partial derivatives are *not* continuous at (a,b); thus we cannot drop the hypothesis of continuity at (a,b).

What we have proved is essentially a commutative law: $D_1D_2 = D_2D_1$. Like most commutative laws, it extends to products of more than two terms. Precisely: *In any mixed partial derivative, the order of differentiation is irrelevant as long as all the derivatives that occur are continuous in an open set containing the point where the derivative is taken.* For example, if f_{xx}, f_{xy}, f_{yx}, f_{xxy}, f_{xyx}, and f_{yxx} are all continuous in an open set U, then Theorem 10 applies at every point in U, so $f_{xy} = f_{yx}$ throughout U; differentiating this with respect to x shows that $f_{xyx} = f_{yxx}$ throughout U. Further, applying

Theorem 10 to f_x instead of f, we get $f_{xyx} = f_{xxy}$; thus

$$f_{yxx} = f_{xyx} = f_{xxy} ,$$

or

$$D_1^2D_2f = D_1D_2D_1f = D_2D_1^2f.$$

PROBLEMS

Problems 1 and 2 are just routine differentiation. The others fall into three groups: Problems 3–8 concern the *wave equation* $f_{xx} = c^2f_{yy}$, which governs the motion of a vibrating string (as in a violin, guitar, piano, etc.). Problems 9–14 concern the *Laplace equation* $f_{xx} + f_{yy} = 0$, which arises in the study of temperature distribution. The last four are related directly to Theorem 10 and its proof.*

1. Let $f(x,y) = x \cos (x + y)$. Compute

(a) f_{xy} (c) $D_1^2D_2 f$ (e) $\dfrac{\partial^3 f}{\partial x \partial y \partial x}$

(b) f_{yx} (d) $D_2D_1^2f$

2. Define a function f of your choice, and show by direct calculation that $f_{xy} = f_{yx}$, $f_{xyy} = f_{yxy}$ wherever these derivatives are all continuous.

3. Prove that the following functions satisfy $\dfrac{\partial^2 f}{\partial x^2} = \dfrac{\partial^2 f}{\partial y^2}$.

(a) $\cos (x - y)$ (d) $\cos x \sin y$
(b) $\sin(x + y)$ (e) $\cos 3x \sin 3y$
(c) $e^{x+y} + e^{(x-y)^2}$ (f) $\cos 2x \sin 2y$

4. Prove that the following functions satisfy $f_{xx} = c^2f_{yy}$ where c is a constant.
(a) $f(x,y) = \cos (cx - y)$
(b) $f(x,y) = \log (cx + y)$
(c) $f(x,y) = \cos (cx + y) + e^{cx-y}$

5. (a) Prove that if u and v are functions of one variable such that u'' and v'' exist, then $f(x,y) = u(x + y) + v(x - y)$ satisfies

$$\frac{\partial^2 f}{\partial x^2} = \frac{\partial^2 f}{\partial y^2} .$$

(b) With u and v as in part (a), prove that $f(x,y) = u(cx + y) + v(cx - y)$ satisfies

$$\frac{\partial^2 f}{\partial x^2} = c^2 \frac{\partial^2 f}{\partial y^2} .$$

---

* You can also do Problem 10(a), p. 140.

6. (a) Show that every first degree polynomial f satisfies

$$\frac{\partial^2 f}{\partial x^2} = \frac{\partial^2 f}{\partial y^2}.$$

(b) Show that a homogeneous second degree polynomial $f(x,y) = Ax^2 + Bxy + Cy^2$ satisfies

$$\frac{\partial^2 f}{\partial x^2} = \frac{\partial^2 f}{\partial y^2}$$

if and only if $A = C$.

7. Define an operator $D_1 + D_2$ by $(D_1 + D_2)f = f_x + f_y$, and similarly $(D_1 - D_2)f = f_x - f_y$. Prove that $(D_1 - D_2)(D_1 + D_2) = D_1^2 - D_2^2$, or in other words, $(D_1 - D_2)((D_1 + D_2)f) = D_1^2 f - D_2^2 f$ for every function f having continuous second derivatives.

8. Suppose that f has continuous partial derivatives of order ≤ 2, and that $f_{xx} = f_{yy}$ at every point in R^2. This problem shows that there are functions u and v such that $f(x,y) = u(x - y) + v(x + y)$. (This is a converse of Problem 5(a).)

(a) Define $g(s,t) = f(s + t, s - t)$. Prove that

$$D_2\, g(s,t) = D_1 f(s + t, s - t) - D_2 f(s + t, s - t)$$

or, in slightly sloppy notation, $g_t = f_x - f_y$. (Apply the chain rule, §3.4.)

(b) Prove that $D_1 g(s,t) = D_1 f(s + t, s - t) + D_2 f(s + t, s - t)$, or $g_s = f_x + f_y$.

(c) Prove that $g_{st} = f_{xx} - f_{yy}$.

(d) Suppose $h(s,t)$ is defined for all s and t, and $h_t \equiv 0$. Prove that there is a function $H(s)$ such that $h(s,t) \equiv H(s)$. Prove that H is continuous if h is.

(e) Suppose that $f_{xx} = f_{yy}$, and g is defined as in part (a). Prove that $g_s = H(s)$ for some continuous function H. (Use parts (c) and (d).)

(f) Continuing part (e), prove that $g(s,t) = g(0, t) + \int_0^s H(r)\, dr$.

(g) Continuing part (f), prove that there are functions u and v such that $f(x,y) = u(x - y) + v(x + y)$.

$$\left(\text{Hint: } \left.\begin{aligned} x &= s + t \\ y &= s - t \end{aligned}\right\} \Leftrightarrow \left\{\begin{aligned} s &= \tfrac{1}{2}(x + y) \\ t &= \tfrac{1}{2}(x - y) \end{aligned}\right.\right)$$

9. (a) Show that every first degree polynomial f satisfies Laplace's equation

$$\frac{\partial^2 f}{\partial x^2} + \frac{\partial^2 f}{\partial y^2} = 0.$$

(b) Show that a homogeneous second degree polynomial $f(x,y) = Ax^2 + Bxy + Cy^2$ satisfies Laplace's equation if and only if $A + C = 0$.

(c) Prove that every second degree polynomial f satisfying

$$\frac{\partial^2 f}{\partial x^2} + \frac{\partial^2 f}{\partial y^2} = 0$$

is a linear combination of the functions 1, x, y, $x^2 - y^2$, and xy, i.e. $f(x,y) = c_1 + c_2 x + c_3 y + c_4(x^2 - y^2) + c_5 xy$ for some constants $c_1, \ldots, c_5$.

10. Which of the following functions satisfy Laplace's equation? (Three do and two do not.)

(a) $e^{-y} \cos x$ (b) $e^{-2x} \cos 2y$

(c) $\sin y \cos x$ (d) $e^{-2x} \cos 3y$

(e) $\log (x^2 + y^2)$ (Disregard the point $(x,y) = \mathbf{0}$, where the function is not defined.)

11. This problem concerns Laplace's equation in polar coordinates. Suppose that all the second derivatives of f are continuous, and define a function g by $g(r,\theta) = f(r \cos \theta, r \sin \theta)$.

(a) Prove that

$$g_r(r,\theta) = \cos \theta D_1 f(r \cos \theta, r \sin \theta) + \sin \theta D_2 f(r \cos \theta, r \sin \theta).$$

(Hint: Apply the chain rule, §3.4.)

(b) Prove that

$$g_\theta(r,\theta) = -r \sin \theta D_1 f(r \cos \theta, r \sin \theta) + r \cos \theta D_2 f(r \cos \theta, r \sin \theta).$$

(c) Find corresponding expressions for g_{rr} and $g_{\theta\theta}$, and prove that for $r \neq 0$,

$$g_{rr} + \frac{1}{r} g_r + \frac{1}{r^2} g_{\theta\theta} = f_{xx} + f_{yy}.$$

(You will need Theorem 10.)

12. Suppose that $f(x,y)$ is a function of $r = \sqrt{x^2 + y^2}$ only, that is, $f(r \cos \theta, r \sin \theta) = G(r)$ for some function G. Suppose that G has a continuous second derivative for $r > 0$.

(a) Using Problem 11(c), prove that if $f_{xx} + f_{yy} = 0$, then $rG'' = -G'$.

(b) Prove that $G' = A/r$ for some constant A.

(c) Prove that $G = A \log r + B$ for constants A and B.

13. Suppose that $f(r\cos\theta, r\sin\theta) = G(r)\cos\theta$.
(a) Using Problem 11(c), prove that

$$f_{xx} + f_{yy} = \left(G'' + \frac{1}{r}G' - \frac{1}{r^2}G\right)\cos\theta.$$

(b) Prove that $(Ar^{-1} + Br)\cos\theta$ satisfies Laplace's equation.
(c) Prove that

$$A\,\frac{\cos\theta}{r} = D_1 F(r\cos\theta, r\sin\theta),$$

where $F(x,y) = A\log\sqrt{x^2 + y^2}$.

14. Suppose that $f(r\cos\theta, r\sin\theta) = G(r)(a\cos n\theta + b\sin n\theta)$. Prove that $f_{xx} + f_{yy} = 0$ if $G(r) = Ar^{-n} + Br^n$ for some constants A and B.

15. Derive a second difference quotient approximating $f_{xy}(a,b)$, and show that it is the same as the quotient $Q(h)$ in (3) above that approximates $f_{yx}(a,b)$.

16. Prove Lemma 2. (Hint: Begin by considering the function $F(x) = f(x, b+h) - f(x,b)$.)

17. (a) Obtain the second difference quotient

$$Q_{hh} = \frac{f(a+2h,b) - 2f(a+h,b) + f(a,b)}{h^2}$$

as an approximation to $f_{xx}(a,b)$.
(b) Suppose that f_{xx} is continuous at (a,b); prove that

$$\lim_{h\to 0} Q_{hh} = f_{xx}(a,b).$$

18. Let

$$f(x,y) = \frac{xy(x^2 - y^2)}{x^2 + y^2}$$

if $x^2 + y^2 \neq 0$, and $f(0,0) = 0$.
(a) Compute f_x and f_y, and show that they are continuous. (To compute $f_x(0,0)$, you will have to use the defining formula (1); similarly for $f_y(0,0)$.)
(b) Compute $f_{xy}(0,0)$ and $f_{yx}(0,0)$; note that they are *not* equal, but that this does not contradict Theorem 10.
(Notice that f is homogeneous of degree 2, in the sense explained in Problem 7, §3.4. Homogeneous functions provide many other curious examples, for instance the function $h(x,y) = xy(x^2 + y^2)^{-1}$ in §3.3, which has derivatives everywhere, but is not continuous at the origin.)

3.7 THE TAYLOR EXPANSION

The Taylor expansion is a way of approximating a given function near a given point by polynomials. Thanks to the chain rule and Theorem 10 on mixed partials, the expansion for functions of two variables is obtained easily from the one-variable version.

Suppose that f is defined throughout a disk $D = \{\mathbf{P}: |\mathbf{P} - \mathbf{A}| < r\}$ centered at the point $\mathbf{A} = (a,b)$, and that all the partial derivatives we write down are continuous in D. Given a vector $\mathbf{H} = (h,k)$ with $|\mathbf{H}| < r$, the point $\mathbf{A} + \mathbf{H}$ lies in D; we want to expand $f(\mathbf{A} + \mathbf{H})$ as a polynomial in h and k, plus a remainder term. To do this, look at the function

$$g(t) = f(\mathbf{A} + t\mathbf{H}), \qquad 0 \le t \le 1, \tag{1}$$

which gives the values of f along the straight line segment from $\mathbf{A}$ to $\mathbf{A} + \mathbf{H}$. By the mean value theorem, $g(1) - g(0) = (1 - 0)g'(\theta)$ with $0 < \theta < 1$, or

$$g(1) = g(0) + g'(\theta), \qquad 0 < \theta < 1. \tag{2}$$

By (1), $g(0) = f(\mathbf{A})$ and $g(1) = f(\mathbf{A} + \mathbf{H})$, and by the chain rule, $g'(t) = \mathbf{H}\cdot\nabla f(\mathbf{A} + t\mathbf{H})$, so (2) becomes

$$f(\mathbf{A} + \mathbf{H}) = f(\mathbf{A}) + \mathbf{H}\cdot\nabla f(\mathbf{A} + \theta\mathbf{H}), \qquad 0 < \theta < 1. \tag{3}$$

This is the *Mean Value theorem for functions of two variables.*

Formula (3) is the beginning of the Taylor expansion of f. To expand further, take another term in the expansion of g,

$$g(t) = g(0) + tg'(0) + \frac{t^2}{2!}g''(\theta t), \qquad 0 < \theta < 1,$$

then set $t = 1$, obtaining

$$g(1) = g(0) + g'(0) + \frac{1}{2!}g''(\theta), \qquad 0 < \theta < 1. \tag{4}$$

To rewrite this result in terms of f, we have to differentiate the function

$$\begin{aligned} g'(t) &= \mathbf{H}\cdot\nabla f(\mathbf{A} + t\mathbf{H}) \\ &= hD_1 f(a + th, b + tk) + kD_2 f(a + th, b + tk). \end{aligned} \tag{5}$$

By the chain rule,

$$\frac{d[D_1 f(a + th, b + tk)]}{dt} = hD_1D_1 f(a + th, b + tk) + kD_2D_1 f(a + th, b + tk),$$

and similarly

$$\frac{d[D_2 f]}{dt} = hD_1D_2 f + kD_2D_2 f.$$

Thus, differentiating (5) and recalling that $D_1D_2 = D_2D_1$, we find

$$g''(t) = h^2D_1^2f(\mathbf{A} + t\mathbf{H}) + 2hkD_1D_2f(\mathbf{A} + t\mathbf{H}) + k^2D_2^2f(\mathbf{A} + t\mathbf{H}).$$

Putting this in (4), we obtain the *first degree Taylor expansion of f with remainder:*

$$f(\mathbf{A} + \mathbf{H}) = f(\mathbf{A}) + hD_1f(\mathbf{A}) + kD_2f(\mathbf{A})$$
$$+ \frac{1}{2}h^2D_1^2f(\mathbf{A} + \theta\mathbf{H}) + hkD_1D_2f(\mathbf{A} + \theta\mathbf{H}) + \frac{1}{2}k^2D_2^2f(\mathbf{A} + \theta\mathbf{H}). \quad (6)$$

Example 1. If $f(x,y) = e^x \cos y$, then $f_x = e^x \cos y$, $f_y = -e^x \sin y$, $f_{xx} = e^x \cos y$, $f_{xy} = -e^x \sin y$, $f_{yy} = -e^x \cos y$. Hence (6) becomes

$$e^{a+h} \cos (b + k) = e^a \cos b + he^a \cos b + k(-e^a \sin b)$$
$$+ \tfrac{1}{2}h^2e^{a+\theta h} \cos (b + \theta k) - hke^{a+\theta h} \sin (b + \theta k)$$
$$- \tfrac{1}{2}k^2e^{a+\theta h} \cos (b + \theta k).$$

Formula (6) shows how to approximate f by a second degree polynomial, and how good the approximation is. Precisely:

Theorem 11. *If f has continuous partial derivatives of order ≤ 2 in the disk $D = \{\mathbf{P}: |\mathbf{P} - \mathbf{A}| < r\}$, then*

$$\lim_{\mathbf{H}\to 0} \frac{f(\mathbf{A} + \mathbf{H}) - f_2(\mathbf{H})}{|\mathbf{H}|^2} = 0, \quad (7)$$

where $f_2(\mathbf{H}) = f_2(h,k)$ is the second degree polynomial in h and k given by

$$f(\mathbf{A}) + hf_x(\mathbf{A}) + kf_y(\mathbf{A}) + \frac{h^2}{2} f_{xx}(\mathbf{A}) + hkf_{xy}(\mathbf{A}) + \frac{k^2}{2} f_{yy}(\mathbf{A}).$$

Proof. By (6),

$$\frac{f(\mathbf{A} + \mathbf{H}) - f_2(\mathbf{H})}{|\mathbf{H}|^2} = \frac{h^2}{2|\mathbf{H}|^2}[f_{xx}(\mathbf{A} + \theta\mathbf{H}) - f_{xx}(\mathbf{A})]$$
$$+ \frac{hk}{|\mathbf{H}|^2}[f_{xy}(\mathbf{A} + \theta\mathbf{H}) - f_{xy}(\mathbf{A})]$$
$$+ \frac{k^2}{2|\mathbf{H}|^2}[f_{yy}(\mathbf{A} + \theta\mathbf{H}) - f_{yy}(\mathbf{A})]. \quad (8)$$

Because the second derivatives of f are continuous, the three terms in square brackets have limit 0 as $\mathbf{H} \to \mathbf{0}$. Further,

$$\frac{h^2}{|\mathbf{H}|^2} \leq 1, \qquad \frac{k^2}{|\mathbf{H}|^2} \leq 1, \qquad \text{and} \qquad \frac{|hk|}{|\mathbf{H}|^2} \leq 1,$$

so the right-hand side of (8) has limit zero as $\mathbf{H} \to \mathbf{0}$, and the proof is done.

Formula (7) should be compared to the condition for differentiability of f at $\mathbf{A}$,

$$\lim_{\mathbf{H}\to 0} \frac{f(\mathbf{A}+\mathbf{H}) - f_1(\mathbf{H})}{|\mathbf{H}|} = 0,$$

where $f_1(\mathbf{H}) = f(\mathbf{A}) + \mathbf{H}\cdot\nabla f(\mathbf{A})$. In (7) there is a second degree polynomial f_2 instead of the first degree polynomial f_1, and a correspondingly closer approximation, since the denominator is $|\mathbf{H}|^2$ instead of $|\mathbf{H}|$.

Theorem 11 and its extension to polynomials of degree n is fundamental in the study of functions of several variables. The simplest application, concerning maxima and minima, is given in the next section.

It is easy, in principle, to extend Theorem 11 and obtain approximations by polynomials of degree higher than 2; the only difficulty is in the notation. We begin with the expansion

$$g(1) = \sum_{m=0}^{n-1} \frac{1}{m!} g^{(m)}(0) + \frac{1}{n!} g^{(n)}(\theta), \qquad 0 < \theta < 1, \tag{9}$$

where $g(t) = f(\mathbf{A} + t\mathbf{H})$ as before. To express the derivatives of g in terms of f and $\mathbf{H}$, we use the symbol

$$\mathbf{H}\cdot\nabla = (hD_1 + kD_2).$$

(This is the inner product of $\mathbf{H} = (h,k)$ with the "vector" $\nabla = (D_1, D_2)$.) By formula (5), differentiating a function $f(\mathbf{A} + t\mathbf{H})$ with respect to t is the same as "multiplying" f by $\mathbf{H}\cdot\nabla$; hence differentiating n times is the same as multiplying n times by $\mathbf{H}\cdot\nabla$, and (9) yields the nth degree Taylor expansion of f in the form

$$f(\mathbf{A}+\mathbf{H}) = \sum_{m=0}^{n-1} \frac{1}{m!}((\mathbf{H}\cdot\nabla)^m f)(\mathbf{A}) + \frac{1}{n!}((\mathbf{H}\cdot\nabla)^n f)(\mathbf{A}+\theta\mathbf{H}). \tag{10}$$

This looks less mysterious when we work out the expressions $(\mathbf{H}\cdot\nabla)^m f$:

$$(\mathbf{H}\cdot\nabla)f = hD_1 f + kD_2 f \tag{11}$$

$$(\mathbf{H}\cdot\nabla)^2 f = (\mathbf{H}\cdot\nabla)((\mathbf{H}\cdot\nabla)f) = hD_1((\mathbf{H}\cdot\nabla)f) + kD_2((\mathbf{H}\cdot\nabla)f);$$

substituting (11) for $(\mathbf{H}\cdot\nabla)f$, and noting that $D_1D_2 = D_2D_1$, we get

$$(\mathbf{H}\cdot\nabla)^2 f = h^2D_1^2 f + 2hkD_1D_2 f + k^2D_2^2 f.$$

Similarly,

$$\begin{aligned}(\mathbf{H}\cdot\nabla)^3 f &= hD_1((\mathbf{H}\cdot\nabla)^2 f) + kD_2((\mathbf{H}\cdot\nabla)^2 f)\\ &= h^3D_1^3 f + 3h^2kD_1^2D_2 f + 3hk^2D_1D_2^2 f + k^3D_2^3 f,\end{aligned}$$

and generally we obtain the binomial expansion of $(hD_1 + kD_2)^m f$:

$$\begin{aligned}(\mathbf{H}\cdot\nabla)^m f &= h^mD_1^m f + mh^{m-1}kD_1^{m-1}D_2 f + \cdots + k^mD_2^m f\\ &= \sum_{l=0}^{m} \frac{m!}{l!(m-l)!} h^l k^{m-l} D_1^l D_2^{m-l} f.\end{aligned} \tag{12}$$

Putting this in (10) gives an alternate form of the Taylor expansion,

$$f(\mathbf{A} + \mathbf{H}) = \sum_{m=0}^{n-1} \sum_{l=0}^{m} \frac{1}{l!(m-l)!} h^l k^{m-l} (D_1{}^l D_2{}^{m-l} f)(\mathbf{A})$$

$$+ \sum_{l=0}^{n} \frac{1}{l!(n-l)!} h^l k^{n-l} (D_1{}^l D_2{}^{n-l} f)(\mathbf{A} + \theta\mathbf{H}) \qquad 0 < \theta < 1. \qquad (13)$$

From the Taylor expansion (10) or (13) follows

Theorem 12. *Suppose that f is defined in the disk $D = \{\mathbf{P}: |\mathbf{P} - \mathbf{A}| < r\}$, and that all the partial derivatives of f of order $\leq n$ are continuous in D. Let*

$$f_n(\mathbf{H}) = \sum_{m=0}^{n} \frac{1}{m!} (\mathbf{H} \cdot \nabla)^m f(\mathbf{A}). \qquad (14)$$

Then

$$\lim_{|\mathbf{H}| \to 0} \frac{f(\mathbf{A} + \mathbf{H}) - f_n(\mathbf{H})}{|\mathbf{H}|^n} = 0. \qquad (15)$$

The proof is just like Theorem 11; the details are left to you.

Example 2. Taking $f(x,y) = e^x \cos y$ as in Example 1, we find the third degree polynomial approximation

$$\begin{aligned} f_3(h,k) &= e^a \cos b + he^a \cos b - ke^a \sin b \\ &\quad + \tfrac{1}{2}(h^2e^a \cos b - 2hke^a \sin b - k^2e^a \cos b) \\ &\quad + \tfrac{1}{6}(h^3e^a \cos b - 3h^2ke^a \sin b - 3hk^2e^a \cos b + k^3e^a \sin b). \end{aligned}$$

According to Theorem 12, then,

$$\lim_{(h,k) \to 0} \frac{e^{a+h} \cos(b+k) - f_3(h,k)}{(h^2 + k^2)^{3/2}} = 0.$$

In particular, taking $\mathbf{A} = (a,b)$ to be the origin, we get for our approximation to $e^h \cos k$ the polynomial

$$f_3(h,k) = 1 + h + \tfrac{1}{2}h^2 - \tfrac{1}{2}k^2 + \tfrac{1}{6}h^3 - \tfrac{1}{2}hk^2.$$

(You would obtain the same result by multiplying the one-variable expansions of e^h and $\cos k$, and neglecting all terms of degree >3.)

PROBLEMS

1. Find the second degree Taylor polynomial f_2 for the given function f at the given point $\mathbf{A}$.

(a) $f(x,y) = \sin(xy)$, $\mathbf{A} = (0,0)$
(b) $f(x,y) = \sin(xy)$, $\mathbf{A} = (\pi,1)$
(c) $f(x,y) = e^{-x^2-y^2}$, $\mathbf{A} = (0,0)$

2. Find the third degree Taylor polynomial

$$\sum_{m=0}^{3} \frac{1}{m!} (\mathbf{H}\cdot\nabla)^m f(\mathbf{A})$$

for the functions f and points $\mathbf{A}$ given in Problem 1.

3. (a) Find the second degree Taylor polynomial at $\mathbf{A} = \mathbf{0}$ for the function

$$f(x,y) = \begin{cases} \dfrac{\sin xy}{x}, & x \neq 0 \\ y, & x = 0. \end{cases}$$

(b) Take the third degree Taylor polynomial $t - t^3/6$ for $\sin t$, substitute $t = hk$, divide by x, and compare the result with the answer in part (a); notice that the difference is a polynomial containing no terms of degree ≤ 2.

4. Prove that when f is a second degree polynomial and $\mathbf{A}$ is any given point, then $f = f_2$, where f_2 is the second degree Taylor polynomial of f at the point $\mathbf{A}$. (Hint 1: You can use formula (6), and notice that the second derivatives of f are all constant. Hint 2: Alternatively, you can use formula (10) with $n = 3$, and notice that the third derivatives of f are all zero.)

5. Suppose that the second derivatives of f are all constant on R^2. Prove that f is a second degree polynomial of degree ≤ 2. (Hint: Use (6).)

6. Suppose that the nth derivatives of f are all identically zero on R^2. Prove that f is a polynomial of degree $< n$.

7. Prove that formula (3) in the text is valid whenever f is differentiable at every point of the closed segment from $\mathbf{A}$ to $\mathbf{A} + \mathbf{H}$.

8. (a) Suppose f is differentiable at every point of a disk D, and that $|\nabla f| \leq M$ in D, where M is a constant. Prove that when $\mathbf{A}$ and $\mathbf{A} + \mathbf{H}$ are in D, then $|f(\mathbf{A} + \mathbf{H}) - f(\mathbf{A})| \leq M|\mathbf{H}|$. (Hint: The segment from $\mathbf{A}$ to $\mathbf{A} + \mathbf{H}$ lies in D, so Problem 7 applies.)

(b) A set S is *convex* if, whenever it contains two points $\mathbf{P}$ and $\mathbf{Q}$, it contains the segment between them. Suppose f is differentiable in a convex set S, and $|\nabla f| \leq M$ there. Prove that for all points $\mathbf{P}$ and $\mathbf{Q}$ in S,

$$|f(\mathbf{P}) - f(\mathbf{Q})| \leq M \cdot |\mathbf{P} - \mathbf{Q}|.$$

9. (a) Suppose f is differentiable at $\mathbf{A}$ and $|f(\mathbf{A}+\mathbf{H})-f(\mathbf{A})| \le M|\mathbf{H}|$ for some constant M. Prove that $\nabla f(\mathbf{A}) \le M$. (Hint: By the chain rule,

$$\nabla f(\mathbf{A})\cdot\mathbf{U} = \lim_{t\to 0}\frac{f(\mathbf{A}+t\mathbf{U})-f(\mathbf{A})}{t}$$

for every constant vector $\mathbf{U}$. Show that $|\nabla f(\mathbf{A})\cdot\mathbf{U}| \le M|\mathbf{U}|$, then set $\mathbf{U} = \nabla f(\mathbf{A})$.)

(b) From part (a) and Problem 8(b), show that *if f is differentiable at every point of an open convex set S, then the following conditions* (i) *and* (ii) *are equivalent:*

(i) $|\nabla f(\mathbf{P})| \le M$ at every point $\mathbf{P}$ in S

(ii) $|f(\mathbf{P})-f(\mathbf{Q})| \le M|\mathbf{P}-\mathbf{Q}|$ for every pair of points $\mathbf{P}$ and $\mathbf{Q}$ in S.

10. Prove Theorem 12.

3.8 MAXIMA AND MINIMA

Suppose that f is defined in an open set containing $\mathbf{A}$. Then $\mathbf{A}$ is called a *local maximum of f* if $f(\mathbf{A}) \ge f(\mathbf{P})$ for all points $\mathbf{P}$ in some disk centered at $\mathbf{A}$.

Theorem 13. *If $\mathbf{A}$ is a local maximum, then the gradient* $\nabla f(\mathbf{A}) = \mathbf{0}$.

Proof. For any constant $\mathbf{H}$, the function

$$F(t) = f(\mathbf{A}+t\mathbf{H})$$

has a local maximum at $t = 0$, hence

$$0 = F'(0) = \mathbf{H}\cdot\nabla f(\mathbf{A}).$$

In particular, setting $\mathbf{H} = \nabla f(\mathbf{A})$, we get $0 = |\nabla f(\mathbf{A})|^2$. *Q.E.D.*

When $\nabla f(\mathbf{A}) = \mathbf{0}$, then $\mathbf{A}$ is called a *critical point* of f. We have shown that every local maximum occurs at a critical point; and it is easy to see that every local minimum also occurs at a critical point. Some critical points, however, are neither maxima nor minima. Consider the three examples

$$f(x,y) = -x^2 - y^2$$
$$g(x,y) = x^2 + y^2$$
$$h(x,y) = x^2 - y^2.$$

All three have a vanishing gradient at the point $\mathbf{A} = \mathbf{0}$, but f has a local *maximum* there, g has a local *minimum*, and h has neither; $h(0,0) = 0$, but in any disk about $\mathbf{0}$ there are points along the x axis where $h(x,y) = x^2 > 0$, and points along the y axis where $h(x,y) = -y^2 < 0$. The graph of h at this point looks like a saddle (see Fig. 50). Moving from "front to back," $(0,0)$ is a minimum, but moving from "side to side" it is a maximum.

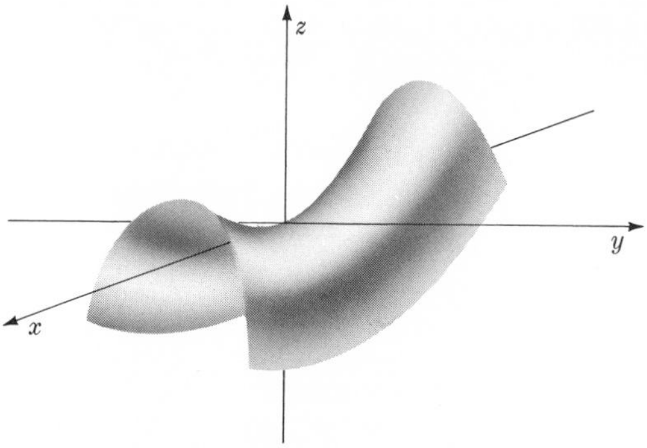

FIGURE 3.50   Graph of $h(x,y) = x^2 - y^2$ near the origin

The second derivatives of f usually distinguish between maxima, minima, and saddle points.

Theorem 14.   *Suppose f has continuous derivatives of order ≤ 2 in a disk centered at $\mathbf{A}$, and that $\nabla f(\mathbf{A}) = 0$. Then $\mathbf{A}$ is* imp.
 (i) *a local maximum point of f if $f_{xx} f_{yy} > (f_{xy})^2$ and $f_{xx} + f_{yy} < 0$;*
 (ii) *a local minimum point of f if $f_{xx} f_{yy} > (f_{xy})^2$ and $f_{xx} + f_{yy} > 0$;*
 (iii) *a saddle point of f if $f_{xx} f_{yy} < (f_{xy})^2$.*
 (iiii) $f_{xx} f_{yy} = (f_{xy})^2 \Rightarrow$ No way to tell
In the remaining case, where $f_{xx} f_{yy} = (f_{xy})^2$, the test fails. The proof, based on the Taylor expansion, is outlined in the problems below.

The three examples f, g, h given above are useful mnemonic aids for the three conditions in Theorem 14. It is obvious that f has a maximum, g a minimum, h a saddle point; and it is easy to check that f is in case (i), g in case (ii), and h in case (iii),

$$h_{xx} h_{yy} = -4 < (h_{xy})^2.$$

The proof of Theorem 14 will show that in the special case where f is a polynomial of degree 2, the criteria in (i) and (ii) give *absolute* maxima and minima; i.e. in case (i), $f(\mathbf{A}) \geq f(\mathbf{P})$ for all $\mathbf{P}$ in R^2, and in case (ii), $f(\mathbf{A}) \leq f(\mathbf{P})$ for all $\mathbf{P}$ in R^2.

Example 1. Let $f(x,y) = x^2 - 2xy + 2y^2 + x - 5$. We have $\nabla f(x,y) = (2x - 2y + 1, -2x + 4y)$, so $\nabla f = \mathbf{0}$ when

$$2x - 2y = -1$$
$$-2x + 4y = 0,$$

which gives $x = -1$, $y = -\frac{1}{2}$. Thus we apply Theorem 14 at the critical point $\mathbf{A} = (-1,-\frac{1}{2})$. We find

$$f_{xx} = 2, \qquad f_{xy} = -2, \qquad f_{yy} = 4,$$

so

$$f_{xx}f_{yy} = 8 > (f_{xy})^2 = 4, \qquad f_{xx} + f_{yy} = 6 > 0,$$

and we are in case (ii), the minimum-point case. This is easy to see from the contour graph in Fig. 51.

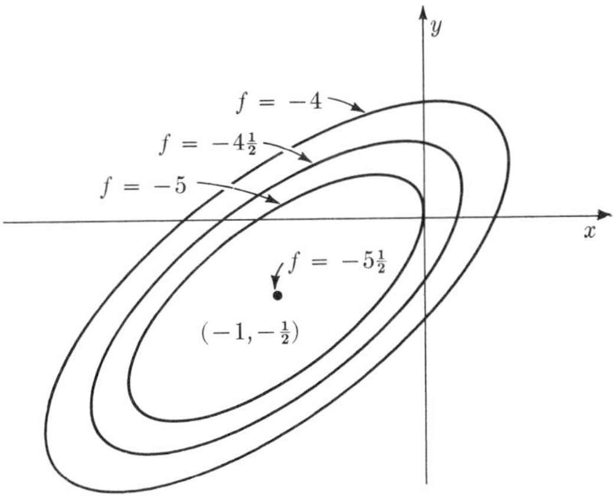

FIGURE 3.51 Contour graph of $f(x,y) = x^2 - 2xy + 2y^2 + x - 5$

Incidentally, the criteria in Theorem 14 can help in plotting the contour lines of quadratics; when there is a maximum or minimum, the contour lines are *ellipses* with center at the critical point $\mathbf{A}$ (as in Fig. 51). When there is a saddle point, the contours are *hyperbolas* with center at the critical point $\mathbf{A}$; the particular contour $\{\mathbf{P}: f(\mathbf{P}) = f(\mathbf{A})\}$ is a degenerate hyperbola, consisting of two lines that form the *asymptotes* of the other hyperbolas. (See Fig. 52.) When there are *no* critical points, the contour lines are parabolas, and their vertices all lie on a line where $|\nabla f|^2$ is minimum (See Fig. 53.) All this is proved in analytic geometry (without referring to critical points and second derivatives, of course).

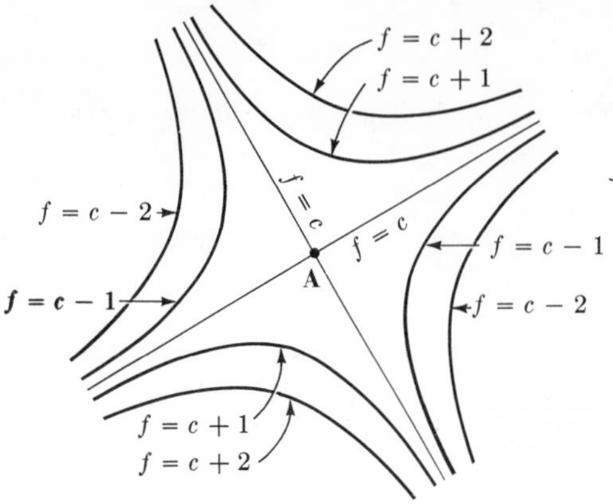

FIGURE 3.52 $c = f(\mathbf{A})$

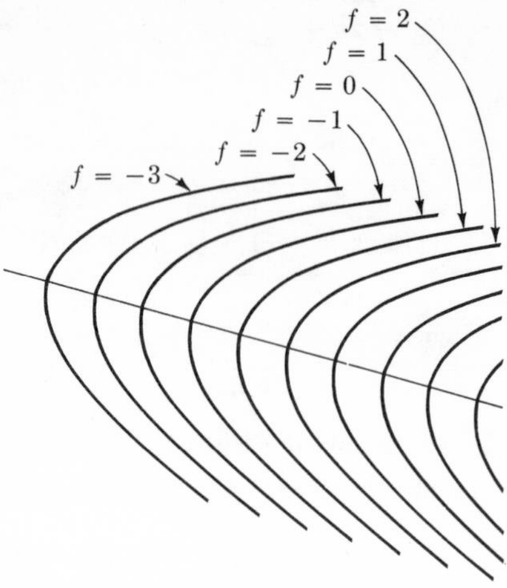

FIGURE 3.53

Example 2. Find the maximum and minimum of $f(x,y) = xy - y + x - 1$ in the closed disk $D = \{\mathbf{P}: |\mathbf{P}| \leq 2\}$. *Solution.* We first look for a *local* maximum in the open disk $\{\mathbf{P}: |\mathbf{P}| < 2\}$. Since $\nabla f(x,y) = (y + 1, x - 1)$, the only critical point is at $x = 1$, $y = -1$. By applying Theorem 14 you can show that this is a saddle point. Hence there can be no maximum or minimum in the open disk; if they exist at all, the maximum and minimum must occur on the boundary. To check this, represent the boundary of D parametrically by

$$x = 2 \cos \theta, \qquad y = 2 \sin \theta,$$

and seek the maximum and minimum of

$$f(2 \cos \theta, 2 \sin \theta) = 4 \cos \theta \sin \theta - 2 \sin \theta + 2 \cos \theta - 1.$$

By the usual one-variable methods we find that among all points on the circle $\{\mathbf{P}: |\mathbf{P}| = 2\}$, f assumes a *maximum* at

$$\left(\frac{1 + \sqrt{3}}{\sqrt{2}}, \frac{\sqrt{3} - 1}{\sqrt{2}}\right) \quad \text{and at} \quad \left(\frac{1 - \sqrt{3}}{\sqrt{2}}, -\frac{\sqrt{3} + 1}{\sqrt{2}}\right),$$

and a *minimum* at $(-\sqrt{2}, \sqrt{2})$. Now we have shown that there is no maximum or minimum in the open disk, but that considering only the points on the boundary circle, f assumes a maximum of

$$f\left(\frac{1 + \sqrt{3}}{\sqrt{2}}, \frac{\sqrt{3} - 1}{\sqrt{2}}\right) = \sqrt{2},$$

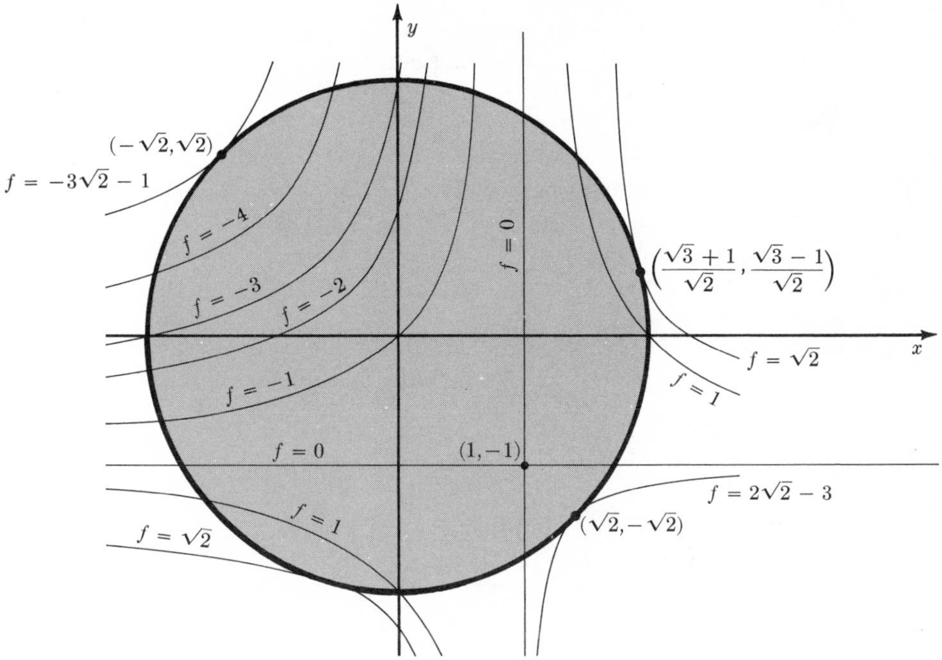

FIGURE 3.54

and a minimum of $f(-\sqrt{2}, \sqrt{2}) = -3\sqrt{2} - 1$. It follows from the special nature of f that $\max_D f = \sqrt{2}$ and $\min_D f = -3\sqrt{2} - 1$, because every value assumed by f in D is actually assumed on the boundary. This is clear from Fig. 54, since every contour line having a point in D must intersect the boundary of D. (We omit the analytic proof.)

Remark 1. The function f in Example 2 satisfies *Laplace's equation* $f_{xx} + f_{yy} = 0$ for steady state temperature distribution. The property that the maximum and minimum of f are achieved on the boundary of D holds for *every* function f satisfying $f_{xx} + f_{yy} = 0$ in D.

Remark 2. The maximum and minimum on the boundary can be found by the method of Lagrange multipliers given in §3.5, instead of by parametrizing the boundary.

Remark 3. The discussion of maximum and minimum problems is simplified when it is known beforehand that a maximum and minimum exist. For functions of one variable, a function f that is continuous on a closed bounded interval I assumes a maximum and a minimum on I. For functions of two variables, there is an analogous *Maximum Value theorem: A function f that is continuous on a closed bounded set S in the plane assumes a maximum and a minimum on S.* The proof goes beyond the scope of this book, but we should at least describe what a closed, bounded set is. A set is *bounded* if it is contained in some disk $\{\mathbf{P}: |\mathbf{P}| \le r\}$. A set is *closed* if (intuitively speaking) it contains all its boundary points. Thus, for example, any closed disk $\{\mathbf{P}: |\mathbf{P} - \mathbf{A}| \le r\}$ is closed and bounded; so is any closed rectangle $\{(x,y): a \le x \le b,\ c \le y \le d\}$.

Returning to Example 2, we see by the maximum value theorem that f *must* have a maximum and minimum on the given closed disk D; since there is no maximum or minimum in the open disk, they must occur on the boundary, hence they are the points we found by considering the function $f(2\cos\theta, 2\sin\theta)$. Thus, the special argument at the end of Example 2 (based on the observation that the contour lines intersect the boundary of D if they intersect D at all) is replaced by a very general argument, based on the fact that a maximum and minimum must exist.

PROBLEMS

1. For the following functions, find all critical points, and for each such point decide which case of Theorem 14 applies (if any).

(a) $x^2 + 2x + 3y^2 + 4y + 1$ (d) $x^2 + xy$
(b) $x^3 + y^3 - 3xy$ (e) $x^2 + y$
(c) $\log (3x^2 + y^2 + 2x + 10)$

2. Decide whether the given contour line is an ellipse, a hyperbola, or a parabola. If it is an ellipse, find the center; if a hyperbola, find the center and asymptotes; if a parabola, find the axis. (See the remarks after Example 1.)

(a) $x^2 + xy = c$ (c) $y^2 - 2xy + x - y = c$
(b) $x^2 + 2xy + y^2 + x - y = c$ (d) $2x^2 + 2xy + 5y^2 + x - 2y = c$

3. Find the maximum and minimum of the following functions over the unit disk $D = \{\mathbf{P}: |\mathbf{P}| \le 1\}$.

(a) The function in Problem 1(d) (c) The function in Problem 1(c)
(b) The function in Problem 1(e)

4. Suppose that f solves Laplace's equation $f_{xx} + f_{yy} = 0$, and that $\mathbf{A}$ is a critical point of f, i.e. $\nabla f(\mathbf{A}) = \mathbf{0}$. Prove that either (i) f_{xx}, f_{yy}, and f_{xy} all vanish at $\mathbf{A}$ or (ii) $\mathbf{A}$ is a *saddle point.*

5. (Method of least squares.) Given a number of points $\mathbf{P}_1 = (x_1, y_1), \ldots, \mathbf{P}_n = (x_n, y_n)$ in the plane, the problem arises of finding the equation $y = mx + b$ of a straight line which "most closely" passes through the given points. The usual solution is to take the equation $y = mx + b$ for which the following sum of squares is minimum:

$$S(m,b) = \sum_1^n (y - y_j)^2 = \sum_1^n (mx_j + b - y_j)^2.$$

(a) Show that if there are just two points $\mathbf{P}_1$ and $\mathbf{P}_2$, and $x_1 \neq x_2$, then $S(m,b)$ has a minimum of zero, and the corresponding line actually passes through the two given points.

(b) Find m and b to minimize $S(m,b)$ if the given points are $(0,2)$, $(1,1)$, and $(4,-1)$.

(c) In the case of n points $(x_1,y_1), \ldots, (x_n,y_n)$, show that $\partial S/\partial m = 0$ and $\partial S/\partial b = 0$ if and only if

$$m\left(\sum_1^n x_j\right) + nb = \sum_1^n y_j \tag{16}$$

and

$$m\left(\sum_1^n x_j^2\right) + b\left(\sum_1^n x_j\right) = \sum_1^n x_j y_j\,. \tag{17}$$

(d) Show that the simultaneous equations (16) and (17) have a unique solution for m and b if

$$\left(\sum_1^n x_j\right)^2 \neq n \sum_1^n x_j^2.$$

(See Problem 22, §1.5.)

(e) Show that $(\sum_1^n x_j)^2 < n \sum_1^n x_j^2$ unless the x_j are all equal, in which case $(\sum_1^n x_j)^2 = n \sum_1^n x_j^2$. (Hint: Notice that $\sum_1^n x_j$ is the dot product of $\mathbf{X} = (x_1, \ldots, x_n)$ and $\mathbf{A} = (1, \ldots, 1)$. Use the fact that $|\mathbf{X}\cdot\mathbf{A}| < |\mathbf{X}|\cdot|\mathbf{A}|$ if $\mathbf{X}$ and $\mathbf{A}$ are not parallel, and $|\mathbf{X}\cdot\mathbf{A}| = |\mathbf{X}|\cdot|\mathbf{A}|$ if $\mathbf{X}$ and $\mathbf{A}$ are parallel.)

(f) Use part (e) and Theorem 14 to show that, unless the x_j are all equal, the function $S(m,b)$ has a unique minimum given by (1) and (2). (Note that $S(m,b)$ is a polynomial of degree 2 in m and b, so Theorem 14 gives absolute maxima and minima.)

6. This problem proves Theorem 14 in the simplest interesting case, that of a homogeneous quadratic polynomial $f(x,y) = \alpha x^2 + 2\beta xy + \gamma y^2$. Prove the following:

(a) $f_{xx} = 2\alpha$, $f_{xy} = 2\beta$, $f_{yy} = 2\gamma$.

(b) $f(r\cos\theta, r\sin\theta) = \frac{1}{2}r^2[(\alpha+\gamma) + 2\beta\sin 2\theta + (\alpha-\gamma)\cos 2\theta]$.

(c) $f(r\cos\theta, r\sin\theta) = \frac{1}{2}r^2[(\alpha+\gamma) + \sqrt{(\alpha-\gamma)^2 + 4\beta^2}\cos(2\theta-\varphi)]$, where

$$\cos\varphi = \frac{\alpha-\gamma}{\sqrt{(\alpha-\gamma)^2+4\beta^2}} \quad\text{and}\quad \sin\varphi = \frac{2\beta}{\sqrt{(\alpha-\gamma)^2+4\beta^2}}\,.$$

(d) On the circle $\{\mathbf{P}: |\mathbf{P}| = r\}$, f has the maximum value

$$\tfrac{1}{2}r^2\left(\alpha+\gamma+\sqrt{(\alpha-\gamma)^2+4\beta^2}\right)$$

and minimum value $\frac{1}{2}r^2\left(\alpha+\gamma-\sqrt{(\alpha-\gamma)^2+4\beta^2}\right)$.

(e) The maximum and minimum in part (d) have opposite signs if and only if $4\alpha\gamma < 4\beta^2$, or $f_{xx}f_{yy} < (f_{xy})^2$.

(f) If $4\alpha\gamma > 4\beta^2$, then the maximum and minimum are both positive if $\alpha + \gamma > 0$, and both negative if $\alpha + \gamma < 0$.

(g) From (d)–(f), deduce that (0,0) is a *saddle point* for f if $f_{xx}f_{yy} < (f_{xy})^2$; a *maximum* if $f_{xx}f_{yy} > (f_{xy})^2$ and $f_{xx} + f_{yy} < 0$; and a *minimum* if $f_{xx}f_{yy} > (f_{xy})^2$ and $f_{xx} + f_{yy} > 0$.

(h) If $4\alpha\gamma = 4\beta^2$, prove that α and γ have the same sign, and $f(x,y) = \pm(\sqrt{|\alpha|}x \pm \sqrt{|\gamma|}y)^2$. What can be said about maxima or minima of f in this case? (This is the only case not covered in parts (e) and (f).)

7. This problem proves Theorem 14 in general. Suppose f has continuous second partial derivatives in a disk centered at $\mathbf{A} = (a,b)$, and that $\nabla f(\mathbf{A}) = \mathbf{0}$. Set $2\alpha = f_{xx}(\mathbf{A})$, $2\beta = f_{xy}(\mathbf{A})$, $2\gamma = f_{yy}(\mathbf{A})$.

(a) Prove that $f(a + h, b + k) = f(a,b) + \alpha h^2 + 2\beta hk + \gamma k^2 + R(h,k)$ where, setting $\mathbf{H} = (h,k)$, we have

$$\lim_{\mathbf{H}\to 0} \frac{R(\mathbf{H})}{|\mathbf{H}|^2} = 0.$$

(b) Prove that if f is a polynomial of degree two, then $R(\mathbf{H}) \equiv 0$. (Hint: In formula (8) of §3.7, note that f_{xx}, f_{yy}, and f_{xy} are constant.)

(c) Using (a) and (b), prove the remark after Theorem 14, about polynomials of degree two. (See Problem 6(g).)

(d) Suppose $\alpha + \gamma > 0$ and $\alpha\gamma > \beta^2$. Prove that $\mathbf{A}$ gives a local minimum. (Hint: Let m be the minimum of

$$\frac{\alpha h^2 + 2\beta hk + \gamma k^2}{h^2 + k^2};$$

by Problem 6(f), $m > 0$. Prove that when $|\mathbf{H}|$ is so small that $|R(\mathbf{H})|/|\mathbf{H}|^2 < m$, then $f(\mathbf{A} + \mathbf{H}) \geq f(\mathbf{A})$; in fact $f(\mathbf{A} + \mathbf{H}) > f(\mathbf{A})$ unless $\mathbf{H} = \mathbf{0}$.)

(e) Suppose $\alpha + \gamma < 0$ and $\alpha\gamma > \beta^2$. Prove that $\mathbf{A}$ gives a local maximum.

(f) Prove that if $\alpha\gamma < \beta^2$, then $\mathbf{A}$ is a saddle point.

Chapter IV

Double Integrals, Vector Fields, and Line Integrals

The title of this chapter suggests a collection of random topics; in fact, however, the topics are united in *Green's theorem*, an important two-dimensional version of the fundamental theorem of calculus, relating the line integral of a vector field to a double integral.

§4.1 Double integrals and Leibniz' rule for differentiating integrals. (Here, for the first time, we give a theorem without the proof.)

§4.2 Vector fields

§4.3 Line integrals

§4.4 Green's theorem

§4.5 Green's theorem applied to the problem of change of variable in double integrals.

4.1 DOUBLE INTEGRALS

The main theorems about integrating functions of two variables are important and conceptually clear, but difficult to formulate and prove. In fact, the first really good theory was not developed until recently, by Henri Lebesgue (1902) and Guido Fubini (1910), to mention two of the most famous names. We will begin with the general ideas, and make only a few steps toward formulating and proving the theorems.

Suppose f is a function defined in a set S of the plane, and $f \geq 0$ on S. Then the double integral $\iint_S f$ means, intuitively, the volume of the region lying over S and under the graph of f.

Example 1. S is the unit disk $\{P: |P| \leq 1\}$, and $f(x,y) = \sqrt{1 - x^2 - y^2}$. The region lying over S and under the graph of f is the upper half of the unit ball $\{(x,y,z): x^2 + y^2 + z^2 \leq 1\}$; hence

$$\iint_S f = \tfrac{1}{2}\,(\tfrac{4}{3}\pi 1^3) = \tfrac{2}{3}\pi.$$

(See Fig. 1.)

Example 2. S is the square $\{(x,y): 0 \leq x \leq 1, 0 \leq y \leq 1\}$, and $f(x,y) = y$. The region lying over S and under the graph of f is a wedge, a unit cube sliced in half, so $\iint_S f = \frac{1}{2}$. (See Fig. 2.)

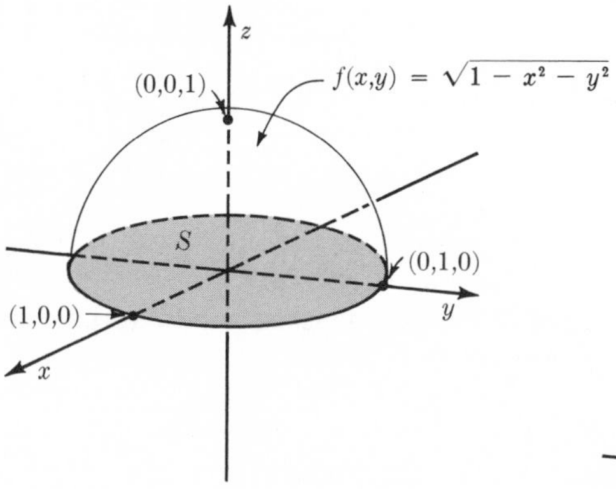

FIGURE 4.1

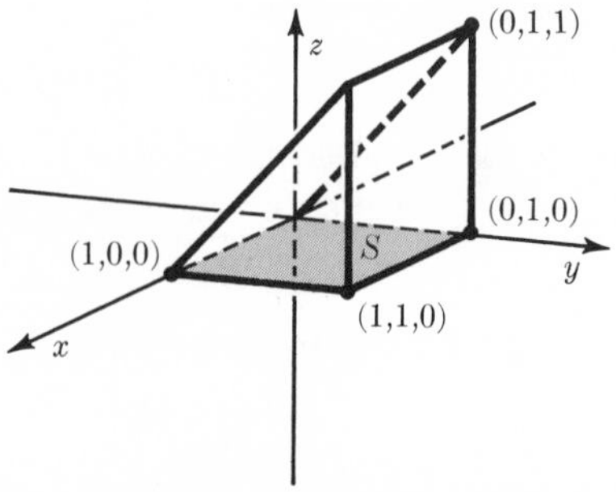

FIGURE 4.2

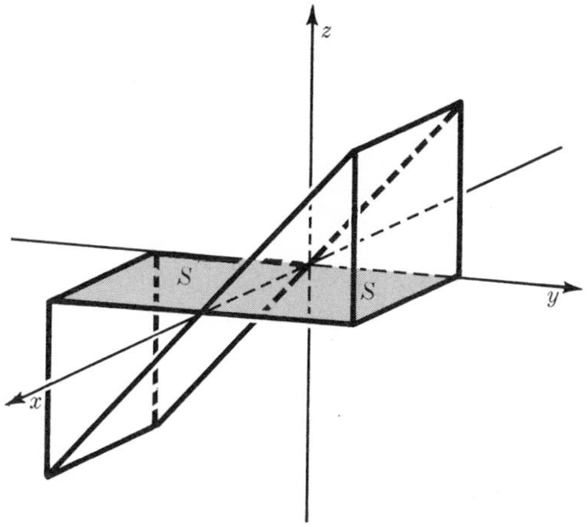

FIGURE 4.3

When f takes negative values in part of S, then $\iint_S f$ means, intuitively, the volume lying under the graph of f and over S, *minus* the volume lying over the graph and under S. In other words, volumes above the xy plane are taken as positive, and those below the xy plane as negative.

For example, if S is the rectangle $\{(x,y): -1 \leq x \leq 1, 0 \leq y \leq 1\}$, and $f(x,y) = y$, then $\iint_S f$ is the difference in the volumes of two congruent wedges, so $\iint_S f = 0$. (See Fig. 3.)

Obviously, simple pictures like these can evaluate only very special integrals. A much more general method is suggested by the formula for a volume of revolution. Recall that if we take the graph of a function g on an interval $[a,b]$ and revolve it about the x axis, we enclose a volume

$$V = \int_a^b \pi g(x)^2\, dx.$$

Here, $\pi g(x)^2$ is the area of a cross section of the enclosed volume, and the volume itself is the integral of these cross-sectional areas (Fig. 4).

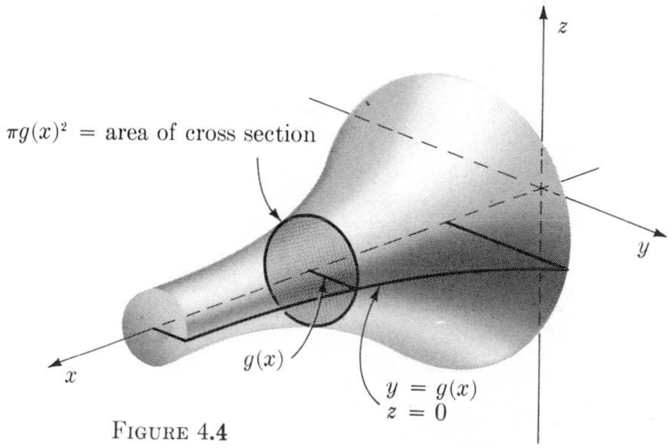

FIGURE 4.4

Now consider a function $f \geq 0$ defined on a rectangle

$$S = \{(x,y): a \leq x \leq b,\ c \leq y \leq d\};$$

then $\iint_S f$ is the volume shown in Fig. 5. Let $A(x)$ denote the area of a typical cross section by a plane perpendicular to the x axis at $(x,0,0)$. By analogy with volumes of revolution, the volume $\iint_S f$ should be

$$\iint_S f = \int_a^b A(x)\, dx. \tag{1}$$

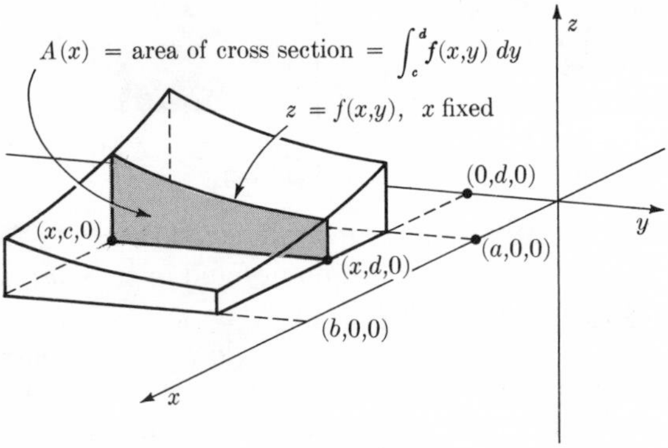

FIGURE 4.5

Further, for any fixed x, the cross-sectional area $A(x)$ is the area under the graph of a function of one variable, $g(y) = f(x,y)$, so

$$A(x) = \int_c^d f(x,y)\, dy. \tag{2}$$

Putting (2) into (1), we get

$$\iint_S f = \int_a^b \left[\int_c^d f(x,y)\, dy\right] dx. \tag{3}$$

This formula reduces the evaluation of $\iint_S f$ to the evaluation of two ordinary integrals, a question we have already studied.

Example 3. $S = \{(x,y): 0 \leq x \leq 1,\ 1 \leq y \leq 2\}$

$$f(x,y) = xe^{xy}$$

$$\iint_S f = \int_0^1 \left[\int_1^2 xe^{xy}\, dy\right] dx = \int_0^1 [e^{xy}]_{y=1}^{y=2}\, dx$$

$$= \int_0^1 (e^{2x} - e^x)\, dx = [\tfrac{1}{2}e^{2x} - e^x]_0^1 = \tfrac{1}{2}e^2 - e + \tfrac{1}{2}.$$

The same method can be applied when S is bounded by the graphs of two functions $\varphi_1(x)$ and $\varphi_2(x)$ on an interval $[a,b]$,

$$S = \{(x,y): a \leq x \leq b,\ \varphi_1(x) \leq y \leq \varphi_2(x)\}, \tag{4}$$

where we assume that $\varphi_1 \leq \varphi_2$ on the interval $[a,b]$. As shown in Fig. 6, a typical cross section perpendicular to the x axis has area

$$A(x) = \int_{\varphi_1(x)}^{\varphi_2(x)} f(x,y)\, dy,$$

so the total volume is

$$\iint_S f = \int_a^b A(x)\, dx = \int_a^b \left[\int_{\varphi_1(x)}^{\varphi_2(x)} f(x,y)\, dy\right] dx. \tag{5}$$

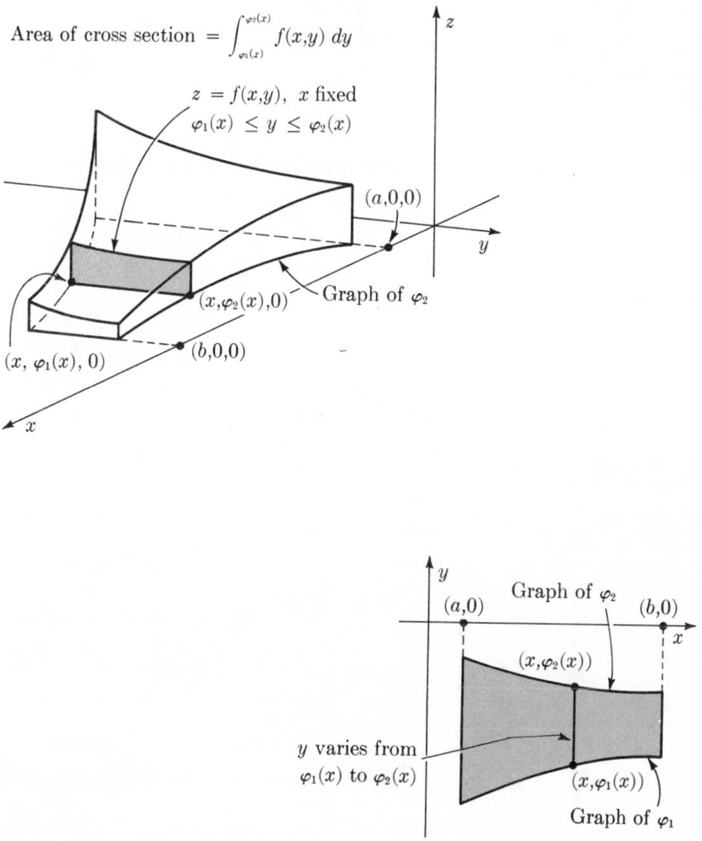

FIGURE 4.6

Example 4. For the double integral illustrated in Fig. 1 we have

$$S = \{(x,y): -1 \le x \le 1, -\sqrt{1-x^2} \le y \le \sqrt{1-x^2}\} \quad \text{(the unit disk)}$$

$$f(x,y) = \sqrt{1-x^2-y^2},$$

$$\iint_S f = \int_{-1}^{1}\left[\int_{-\sqrt{1-x^2}}^{\sqrt{1-x^2}} \sqrt{1-x^2-y^2}\,dy\right]dx$$

$$= \int_{-1}^{1}\left[\frac{1-x^2}{2}\arcsin\frac{y}{\sqrt{1-x^2}} + \frac{1}{2}y\sqrt{1-x^2-y^2}\right]_{y=-\sqrt{1-x^2}}^{y=\sqrt{1-x^2}} dx$$

$$= \int_{-1}^{1}\frac{\pi}{2}(1-x^2)\,dx = \frac{\pi}{2}\left[x - \frac{x^3}{3}\right]_{-1}^{1} = \frac{\pi}{2}\cdot\frac{4}{3} = \frac{2\pi}{3}.$$

(Here we used the integral $\int \sqrt{a^2-y^2}\,dy = \frac{a^2}{2}\arcsin\frac{y}{a} + \frac{1}{2}y\sqrt{a^2-y^2}$.)

The restriction $f \ge 0$ was made only to simplify the picture; the same method works, regardless of the sign of f. And, of course, we could just as well take sections perpendicular to the y axis (Fig. 7): if

$$S = \{(x,y): \psi_1(y) \le x \le \psi_2(y),\ c \le y \le d\}, \tag{6}$$

where $\psi_1 \le \psi_2$ on the interval $[c,d]$, then a typical cross section has area

$$A(y) = \int_{\psi_1(y)}^{\psi_2(y)} f(x,y)\,dx,$$

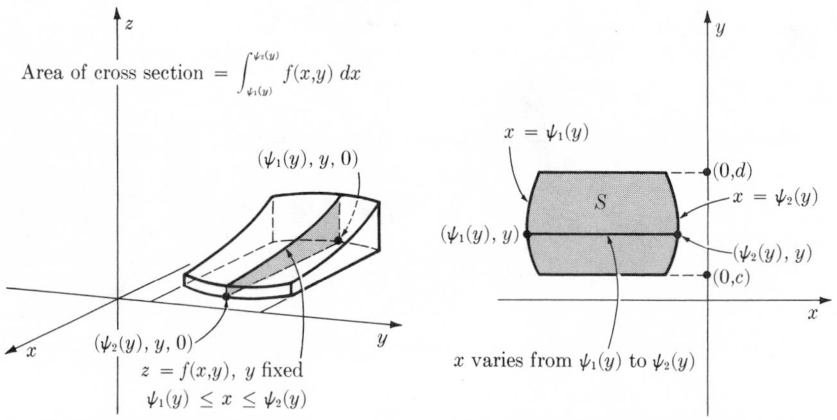

FIGURE 4.7

and

$$\iint_S = \int_c^d A(y)\,dy = \int_c^d \left[\int_{\psi_1(y)}^{\psi_2(y)} f(x,y)\,dx \right] dy. \tag{7}$$

In both (5) and (7) there is an "inner integral" (the one in square brackets) and an "outer integral"; the inner integral has variable limits, and the outer integral has constant limits. When the inner integral is with respect to x (as in (7)), its limits depend on y, and in the evaluation of $\int f(x,y)\,dx$ we keep y constant. When the inner integral is with respect to y (as in (5)), its limits depend on x, and in $\int f(x,y)\,dy$ we keep x constant.

Example 5. $S = \{(x,y): 0 \le y \le x^2, 0 \le x \le 2\}$ (see Fig. 8(a))

$$f(x,y) = x + y.$$

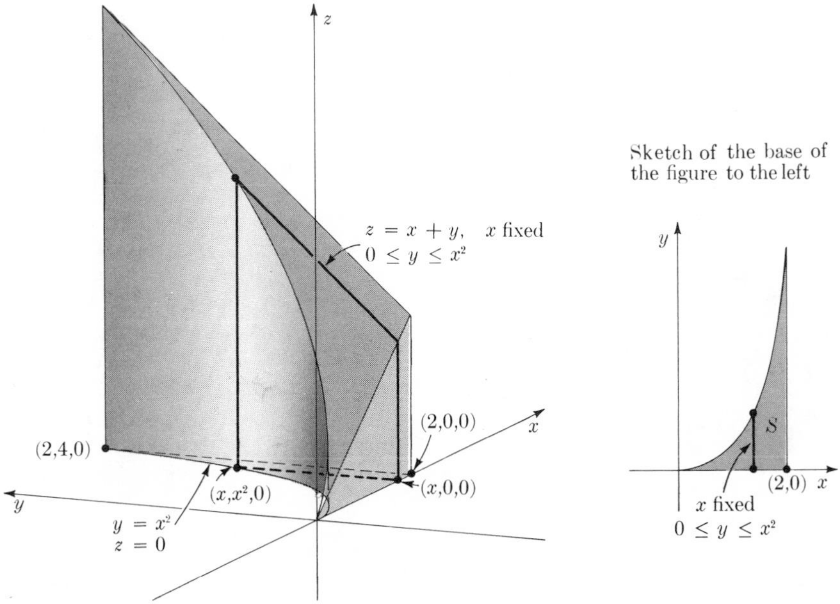

FIGURE 4.8 (a)

The set S is given in the form (4), with $\varphi_1 = 0$ and $\varphi_2 = x^2$, so we have, as in (5),

$$\iint_S f = \int_0^2 \left[\int_0^{x^2} (x+y)\,dy \right] dx = \int_0^2 \left[xy + \frac{y^2}{2} \right]_{y=0}^{y=x^2} dx$$

$$= \int_0^2 \left[x^3 + \frac{x^4}{2} \right] dx = \left[\frac{x^4}{4} + \frac{x^5}{10} \right]_0^2 = \frac{36}{5}.$$

The same set can also be described in the form (6),

$$S = \{\, (x,y) \colon \sqrt{y} \le x \le 2,\ 0 \le y \le 4\} \qquad \text{(see Fig. 8 (b))},$$

so

$$\iint_S f = \int_0^4 \left[\int_{\sqrt{y}}^2 (x+y)\,dx \right] dy = \int_0^4 \left[\frac{x^2}{2} + xy \right]_{x=\sqrt{y}}^{x=2} dy$$

$$= \int_0^4 \left(2 + 2y - \frac{y}{2} - y^{3/2} \right) dy$$

$$= \left[2y + y^2 - \frac{y^2}{4} - \frac{2}{5} y^{5/2} \right]_0^4 = \frac{36}{5}.$$

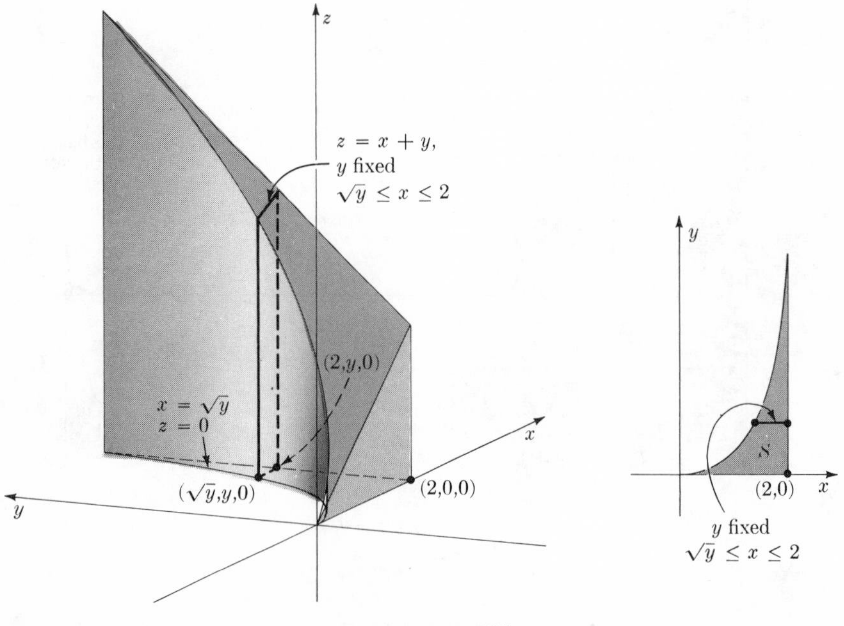

FIGURE 4.8 (b)

We have written the "repeated integral"

$$\int_a^b \left[\int_{\varphi_1(x)}^{\varphi_2(x)} f(x,y)\, dy \right] dx$$

with square brackets to show clearly how it is to be evaluated; first take

$$\int_{\varphi_1(x)}^{\varphi_2(x)} f(x,y)\, dy,$$

and then integrate the result with respect to x. Usually it is written simply

$$\int_a^b \int_{\varphi_1(x)}^{\varphi_2(x)} f(x,y)\, dy\, dx,$$

with the understanding that the "inner integral" is to be evaluated first.

This whole discussion has been based on an analogy and a few pictures. Two important theorems give these pictures the necessary rigorous basis.

Theorem 1. *Let f be continuous on the set*

$$S = \{(x,y) : a \leq x \leq b,\ \varphi_1(x) \leq y \leq \varphi_2(y)\}, \tag{4}$$

where φ_1 and φ_2 are continuous on $[a, b]$ and $\varphi_1 \leq \varphi_2$. Let

$$G(x) = \int_{\varphi_1(x)}^{\varphi_2(x)} f(x,y)\, dy.$$

Then G is continuous on $[a,b]$.

Similarly, if S is the set

$$S = \{(x,y) : \psi_1(y) \leq x \leq \psi_2(y),\ c \leq y \leq d\}, \tag{6}$$

where ψ_1 and ψ_2 are continuous and $\psi_1 \leq \psi_2$, then

$$H(y) = \int_{\psi_1(y)}^{\psi_2(y)} f(x,y)\, dx$$

is continuous on $[c,d]$.

Theorem 2. *If the same set S is described both by (4) and by (6), then*

$$\int_a^b \left[\int_{\varphi_1(x)}^{\varphi_2(x)} f(x,y)\, dy \right] dx = \int_c^d \left[\int_{\psi_1(y)}^{\psi_2(y)} f(x,y)\, dx \right] dy. \tag{8}$$

If these theorems could be proved intelligibly in a page or two, we would do it, but in fact they are by-products of a thorough investigation of double integration, as well as the deeper properties of continuous functions of two variables. Rather than give "ad hoc" direct proofs of such special results, we refer you to the general theory as expounded in the references listed at the end of this section.

The common value of the two integrals in (8) is called the *double integral* of f over S, denoted

$$\iint_S f \qquad \text{or} \qquad \iint_S f(x,y)\,dx\,dy.$$

Since we are defining the double integral by (8), the linearity property

$$\iint_S (\alpha f + \beta g) = \alpha \iint_S f + \beta \iint g \qquad (\alpha \text{ and } \beta \text{ are constants})$$

follows from the linearity of the single integral (Problem 7). Similarly,

$$f \leq g \;\Rightarrow\; \iint_S f \leq \iint_S g.$$

Theorems 1 and 2 have an important corollary, *Leibniz' rule* for differentiating under the integral sign:

Theorem 3. *Suppose $D_1 f(t,y)$ is continuous on the rectangle*

$$R = \{(t,y) : a \leq t \leq b,\ c \leq y \leq d\}.$$

Then the function

$$G(t) = \int_c^d f(t,y)\,dy$$

has the derivative

$$G'(t) = \int_c^d D_1 f(t,y)\,dy.$$

Proof. Consider $f(t,y)$ as a function of t, with y held fixed. By the fundamental theorem of calculus

$$f(t,y) = f(a,y) + \int_a^t D_1 f(x,y)\,dx;$$

hence

$$G(t) = \int_c^d f(t,y)\,dy = \int_c^d f(a,y)\,dy + \int_c^d \left[\int_a^t D_1 f(x,y)\,dx\right] dy$$

$$= \int_c^d f(a,y)\,dy + \int_a^t \left[\int_c^d D_1 f(x,y)\,dy\right] dx,$$

by Theorem 2. The first term in the last line is constant, so its derivative is zero. The second term is

$$\int_a^t H(x)\,dx, \quad \text{where} \quad H(x) = \int_c^d D_1 f(x,y)\,dy.$$

By Theorem 1, H is continuous, so by the fundamental theorem of calculus $G(t) = \int_a^t H(x)\,dx$ has the derivative

$$G'(t) = H(t) = \int_c^d D_1 f(t,y)\,dy. \quad Q.E.D.$$

Perhaps it is fitting to write Leibniz' rule in Leibniz notation:

$$\frac{d}{dt}\int_c^d f(t,y)\,dy = \int_c^d \frac{\partial f}{\partial t}(t,y)\,dy.$$

Thus, under appropriate conditions, the derivative d/dt can be moved from the outside of the integral sign to the inside. (But once inside, it has to be rewritten as $\partial/\partial t$, since it now applies to a function of two variables.) In this guise, it is easy to see how the rule works when other letters are used for the variables; for example,

$$\frac{d}{dx}\int_a^b f(x,s)\,ds = \int_a^b \frac{\partial f}{\partial x}(x,s)\,ds,$$

$$\frac{d}{dt}\int_a^b f(t,x)\,dx = \int_a^b \frac{\partial f}{\partial t}(t,x)\,dx.$$

Further, since s is held constant in computing $\partial f(t,s,x)/\partial t$, we have

$$\frac{\partial}{\partial t}\int_a^b f(t,s,x)\,dx = \int_a^b \frac{\partial f}{\partial t}(t,s,x)\,dx.$$

Example 6. Let

$$G(t) = \int_0^1 \sin(t + y)\, dy.$$

Applying Theorem 3 with $f(t, y) = \sin(t + y)$, we find $D_1 f(t,y) = f_t = \cos(t + y)$; hence

$$G'(t) = \int_0^1 \cos(t + y)\, dy = [\sin(t + y)]_0^1$$
$$= \sin(t + 1) - \sin t.$$

We can check this by first evaluating the integral for $G(t)$, obtaining $G(t) = -\cos(t + 1) + \cos t$, which yields $G'(t) = \sin(t + 1) - \sin t$.

Example 7. Let

$$G(t) = \int_1^2 \frac{1}{y} e^{ty}\, dy.$$

Applying Theorem 3 with

$$f(t,y) = \frac{1}{y} e^{ty},$$

we find $D_1 f(t,y) = f_t = e^{ty}$; hence

$$G'(t) = \int_1^2 e^{ty}\, dy = \left[\frac{1}{t} e^{ty}\right]_1^2 = \frac{e^{2t} - e^t}{t}.$$

We cannot check this result by evaluating $G(t)$ explicitly, since none of the standard methods evaluate the integral

$$\int \frac{1}{y} e^{ty}\, dy.$$

In a case like this, Theorem 3 is the only practical way to obtain a useful expression for $G'(t)$.

Example 8. Let

$$G(x,y) = \int_0^x f(s,y)\, ds,$$

where f and f_y are continuous. Find G_x and G_y. *Solution.* By the fundamental theorem of calculus, $G_x(x,y) = f(x,y)$, and by Leibniz' rule,

$$G_y(x,y) = \int_0^x f_y(s,y)\, ds.$$

Example 9. Let

$$H(x,y) = \int_0^{\varphi(x,y)} f(s,y)\, ds,$$

where f, f_y, φ, φ_x, and φ_y are all continuous. Find H_x and H_y.
Solution. We can use the chain rule, with the scheme

$$(x,y) \quad\to\quad (\varphi(x,y),y) \quad\to\quad \int_0^{\varphi(x,y)} f(s,y)\, ds = H(x,y)$$

or

$$(x,y) \quad\to\quad (u,v) \quad\to\quad z$$

where $u = \varphi(x,y)$, $v = y$, and $z = \displaystyle\int_0^u f(s,v)\, ds$. We find

$$\begin{aligned} H_x &= \frac{\partial z}{\partial x} = \frac{\partial z}{\partial u}\frac{\partial u}{\partial x} + \frac{\partial z}{\partial v}\frac{\partial v}{\partial x} \\ &= f(u,v)\cdot\varphi_x + \left(\int_0^u D_2 f(s,v)\, ds\right)\cdot 0 \\ &= f(\varphi(x,y),y)\varphi_x(x,y), \end{aligned}$$

and

$$\begin{aligned} H_y &= \frac{\partial z}{\partial y} = \frac{\partial z}{\partial u}\frac{\partial u}{\partial y} + \frac{\partial z}{\partial v}\frac{\partial v}{\partial y} \\ &= f(u,v)\cdot\varphi_y + \left(\int_0^u D_2 f(s,v)\, ds\right)\cdot 1 \\ &= f(\varphi(x,y),y)\varphi_y(x,y) + \int_0^{\varphi(x,y)} D_2 f(s,y)\, ds. \end{aligned}$$

PROBLEMS

1. Evaluate the following repeated integrals.

(a) $\displaystyle\int_0^\pi \int_0^y y \sin x \, dx\, dy$ (d) $\displaystyle\int_0^1 \int_{\sqrt{x}}^1 dy\, dx$

(b) $\displaystyle\int_1^2 \int_x^{x^2} dy\, dx$ (e) $\displaystyle\int_0^2 \int_1^{e^y} dx\, dy$

(c) $\displaystyle\int_1^3 \int_0^{\log y} e^{x+y}\, dx\, dy$ (f) $\displaystyle\int_0^1 \int_0^{x^2} \frac{1}{1+x^2}\, dy\, dx.$

2. Describe each of the sets in Fig. 9 in the form (4), and in the form (6).

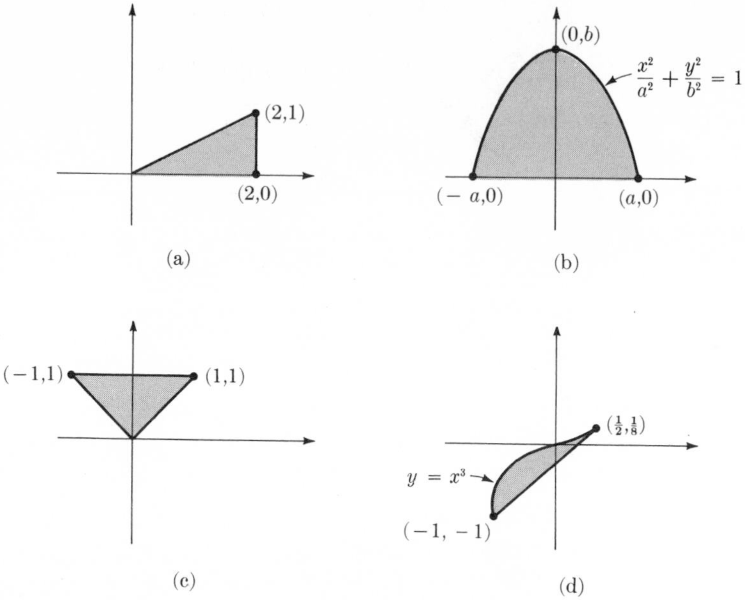

FIGURE 4.9

3. For each of the integrals in Problem 1, sketch the set S over which you are integrating, and rewrite the integral with dx and dy interchanged. If possible, evaluate the new repeated integral, and compare it to the result found in Problem 1. (*Warning:* It is difficult to obtain the limits for the new repeated integral just by looking at the original limits; you need a clear picture of the set S over which you are integrating.)

4. Find the partial derivatives of the following functions by applying the fundamental theorem of calculus and Leibniz' rule.

(a) $f(x,y) = \int_1^x e^{sy}\, ds$

(b) $g(x,y) = \int_1^{x^2} e^{sy}\, ds$

(Hint: $g(x,y) = f(x^2,y)$, with f as in (a); use the chain rule).

(c) $h(x,y) = \int_0^x \sin(sy)\, ds$

(d) $i(x,y) = \int_0^{x^3} \sin(sy)\, ds$

(e) $j(x,y) = \int_0^{x+y} \sin(sy)\, ds$

(Hint: $j(x,y) = h(x + y, y)$; use the chain rule.)

(f) $k(x,y) = \int_0^{\varphi(x)} \sin(sy)\, ds$, where φ is differentiable

(g) $l(x,y) = \int_0^{\varphi(x,y)} \sin(sy)\, ds$, where φ is differentiable

(h) $m(x,y) = \int_{\varphi_1(x,y)}^{\varphi_2(x,y)} \sin(sy)\, ds$ (Hint: $\int_{\varphi_1}^{\varphi_2} = \int_0^{\varphi_2} - \int_0^{\varphi_1}$)

5. Evaluate the integrals in Problem 4(a)–(e), and check the results you found in Problem 4.

6. Suppose that f and f_y are continuous on the rectangle

$$R = \{(x,y): a \le x \le b,\ c \le y \le d\},$$

that φ_1 and φ_2 are differentiable on R, that $a \le \varphi_1 \le b$, and that $a \le \varphi_2 \le b$. Prove that if

$$F(x,y) = \int_{\varphi_1(x,y)}^{\varphi_2(x,y)} f(s,y)\, ds,$$

then

$$F_x(x,y) = f(\varphi_2(x,y),y)\frac{\partial \varphi_2}{\partial x} - f(\varphi_1(x,y),y)\frac{\partial \varphi_1}{\partial x},$$

and

$$F_y(x,y) = \int_{\varphi_1}^{\varphi_2} f_y(s,y)\, ds + f(\varphi_2(x,y),y)\frac{\partial \varphi_2}{\partial y} - f(\varphi_1(x,y),y)\frac{\partial \varphi_1}{\partial y}.$$

(Hint: Do Problem 4 first.)

7. Suppose that S is a region of the type in Theorem 2, and f and g are continuous on S.
   (a) Prove that $\iint_S (\alpha f + \beta g) = \alpha \iint_S f + \beta \iint_S g$ for all constants α and β.
   (b) Prove that if $f \ge g$, then $\iint_S f \ge \iint_S g$.

8. (a) Suppose that U is an open set, f is continuous on U, and $\iint_D f = 0$ for every disk D contained in U. Prove that $f \equiv 0$ in U. (Hint: If $f \not\equiv 0$, then $f(\mathbf{P}_0) \ne 0$ for some point $\mathbf{P}_0$ in U; say $f(\mathbf{P}_0) > 0$.

Since f is continuous and U is open, there is a disk D contained in U such that $f(\mathbf{P}) > \frac{1}{2}f(\mathbf{P}_0)$ for every point $\mathbf{P}$ in R. Now apply Problem 7(b).)

(b) Suppose that S is a region of the type in Theorem 2, f is continuous on S, $f \geq 0$, and $\iint_S f = 0$. Let U be any open set contained in S. Prove that $f \equiv 0$ on U. (Hint: Show that $0 \leq \iint_D f \leq \iint_S f = 0$ for every disk D contained in U.)

References. The following books give a thorough development of double integrals, including the proofs omitted above. We will refer to them again later in connection with Green's theorem and its extensions.

T. M. Apostol, *Mathematical Analysis*, Addison-Wesley, 1957

W. H. Fleming, *Functions of Several Variables*, Addison-Wesley, 1965

M. Spivak, *Calculus on Manifolds*, Benjamin, 1965

4.2 VECTOR FIELDS

A vector field $\mathbf{F}$ over a set S is a function assigning a vector $\mathbf{F}(\mathbf{P})$ to each point $\mathbf{P}$ in S. Here the set S will be in the plane, and the vectors will be in R^2. The two components of $\mathbf{F}(\mathbf{P})$ are often denoted $M(\mathbf{P})$ and $N(\mathbf{P})$; thus $\mathbf{F}(\mathbf{P}) = (M(\mathbf{P}), N(\mathbf{P}))$, where M and N are ordinary real-valued functions on S. To visualize $\mathbf{F}$, picture at each point $\mathbf{P}$ in S an arrow representing $\mathbf{F}(\mathbf{P})$, as in Fig. 10.

The two main physical examples are *force fields* and *velocity fields*. A particle of mass M at the origin attracts a particle of mass m at the point $\mathbf{P}$ by a force $-\gamma mM\mathbf{P}/|\mathbf{P}|^3$, where γ is a gravity constant. The function

$$\mathbf{F}(\mathbf{P}) = -\gamma mM\,|\mathbf{P}|^{-3}\mathbf{P} \qquad (*)$$

is a vector field defined on the set where $|\mathbf{P}| \neq 0$ (Fig. 10(a)); since it describes a force, it is called a *force field.*

For a simple example of a velocity field, imagine that a plate lying on the plane is rotated counterclockwise about the origin at a rate of c radians per minute. Then for any (x,y) in the plane, the point on the plate lying over (x,y) moves with velocity $\mathbf{F}(x,y) = (-cy,cx)$, as you

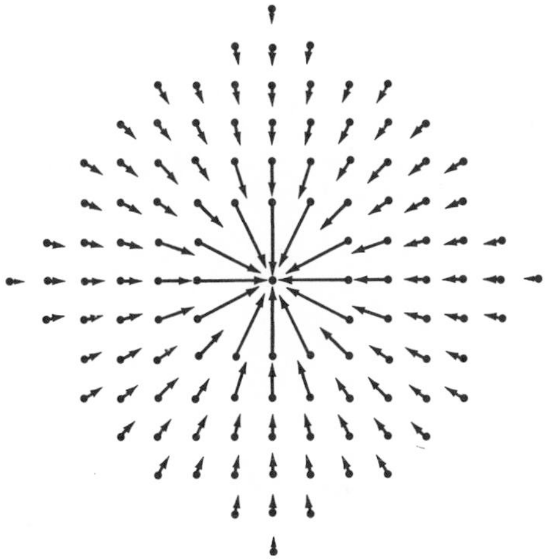

(a) $\mathbf{F}(\mathbf{P}) = \frac{-1}{|\mathbf{P}|^3}\mathbf{P}$

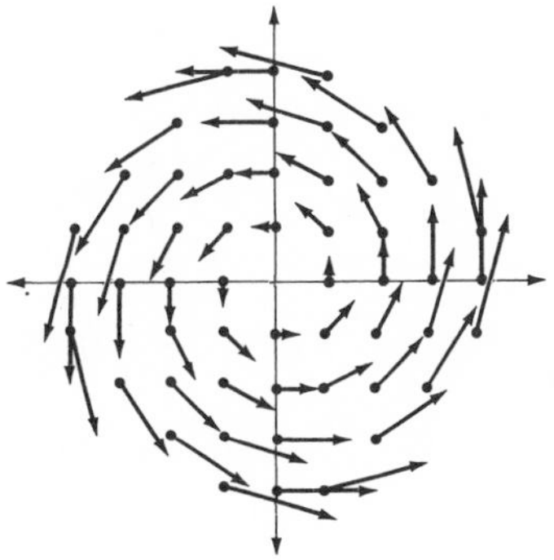

(b) $\mathbf{F}(x,y) = \left(-\frac{y}{2}, \frac{x}{2}\right)$

FIGURE 4.10

can easily check (see Problem 4). This vector field $\mathbf{F}$ is called the *velocity field* of the rotation (Fig. 10(b)).

In a purely mathematical context, vector fields arise from gradients; precisely, if f is differentiable at every point in S, then $\mathbf{F}(\mathbf{P}) = \nabla f(\mathbf{P})$ defines a vector field $\mathbf{F}$ on S. For example, if $f(\mathbf{P}) = \gamma mM/|\mathbf{P}|$, you can check that $\nabla f(\mathbf{P}) = -\gamma mM\,|\mathbf{P}|^{-3}\,\mathbf{P}$, and we get the force field (*) as a gradient. The function f is called a *potential function* of the force $\mathbf{F} = \nabla f$.

Not every vector field is a gradient, though. For example, the velocity field $\mathbf{F}(x,y) = (-cy,cx)$ is not the gradient of any function f. Suppose, on the contrary, that $\mathbf{F}$ were a gradient ∇f; then we would have $f_x = -cy$, $f_y = cx$; hence $f_{xy} = -c$, $f_{yx} = c$, and the mixed partials of f would be continuous but unequal, contradicting Theorem 10 of the previous chapter. Hence there is no function f such that $\nabla f(x,y) = (-cy,cx)$.

This raises the question: Which vector fields are gradients? Or, in physical terms, which force fields have potentials? The answer is easy for a vector field defined over a rectangle:

Theorem 4. *Suppose that* $\mathbf{F} = (M,N)$ *is defined on an open rectangle*

$$R = \{(x,y): a < x < b,\ c < y < d\},$$

and the partial derivatives M_y *and* N_x *are continuous on* R. *Then* $\mathbf{F}$ *is a gradient if and only if* $M_y \equiv N_x$.

Proof. If $\mathbf{F}$ is the gradient of a function f, then $(M,N) = (D_1 f, D_2 f)$, so $D_2M = D_2D_1 f$ and $D_1N = D_1D_2 f$. By the assumptions on D_2M and D_1N, the mixed partials of f are continuous, hence they must be equal, so $D_2M = D_1N$, i.e. $M_y = N_x$.

Conversely, suppose that $D_2M = D_1N$. We must find a function f with $\nabla f = (M,N)$, in other words a function f whose partial derivatives are given, $D_1 f = M$ and $D_2 f = N$. Let $\mathbf{P}_0 = (x_0,y_0)$ be any point in the rectangle R. Since $D_1 f = M$ is prescribed, we must have

$$f(x,y_0) = f(x_0,y_0) + \int_{x_0}^{x} D_1 f(s,y_0)\, ds = f(x_0,y_0) + \int_{x_0}^{x} M(s,y_0)\, ds. \qquad (1)$$

Since $D_2 f = N$ is prescribed, we must have

$$f(x,y) = f(x,y_0) + \int_{y_0}^{y} D_2 f(x,t)\, dt = f(x,y_0) + \int_{y_0}^{y} N(x,t)\, dt;$$

hence, from (1),

$$f(x,y) = f(x_0,y_0) + \int_{x_0}^{x} M(s,y_0)\, ds + \int_{y_0}^{y} N(x,t)\, dt. \qquad (2)$$

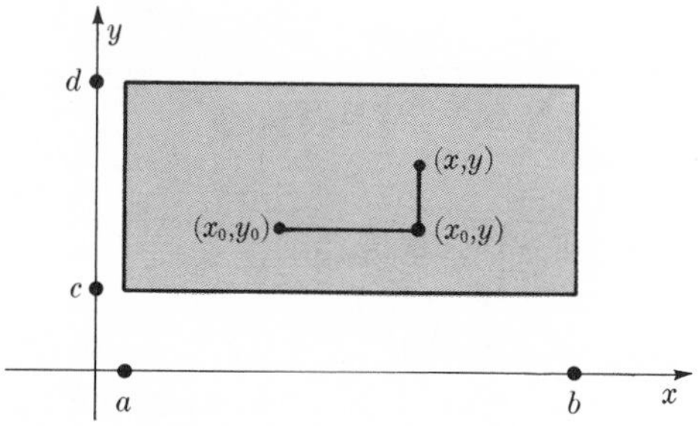

FIGURE 4.11

(Conceptually, the integrals in (2) are taken along the two line segments shown in Fig. 11. When (x,y) is in R, these segments lie entirely in R, so the integrals are defined.) What we have proved is this: If there is a function f with $\nabla f = (M,N)$, it must be given by (2). It remains to be seen whether (2) actually works. By the fundamental theorem of calculus we see immediately that $f_y = N(x,y)$, as desired. Using Leibniz' rule (Theorem 3), we get

$$f_x = M(x,y_0) + \int_{y_0}^{y} N_x(x,t)\, dt,$$

which does not look like M. But $N_x = M_y$, so

$$f_x = M(x,y_0) + \int_{y_0}^{y} M_y(x,t)\,dt$$
$$= M(x,y_0) + M(x,y) - M(x,y_0) = M(x,y). \quad Q.E.D.$$

Theorem 4 is so important that its main hypothesis and its conclusion have special names. A vector field $\mathbf{F} = (M,N)$ is called *closed* if $M_y = N_x$, and *exact* if $\mathbf{F} = \nabla f$ for some function f. In these terms, the theorem says that *a vector field whose domain is a rectangle is closed if and only if it is exact.* When the domain is more general the situation becomes more complicated, but more interesting. Every exact field is still closed; but if the domain S has any "holes" (e.g. if $S = \{\mathbf{P}: |\mathbf{P}| > 0\}$, which has a hole at the origin, Fig. 12), then there are vector fields which are closed (i.e. $M_y = N_x$) but are *not* exact (i.e. (M,N) is not a gradient). Problem 3 gives one example. Problem 7, on the other hand, gives examples of sets "without holes" in which it is easy to prove (as in Theorem 4) that "closed" implies "exact" (Fig. 13).

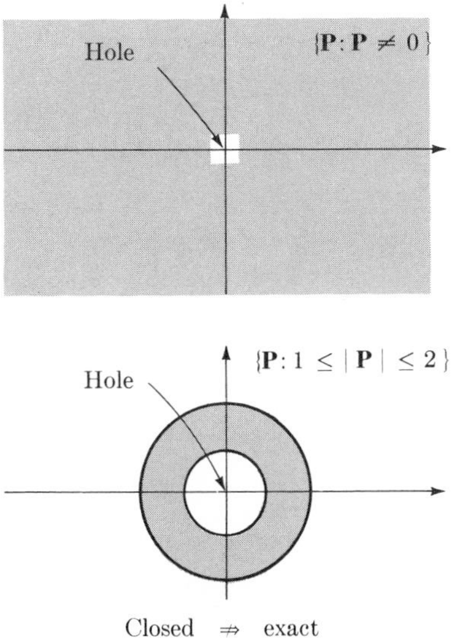

FIGURE 4.12

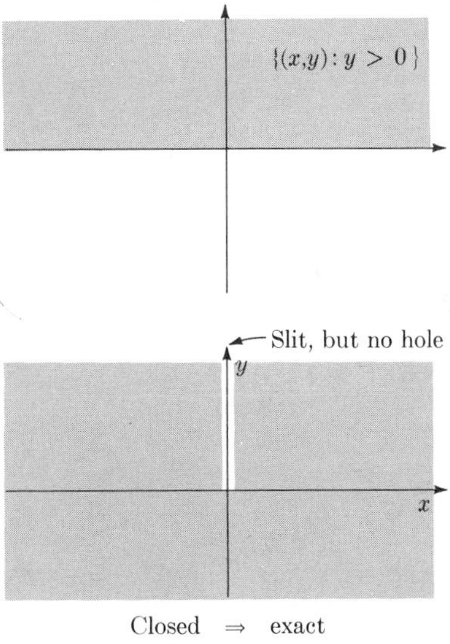

FIGURE 4.13

The proof of Theorem 4 does not merely say that a closed vector field has a potential f; it gives the explicit formula (2). Given a specific M and N and a little luck in evaluating the integrals, you can write down exactly what f is, up to the undetermined constant $f(x_0,y_0)$. This is as much as could be expected, since changing f by a constant does not affect ∇f.

Example 1. $M(x,y) = y, N(x,y) = x$. This vector field is defined in all of R^2, and $M_y = 1$, $N_x = 1$, so it is closed; hence formula (2) defines a potential f. Take $x_0 = 0$, $y_0 = 0$. Then $M(s,y_0) = y_0 = 0$, and $N(x,t) = x$, so formula (2) becomes

$$f(x,y) = f(0,0) + \int_0^x 0\,ds + \int_0^y x\,dt = f(0,0) + xy.$$

You can check that $\nabla f = (M,N)$, as required.

A certain special class of differential equations can be solved by Theorem 4. Suppose we want to solve

$$\varphi'(t) = G(t,\varphi(t)), \tag{3}$$

where $G(x,y)$ is a given function defined on a rectangle, and φ is to be determined by (3). Suppose that G can be written in the special form

$$G(x,y) = -\frac{M(x,y)}{N(x,y)}, \tag{4}$$

where $M_y = N_x$. Because (M,N) is closed, and defined on a rectangle, it is exact; there is an f with $\nabla f = (M,N)$. Then *any differentiable function* φ *such that*

$$f(t,\varphi(t)) = \text{constant} \tag{5}$$

is a solution of (3). For, differentiating (5) by the chain rule gives

$$D_1 f(t,\varphi(t)) + D_2 f(t,\varphi(t))\varphi'(t) = 0.$$

Since $D_1 f = M$ and $D_2 f = N$, we get

$$M(t,\varphi(t)) + N(t,\varphi(t))\varphi'(t) = 0,$$

which on account of (4) reduces to (3). (Notice that if $N = f_y \neq 0$, the implicit function theorem guarantees the existence of φ, at least on a small interval.)

Equation (3) is often written in Leibniz notation with $x = t$ and $y = \varphi(t)$. It then looks like

$$\frac{dy}{dx} = G(x,y),$$

and if $G = -M/N$ this becomes

$$\frac{dy}{dx} = -\frac{M}{N}, \qquad \text{or} \qquad N\frac{dy}{dx} + M = 0,$$

or

$$M\,dx + N\,dy = 0. \tag{6}$$

We have found that φ is a solution if $f(t,\varphi(t)) = \text{constant}$; in other words, φ is a solution if its graph lies along a contour line of f. Summing up briefly: *To solve the equation* (6) *when* $M_y = N_x$, *find a potential* f *with* $\nabla f = (M,N)$. *Then the contour lines of* f *are the graphs of solutions of* (6). Differential equations of this type are called *exact.*

Example 2. In the equation

$$y\,dx + x\,dy = 0 \tag{7}$$

we have $M = y$, $N = x$, hence $M_y = 1$ and $N_x = 1$, so (M,N) is closed. This vector field is the gradient of $f(x,y) = xy$, so the solutions of (7) are the contour lines $xy = c$, or $y = c/x$, where c is a constant. As a check: when $y = c/x$, then $dy/dx = -c/x^2$, hence $x^2\,dy + c\,dx = 0$; but $c = xy$, so $x^2\,dy + xy\,dx = 0$, or $x\,dy + y\,dx = 0$, as required by (7).

PROBLEMS

1. Decide which of the following vector fields are closed. For those $\mathbf{F}$ which are closed, find a potential function f such that $\nabla f = \mathbf{F}$.

(a) $(2xy,x^2)$ (i.e. $M(x,y) = 2xy$, $N(x,y) = x^2$.)
(b) $(2xy,-x^2)$
(c) (e^{x+y},e^{x+y})
(d) $(\sin(xy),\cos(xy))$
(e) (e^y,xe^y)
(f) $(\cos(x+y),\cos(x+y))$
(g) $\left(\dfrac{x}{x^2+y^2},\dfrac{y}{x^2+y^2}\right)$ (Notice that Theorem 4 does not apply; nevertheless, the vector field *is* exact. Find the potential f such that $f(1,0) = 0$.)

2. Of the following differential equations, solve the exact ones. (You need not express y explicitly as a function of x in every case.)

(a) $xe^{xy}\dfrac{dy}{dx} + ye^{xy} = 0$ (d) $x^2\,dx + y^2\,dy = 0$

(b) $ye^{xy}\dfrac{dy}{dx} + xe^{xy} = 0$ (e) $y^2\,dx + x^2\,dy = 0$

(c) $x\,dx + y\,dy = 0$ (f) $(x - y)\,dx + (y^2 - x)\,dy = 0$

3. Let

$$\mathbf{F}(x,y) = \left(\frac{-y}{x^2+y^2},\frac{x}{x^2+y^2}\right)$$

be defined on the set $\{\mathbf{P}: |\mathbf{P}| > 0\}$.

(a) Prove that $\mathbf{F}$ is closed.

(b) Prove that if $\mathbf{F} = \nabla f$, where f is differentiable for $|\mathbf{P}| > 0$, then there are constants c_+ and c_- such that

$$f(x,y) = \arctan\frac{y}{x} + c_+ \quad \text{for } x > 0$$

$$f(x,y) = \arctan\frac{y}{x} + c_- \quad \text{for } x < 0.$$

(Recall that two functions defined in an open connected set and having the same gradient there can differ by at most a constant. See Problem 16, §3.3.)

(c) Prove that if the function f in part (b) is continuous at points on the positive half of the y axis, then $\pi/2 + c_+ = -\pi/2 + c_-$.

(d) Obtain a similar condition for continuity of f along the negative y axis.

(e) Show that the conditions in parts (c) and (d) are incompatible. (This proves that the function f postulated in part (b) cannot exist. Thus, $\mathbf{F}$ is closed, but not exact.)

4. The curve $\boldsymbol{\gamma}(t) = (r\cos(ct), r\sin(ct))$ describes a motion of rotation clockwise about the origin, c radians per unit time. Prove that when the moving point is at (x,y), then its velocity is $(-cy,cx)$. (Thus, $\mathbf{F}(x,y) = (-cy,cx)$ is the velocity field for a rotation of the plane about the origin.)

5. Suppose $\mathbf{F} = (M,N)$ is exact in an arbitrary open set S, and M_y and N_x are continuous in S. Prove that $\mathbf{F}$ is closed in S.

6. Problem 3 shows that a closed vector field need not be exact if it is defined on the set $S = \{\mathbf{P}: |\mathbf{P}| > 0\}$. What goes wrong in the proof of Theorem 4 given above if we replace the rectangle R by this set S?

7. Rectangles are not the only sets for which "closed" implies "exact." Show that the proof of Theorem 4 remains valid when the rectangle R is replaced by

(a) a disk

(b) the whole plane R^2

(c) the upper half plane $\{(x,y): y > 0\}$

(d) the set $S = \{(x,y): x \neq 0 \text{ or } y < 0\}$, which consists of the plane with the upper half of the y axis removed, Fig. 13. (Hint: Take $(x_0,y_0) = (0,-1)$).

(e) Define $\mathbf{F}$ as in Problem 3, and find a function f such that $\nabla f = \mathbf{F}$ for points in the set S given in part (d).

8. It can happen that the equation

$$M\,dx + N\,dy = 0 \tag{8}$$

is not exact, but that the equivalent equation obtained by multiplying by some nonzero function ρ, $\rho M\, dx + \rho N\, dy = 0$, *is* exact, i.e.

$$\frac{\partial \rho M}{\partial y} = \frac{\partial \rho N}{\partial x}.$$

Such a function ρ is called an *integrating factor.* The usual way to find an integrating factor is simply to guess. This doesn't succeed very often, so hints are provided with the following problems. Solve the given equations.

(a) $(1 + xy)\, dx + x^2\, dy = 0$ (Try $\rho(x,y) = e^{xy}$)

(b) $(1 - xy)\, dx - x^2\, dy = 0$

(c) $(xy^2 + y)\, dx - x\, dy = 0$ (Try $\rho(x,y) = y^{-2}$)

(d) $(y^2 + 1)\, dx + (xy - y\sqrt{y^2 + 1})\, dy = 0$ (Try $\rho = (y^2 + 1)^{-1/2}$)

(e) $\dfrac{dy}{dx} = \dfrac{e^x - y}{x}$

4.3 LINE INTEGRALS

In both of the main physical examples of vector fields there arises an important concept, the *line integral* of a vector field over a curve. In a force field, the work done by the force in moving a particle along a curve is given by a line integral; and in a velocity field, the rate of flow across a curve is given by a line integral.

The mathematical definition of line integrals is simple. Given a differentiable curve $\boldsymbol{\gamma}: [a,b] \to R^2$ and a vector field $\mathbf{F}$ which is continuous at every point on $\boldsymbol{\gamma}$, the line integral of $\mathbf{F}$ along $\boldsymbol{\gamma}$ is defined by

$$\int_\gamma \mathbf{F} = \int_a^b (\mathbf{F}\circ\boldsymbol{\gamma})\cdot\boldsymbol{\gamma}'. \tag{1}$$

We will give some examples and remarks on the evaluation and interpretation of (1), and finally prove a theorem relating line integrals and exact vector fields.

Example 1. If $\mathbf{F}(x,y) = (y,x)$ and $\boldsymbol{\gamma}(t) = (r\cos t, r\sin t)$ for $0 \le t \le \pi/4$, then $\boldsymbol{\gamma}'(t) = (-r\sin t, r\cos t)$, so

$$\begin{aligned}\mathbf{F}(\boldsymbol{\gamma}(t))\cdot\boldsymbol{\gamma}'(t) &= (r\sin t, r\cos t)\cdot(-r\sin t, r\cos t)\\ &= r^2(\cos^2 t - \sin^2 t) = r^2\cos(2t);\end{aligned}$$

hence

$$\int_\gamma \mathbf{F} = \int_0^{\pi/4} r^2\cos 2t\, dt = \frac{1}{2}r^2\sin 2t\Big]_0^{\pi/4} = \frac{r^2}{2}.$$

The Leibniz notation for the line integral (1) is

$$\int_\gamma M(x,y)\,dx + N(x,y)\,dy, \tag{2}$$

where M and N are the components of $\mathbf{F}$. To evaluate (2), simply substitute for x and y their values on the given curve, set

$$dx = \frac{dx}{dt}\,dt, \qquad dy = \frac{dy}{dt}\,dt,$$

and evaluate the integral between the given limits on t. Thus if $x = \gamma_1(t)$ and $y = \gamma_2(t)$, $a \le t \le b$, the expression (2) becomes

$$\int_a^b M(\gamma_1(t),\gamma_2(t))\gamma_1'(t)\,dt + N(\gamma_1(t),\gamma_2(t))\gamma_2'(t)\,dt$$

$$= \int_a^b \big(M(\boldsymbol{\gamma}(t))\gamma_1'(t) + N(\boldsymbol{\gamma}(t))\gamma_2'(t)\big)\,dt$$

$$= \int_a^b \mathbf{F}(\boldsymbol{\gamma}(t))\cdot\boldsymbol{\gamma}'(t)\,dt,$$

which is equivalent to the definition (1).

Example 2. In Leibniz notation, the line integral in Example 1 is given as

$$\int_\gamma y\,dx + x\,dy, \qquad x = r\cos t, \quad y = r\sin t, \quad 0 \le t \le \pi/4.$$

Making the indicated substitutions, we get

$$\int_0^{\pi/4} (r\sin t(-r\sin t\,dt) + r\cos t(r\cos t\,dt)) = \int_0^{\pi/4} r^2(\cos^2 t - \sin^2 t)\,dt = \frac{r^2}{2}.$$

Another common notation for line integrals is derived from the formulas

$$\frac{ds}{dt} = |\boldsymbol{\gamma}'(t)|, \qquad \mathbf{T} = \frac{1}{|\boldsymbol{\gamma}'|}\boldsymbol{\gamma}',$$

where s is arc length on the curve and $\mathbf{T}$ is the unit tangent vector (§2.3). Substituting these in (1) suggests

$$\int_\gamma \mathbf{F} = \int_a^b (\mathbf{F}\circ\boldsymbol{\gamma})\cdot\frac{\boldsymbol{\gamma}'}{|\boldsymbol{\gamma}'|}|\boldsymbol{\gamma}'|\,dt = \int_\gamma \mathbf{F}\cdot\mathbf{T}\,ds.$$

Since $\mathbf{T}$ is a unit vector, $\mathbf{F}\cdot\mathbf{T}$ is the component of $\mathbf{F}$ in the tangent direction $\mathbf{T}$, called the *tangential component* of $\mathbf{F}$ (see Fig. 14); the line integral $\int_\gamma \mathbf{F}\cdot\mathbf{T}\,ds$ is the integral of this tangential component with respect to arc length on the curve.

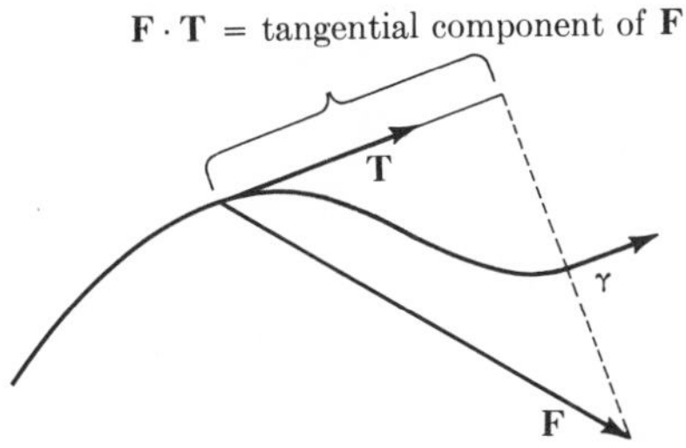

FIGURE 4.14

When **F** is a force, then $\int_\gamma \mathbf{F} = \int_\gamma \mathbf{F}\cdot\mathbf{T}\,ds$ is defined to be the *work* done by **F** in moving a particle along γ from beginning to end.

When $\mathbf{F} = (M,N)$ is the velocity field of a flow, there is a line integral giving the rate of flow across γ from left to right; it is not $\int_\gamma \mathbf{F} = \int_\gamma M\,dx + N\,dy$, but

$$\int_\gamma (-N\,dx + M\,dy). \tag{3}$$

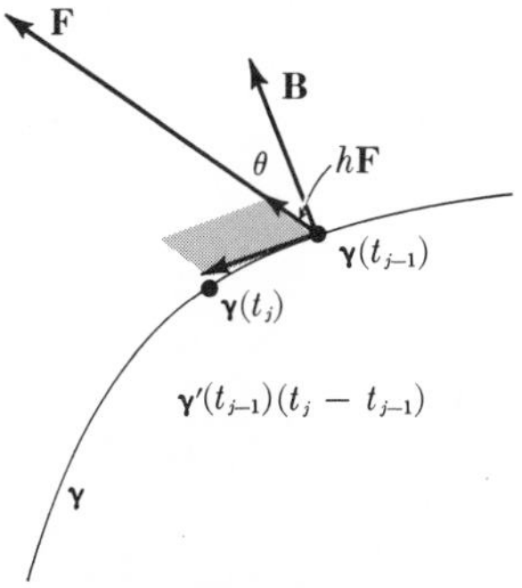

FIGURE 4.15

To see why this integral is interpreted as the rate of flow, consider a small section of the curve from $\gamma(t_{j-1})$ to $\gamma(t_j)$. In a short time interval of length h, the fluid near this part of the curve has a displacement of approximately $h\mathbf{F}(\gamma(t_{j-1}))$. Hence the fluid that has crossed this section of curve in the given time h is contained approximately in the parallelogram in Fig. 15. The parallelogram has sides $h\mathbf{F}(\gamma(t_{j-1}))$ and $\gamma'(t_{j-1})(t_j - t_{j-1})$, so its area is

$$A = h \cdot |\mathbf{F}| \cdot |\gamma'| \cdot (t_j - t_{j-1}) \cos\theta,$$

where θ is the angle between $\mathbf{F}$ and the normal $\mathbf{B}$ to the curve, obtained by rotating $\boldsymbol{\gamma}'(t_{j-1})$ clockwise through an angle $\pi/2$. (Rotating through $\pi/2$ makes the area positive for a flow from left to right, and negative from right to left; rotating through $-\pi/2$ would reverse this.) Since $\mathbf{B} = (\gamma_2'(t_{j-1}), -\gamma_1'(t_{j-1}))$, we have $|\mathbf{B}| = |\boldsymbol{\gamma}'|$, and $|\mathbf{F}|\,|\boldsymbol{\gamma}'| \cos\theta = \mathbf{F}\cdot\mathbf{B}$, so the parallelogram has area

$$A = h(\mathbf{F}\cdot\mathbf{B})(t_j - t_{j-1}).$$

Evaluating the inner product of $\mathbf{B}$ with $\mathbf{F} = (M, N)$, we get $\mathbf{F}\cdot\mathbf{B} = M\gamma_2' - N\gamma_1'$, hence

$$A = h[M(\boldsymbol{\gamma}(t_{j-1}))\gamma_2'(t_{j-1}) - N(\boldsymbol{\gamma}(t_{j-1}))\gamma_1'(t_{j-1})].$$

Adding up these areas for each section of the curve, we get a Riemann sum for

$$h\int_a^b [M(\boldsymbol{\gamma})\gamma_2' - N(\boldsymbol{\gamma})\gamma_1'] = h\int_{\gamma} M\,dy - N\,dx.$$

This is the fluid that crosses in time h, so the *rate* of flow is given by (3).

These physical applications, and the mathematical theory as well, require line integrals not only over smooth differentiable curves (ellipses, parabolas, exponentials, etc.), but over "curves with corners" (rectangles and triangles, for example). To handle this situation, we introduce the concept of a *chain of curves*, namely, a finite sequence of differentiable curves $\boldsymbol{\gamma}^1, \ldots, \boldsymbol{\gamma}^n$, each curve $\boldsymbol{\gamma}^j$ defined on some interval $[a_j, b_j]$. The chain is called *connected* if the endpoint of each curve coincides with the beginning of the next, i.e. $\boldsymbol{\gamma}^{j-1}(b_{j-1}) = \boldsymbol{\gamma}^j(a_j)$. (See Fig. 16.) The *endpoints* of a connected chain are the beginning, $\boldsymbol{\gamma}^1(a_1)$, and the end, $\boldsymbol{\gamma}^n(b_n)$. A connected chain is called *closed* if the beginning and end coincide, that is, if $\boldsymbol{\gamma}^1(a_1) = \boldsymbol{\gamma}^n(b_n)$. (See Fig. 17.)

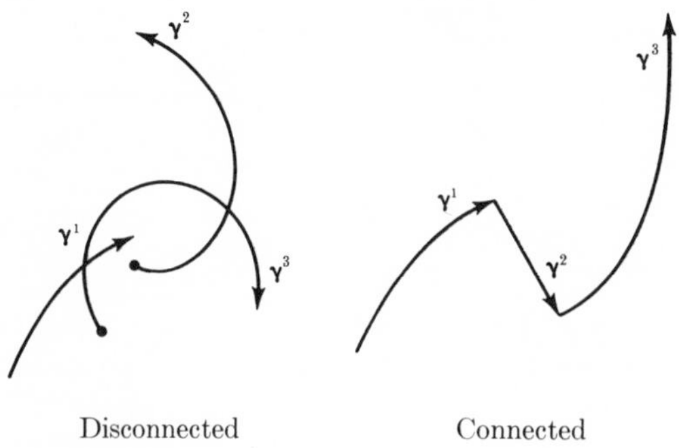

FIGURE 4.16

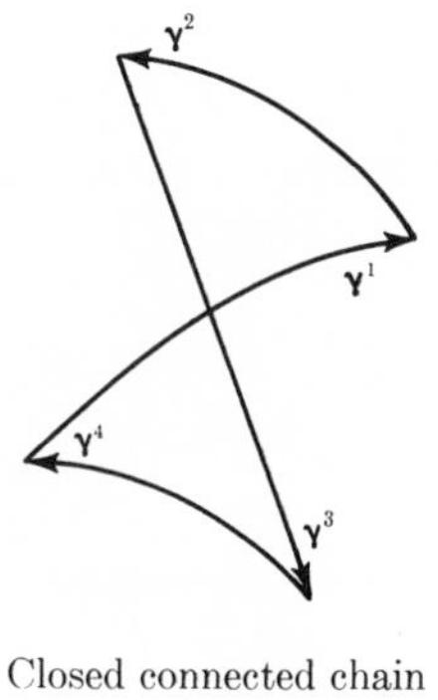

FIGURE 4.17

A chain $\boldsymbol{\gamma}^1, \ldots, \boldsymbol{\gamma}^n$ can be denoted by a single letter $\boldsymbol{\gamma}$. The line integral of $\mathbf{F}$ over such a chain is simply the sum of the integrals over all the pieces,

$$\int_\gamma \mathbf{F} = \sum_{j=1}^{n} \int_{\gamma_j} \mathbf{F}.$$

Now we are ready to take up the connection between exact vector fields and line integrals. The starting point is a simple expression for the integral of a gradient ∇f over a differentiable curve $\boldsymbol{\gamma}$. Using the chain rule and the fundamental theorem of calculus, we find

$$\int_\gamma \nabla f = \int_a^b (\nabla f \circ \boldsymbol{\gamma}) \cdot \boldsymbol{\gamma}' = \int_a^b (f \circ \boldsymbol{\gamma})' = (f \circ \boldsymbol{\gamma})(b) - (f \circ \boldsymbol{\gamma})(a),$$

or

$$\int_\gamma \nabla f = f(\boldsymbol{\gamma}(b)) - f(\boldsymbol{\gamma}(a)). \tag{4}$$

This handy formula bypasses the work of evaluating an integral; but beyond that, it is interesting because, given f, *the value of the integral depends only on the endpoints of the curve* $\boldsymbol{\gamma}$, i.e. it depends only on $\boldsymbol{\gamma}(b)$ and $\boldsymbol{\gamma}(a)$. This is obvious from the right-hand side of (4). The same phenomenon occurs, more generally, if $\boldsymbol{\gamma}$ is a *connected chain* consisting of differentiable curves $\boldsymbol{\gamma}^1, \ldots, \boldsymbol{\gamma}^n$; in this case we have

$$\begin{aligned}\int_\gamma \nabla f = \sum_{j=1}^{n} \int_{\gamma^j} \nabla f &= f(\boldsymbol{\gamma}^1(b_1)) - f(\gamma^1(a_1)) \\ &+ f(\boldsymbol{\gamma}^2(b_2)) - f(\boldsymbol{\gamma}^2(a_2)) \\ &+ f(\boldsymbol{\gamma}^3(b_3)) - f(\boldsymbol{\gamma}^3(a_3)) \\ &+ \cdots \\ &+ f(\boldsymbol{\gamma}^{n-1}(b_{n-1})) - f(\boldsymbol{\gamma}^{n-1}(a_{n-1})) \\ &+ f(\boldsymbol{\gamma}^n(b_n)) - f(\boldsymbol{\gamma}^n(a_n)).\end{aligned}$$

On the right-hand side, all but two terms cancel out (as suggested by the dotted lines), since $\boldsymbol{\gamma}^{j-1}(b_{j-1}) = \boldsymbol{\gamma}^j(a_j)$. Thus the sum reduces to $f(\boldsymbol{\gamma}^n(b_n)) - f(\boldsymbol{\gamma}^1(a_1))$, which depends only on the endpoints of the chain.

This phenomenon, that $\int_\gamma \mathbf{F}$ is determined by the endpoints of $\boldsymbol{\gamma}$, characterizes the exact vector fields:

Theorem 5. *Let* $\mathbf{F}$ *be a continuous vector field defined in an open connected set* S. *Then* $\mathbf{F}$ *is exact if and only if for every connected chain* $\boldsymbol{\gamma}$ *in* S, $\int_{\boldsymbol{\gamma}} \mathbf{F}$ *is determined by the endpoints of* $\boldsymbol{\gamma}$.

Proof. If $\mathbf{F}$ is exact, then $\mathbf{F} = \nabla f$ for some f, so $\int_{\boldsymbol{\gamma}} \mathbf{F} = \int_{\boldsymbol{\gamma}} \nabla f$ is determined by the endpoints, as we have already seen. Conversely, suppose that $\int_{\boldsymbol{\gamma}} \mathbf{F}$ is determined by the endpoints of $\boldsymbol{\gamma}$. Pick a fixed point $\mathbf{P}_0$ in S. Since S is open and connected, each point $\mathbf{P}$ in S can be joined to $\mathbf{P}_0$ by a differentiable curve $\boldsymbol{\gamma}^{\mathbf{P}}$. (This is precisely the *definition* of a connected open set; see the problems in §3.3.) We define a function f by

$$f(\mathbf{P}) = \int_{\gamma^{\mathbf{P}}} \mathbf{F}; \tag{5}$$

because of our assumption about $\mathbf{F}$, *the integral* (5) *gives the same value for* $f(\mathbf{P})$ *no matter what chain of curves* $\boldsymbol{\gamma}^{\mathbf{P}}$ *is chosen from* $\mathbf{P}_0$ *to* $\mathbf{P}$. It remains to show that $\nabla f = \mathbf{F}$; in other words, if $\mathbf{F} = (M,N)$, then $D_1 f = M$ and $D_2 f = N$. We will prove the first equality,

$$D_1 f(x,y) = \lim_{h\to 0} \frac{f(x+h,y) - f(x,y)}{h} = M(x,y), \tag{6}$$

and leave the other to you.

Let $\boldsymbol{\gamma}^{\mathbf{P}}$ be any curve from $\mathbf{P}_0$ to $\mathbf{P} = (x,y)$, and set

$$\boldsymbol{\gamma}^h(t) = (x + th,y), \qquad 0 \le t \le 1.$$

Then $f(x+h,y)$ can be evaluated by integrating over the chain $\boldsymbol{\gamma}$ consisting of $\boldsymbol{\gamma}^{\mathbf{P}}$ and $\boldsymbol{\gamma}^h$ (Fig. 18). Thus, by (5),

$$f(x+h,y) = \int_{\gamma^{\mathbf{P}}} \mathbf{F} + \int_{\gamma^h} \mathbf{F} = f(x,y) + \int_{\gamma^h} \mathbf{F},$$

so $f(x+h,y) - f(x,y) = \int_{\gamma^h} \mathbf{F}$, and

$$\frac{f(x+h,y) - f(x,y)}{h} = \frac{1}{h}\int_{\gamma^h} \mathbf{F} = \frac{1}{h}\int_0^1 \mathbf{F}(x+th,y)\cdot(h,0)\,dt$$

$$\text{(since } (\boldsymbol{\gamma}^h)'(t) = (h,0))$$

$$= \frac{1}{h}\int_0^1 M(x+th,y)h\,dt \qquad \text{(since } \mathbf{F} = (M,N))$$

$$= \frac{1}{h}\int_0^h M(x+s,y)\,ds \qquad \text{(substituting } s = th).$$

Now, as $h \to 0$, this last expression tends to $M(x,y)$, by the fundamental theorem of calculus, so (6) is proved. Similarly, $D_2 f = N$, and Theorem 5 is proved.

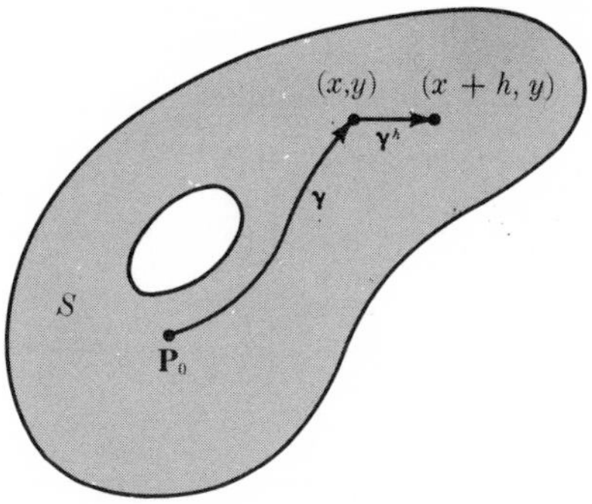

FIGURE 4.18

Corollary 1. *If* γ *is a closed chain and* $\mathbf{F}$ *is exact, then* $\int_\gamma \mathbf{F} = 0$.

Proof. Since $\mathbf{F}$ is exact, we have $\mathbf{F} = \nabla f$. Since γ is connected, we have

$$\int_\gamma \mathbf{F} = \int_\gamma \nabla f = f(\mathbf{P}_2) - f(\mathbf{P}_1) \tag{7}$$

where $\mathbf{P}_1$ and $\mathbf{P}_2$ are the endpoints of the chain. But $\mathbf{P}_2 = \mathbf{P}_1$ (since γ is a closed chain), so (7) shows that $\int_\gamma \mathbf{F} = 0$. *Q.E.D.*

We now have two ways to prove that a vector field $\mathbf{F} = (M,N)$ is *not* exact: (i) show that it is not closed, i.e. $M_y \neq N_x$, or (ii) find a closed chain γ such that $\int_\gamma \mathbf{F} \neq 0$ (which, by the corollary above, implies that $\mathbf{F}$ is not exact.)

It is a little harder to prove that a vector field $\mathbf{F}$ *is* exact. We can (i) find explicitly a function f such that $\nabla f = \mathbf{F}$, or (ii) apply Theorem 4: $\mathbf{F}$ is exact in a rectangle R if $\mathbf{F}$ is closed in R. The second half of Theorem 5 (which says that $\mathbf{F}$ is exact if $\int_\gamma \mathbf{F}$ depends only on the endpoints of γ) is hard to apply, since it has to be checked for *all* chains γ.

Example 3. Problem 3 of the preceding section showed that

$$\mathbf{F}(x,y) = \left(\frac{-y}{x^2+y^2}, \frac{x}{x^2+y^2}\right)$$

is closed, but not exact. Now we can prove the nonexactness very simply by integrating $\mathbf{F}$ around a circle $\gamma(t) = (r\cos t, r\sin t)$, $0 \leq t \leq 2\pi$:

$$\int_\gamma \mathbf{F} = \int_0^{2\pi} (\mathbf{F}\circ\gamma)\cdot\gamma' = \int_0^{2\pi} \left(\frac{-r\sin t}{r^2}, \frac{r\cos t}{r^2}\right)\cdot(-r\sin t, r\cos t)\,dt$$

$$= \int_0^{2\pi} (\sin^2 t + \cos^2 t)\,dt = 2\pi.$$

Since $\boldsymbol{\gamma}$ is a closed curve and the integral is not zero, $\mathbf{F}$ is not exact, by Corollary 1.

Example 4. The line integral in Examples 1 and 2,

$$\int_\gamma y\,dx + x\,dy, \qquad x = r\cos t,\ y = r\sin t,\ 0 \le t \le \pi/4,$$

can be evaluated by formula (4). Since the vector field $\mathbf{F} = (y,x)$ is the gradient of $f(x,y) = xy$, and since the curve begins at $(r,0)$ and ends at $(r/\sqrt{2}, r/\sqrt{2})$ we have

$$\int_\gamma y\,dx + x\,dy = f\left(\frac{r}{\sqrt{2}}, \frac{r}{\sqrt{2}}\right) - f(r,0) = \frac{r}{\sqrt{2}}\cdot\frac{r}{\sqrt{2}} - 0\cdot r = \frac{r^2}{2}.$$

Example 5. Evaluate $\int_\gamma x^2\,dx + xy\,dy$, where $\boldsymbol{\gamma}$ is the straight line segment from $(1,0)$ to $(2,3)$. *Solution.* Strictly speaking, this is not a well-defined problem, since $\int_\gamma \mathbf{F}$ is defined only when $\boldsymbol{\gamma}$ is a curve, i.e. a function from an interval $[a,b]$ to the plane. However, "the straight line from (1,0) to (2,3)" has a natural parametrization of the form $\mathbf{P} = \mathbf{P}_1 + t(\mathbf{P}_2 - \mathbf{P}_1)$, which gives

$$x = 1 + t, \qquad y = 3t, \qquad 0 \le t \le 1, \tag{8}$$

and we use this to evaluate the integral:

$$\int_\gamma x^2\,dx + xy\,dy = \int_0^1 (1+t)^2\,dt + (1+t)3t\cdot 3\,dt$$

$$= \int_0^1 (1 + 11t + 10t^2)\,dt = 1 + \frac{11}{2} + \frac{10}{3}.$$

Example 5 raises an obvious question: What if you use some other parametrization for the given line segment, for example,

$$y = \bar{t}, \qquad x = 1 + \tfrac{1}{3}\bar{t}, \qquad 0 \le \bar{t} \le 3\,? \tag{9}$$

You would find, in fact, the same value for the line integral. The curves given in (8) and (9) are related by a change of parameter, and this does not affect the line integral (see Problem 14 below). It is important, however, that in each parametrization the curve runs *from* $(1,0)$ *to* $(2,3)$, not vice versa; reversing the endpoints would change the sign of the integral, as you can easily check by evaluating $\int x^2\,dx + xy\,dy$ with a parametrization of the segment from $(2,3)$ to $(1,0)$, for example,

$$x = 1 - t, \qquad y = -3t, \qquad -1 \le t \le 0.$$

Example 6. A force $\mathbf{F}$ is called *conservative* if it is exact. Show that the force $\mathbf{F}(x,y) = (y\cos xy, x\cos xy)$ is conservative, and find the work done by this force in moving a particle from the origin to the point $(3,8)$.

Solution. The force **F** is *closed*, since

$$\frac{\partial M}{\partial y} = \frac{\partial}{\partial y}(y \cos xy) = \cos xy - xy \sin xy = \frac{\partial N}{\partial x}.$$

Since **F** is defined in all of R^2, it is exact; you can easily find that **F** is the gradient of $f(xy) = \sin xy$. Hence the work done by **F**, the line integral $\int_\gamma \mathbf{F}$, depends only on the endpoints of $\boldsymbol{\gamma}$. In particular, the work done in moving from the origin to the point $(3,8)$ is $f(3,8) - f(0,0) = \sin 24$.

Example 7. The *divergence* of a flow $\mathbf{F} = (M,N)$ is defined to be $M_x + N_y$. Show that if the flow **F** is defined in a rectangle R, and has zero divergence at every point of R, then the rate of flow across every closed chain in R is zero. *Solution.* The rate of flow across $\boldsymbol{\gamma}$ is $\int_\gamma (-N\,dx + M\,dy)$. From the given equation $M_x + N_y \equiv 0$, it follows that the vector field $(-N, M)$ is closed in R; hence (by Theorem 4) it is exact in R; hence (by the Corollary of Theorem 5) $\int_\gamma (-N\,dx + M\,dy) = 0$ for every closed chain $\boldsymbol{\gamma}$ in R.

PROBLEMS

Problems 10, 12, and 13 concern *change of parameter*, and 17–19 concern the geometric concept of *winding number of a curve.*

1. Compute the following line integrals $\int_\gamma \mathbf{F}$:
   (a) $\mathbf{F}(x,y) = (x^2y, xy^2), \quad \boldsymbol{\gamma}(t) = (t,t^2), \quad 0 \le t \le 1$
   (b) $\int x^2y\,dx + xy^2\,dy, \quad x = c_1t, \quad y = c_2t, \quad 0 \le t \le 1$
   (c) $\mathbf{F}(x,y) = (x \sin y, \cos y), \quad \boldsymbol{\gamma}$ as in part (b)
   (d) $\mathbf{F}(x,y) = (y,x), \quad \boldsymbol{\gamma}$ is the chain with

$$\boldsymbol{\gamma}^1(t) = (t^2,t), \qquad 0 \le t \le 1$$

$$\boldsymbol{\gamma}^2(t) = (1 - t, 1 - t), \qquad 0 \le t \le 1$$

   (e) $\mathbf{F}(x,y) = (-y,0)$, $\boldsymbol{\gamma}$ is the straight line path from (x_1,y_1) to (x_2,y_2) (*Answer:* $\frac{1}{2}(x_1 - x_2)(y_1 + y_2)$.)

2. Obtain a parametric representation for each of the following curves $\boldsymbol{\gamma}$.
   (a) $\boldsymbol{\gamma}$ is the graph of $y = x^3$ from $(0,0)$ to $(1,1)$.
   (b) $\boldsymbol{\gamma}$ is the straight line from a given point (x_1,y_1) to (x_2,y_2).
   (c) $\boldsymbol{\gamma}$ is the upper half of the unit circle, taken from left to right.
   (d) $\boldsymbol{\gamma}$ is a closed chain running counterclockwise around the boundary of the triangle in Fig. 19.

3. Evaluate $\int (dx - dy)$ over each of the curves (or chains) in Problem 2. (This can actually be done without answering Problem 2.)

4. Find the work done by the following forces **F** over the given curves $\boldsymbol{\gamma}$. (Work $= \int_\gamma \mathbf{F}$.)
   (a) $\mathbf{F} = (0,-1), \quad \boldsymbol{\gamma}(t) = (t, 1 - t^2), \quad -1 \le t \le 0$

(b) Same $\mathbf{F}$ and $\boldsymbol{\gamma}$, but $0 \leq t \leq 1$

(c) $\mathbf{F}(\mathbf{P}) = -\mathbf{P}/|\mathbf{P}|^3, \quad \boldsymbol{\gamma}(t) = (\cos t, \sin t), \quad 0 \leq t \leq \pi$

(d) $\mathbf{F}(\mathbf{P}) = -\mathbf{P}/|\mathbf{P}|^3, \quad \boldsymbol{\gamma}(t) = \left(\frac{t}{\sqrt{2}}, \frac{t}{\sqrt{2}}\right), \quad a \leq t \leq b$

(e) $\mathbf{F}(\mathbf{P}) = -\mathbf{P}/|\mathbf{P}|^3, \quad \boldsymbol{\gamma}(t) = (t,0), \quad a \leq t \leq b$

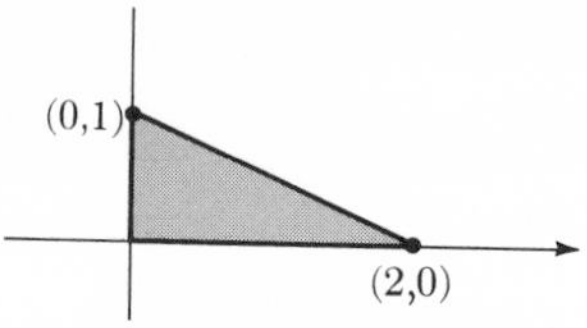

FIGURE 4.19

5. Let $f(\mathbf{P}) = c/|\mathbf{P}|$ for $|\mathbf{P}| \neq 0$, and $\mathbf{F} = \nabla f$.

(a) A particle originally at a point $\mathbf{P}_1$ at distance r_1 from the origin is moved by $\mathbf{F}$ to a point $\mathbf{P}_2$ at distance r_2 from the origin. Find the work done. (Note: By Theorem 5, the answer depends only on the starting point $\mathbf{P}_1$ and ending point $\mathbf{P}_2$, but in this case you will find that it actually depends only on r_1 and r_2.)

(b) Find the work done in moving from a point r_1 units from the origin "all the way to ∞." (When the constant c is properly chosen, and r_1 is taken as the radius of the earth, your answer gives the work required to move the "particle" from the surface of the earth to a point "completely out of the earth's gravity.")

(c) Repeat parts (a) and (b), but with $f(\mathbf{P}) = -\log |\mathbf{P}|$.

6. Let $\mathbf{F}(x,y) = (1,0)$ be the velocity field for a constant flow parallel to the x axis. Find the rate of flow from left to right across each of the five curves shown in Fig. 20. (To interpret "left to right" in each figure, face in the direction of the given curve.)

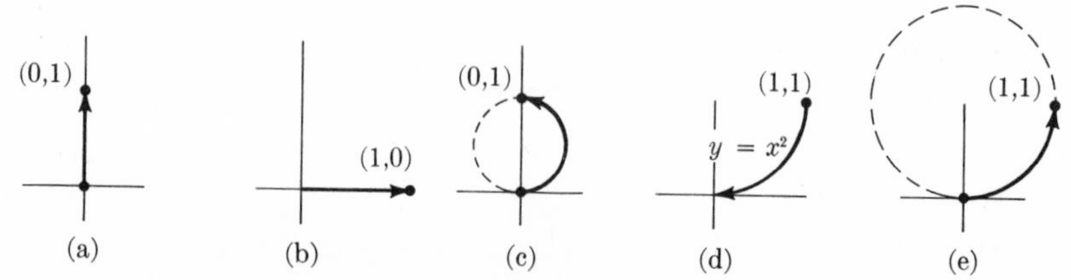

FIGURE 4.20

7. Repeat Problem 6 with $\mathbf{F}(x,y) = (x,0)$.

8. Show that the function $f(x,y)$ constructed in Theorem 4, p. 189, is actually $f(x_0,y_0) + \int_\gamma \mathbf{F}$ for a certain chain $\boldsymbol{\gamma}$ from (x_0,y_0) to (x,y).

9. (a) Show that if $\boldsymbol{\gamma}$ is a *constant* curve, then $\int_\gamma \mathbf{F} = 0$ for every $\mathbf{F}$.
(b) Show that if $\boldsymbol{\gamma}$ is defined on a "one-point interval" $[a,a]$, then $\int_\gamma \mathbf{F} = 0$ for every $\mathbf{F}$.

10. If $\boldsymbol{\gamma}$ is defined on $[a,b]$, its *inverse* $\boldsymbol{\gamma}^{-1}$ is given by

$$\boldsymbol{\gamma}^{-1}(t) = \boldsymbol{\gamma}(-t), \qquad -b \le t \le -a.$$

(a) Prove that $\boldsymbol{\gamma}^{-1}$ runs through exactly the same points as $\boldsymbol{\gamma}$, but starting at $\boldsymbol{\gamma}(b)$ and ending at $\boldsymbol{\gamma}(a)$, i.e. γ^{-1} runs backward over $\boldsymbol{\gamma}$. (See Fig. 21.)
(b) Prove that for any continuous $\mathbf{F}$, $\int_{\gamma^{-1}} \mathbf{F} = -\int_\gamma \mathbf{F}$.

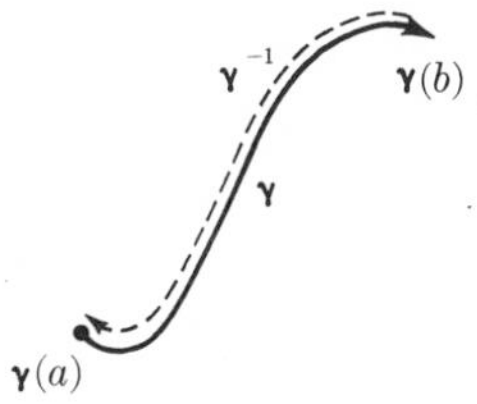

FIGURE 4.21

11. In the second half of Theorem 5, prove that $D_2 f = N$.

12. Suppose that $\boldsymbol{\gamma}$ is a differentiable curve lying in the graph of a function φ defined on $c \le x \le d$, beginning at $(c,\varphi(c))$ and ending at $(d,\varphi(d))$. Prove that

$$\int_\gamma M(x,y)\,dx = \int_c^d M(x,\varphi(x))\,dx.$$

(Hint: If $\boldsymbol{\gamma} = (\gamma_1,\gamma_2)$, then $c \le \gamma_1 \le d$ and $\gamma_2 = \varphi\circ\gamma_1$; make a change of variable in the integral.)

13. (*Change of parameter.*) If $\boldsymbol{\gamma}$ is defined on the interval $[a,b]$ and g is a differentiable function from some interval $[\bar{a},\bar{b}]$ into $[a,b]$, then we can form a new curve $\bar{\boldsymbol{\gamma}} = \boldsymbol{\gamma}\circ g$ defined on $[\bar{a},\bar{b}]$ by the formula

$$\bar{\boldsymbol{\gamma}}(\bar{t}) = \boldsymbol{\gamma}(g(\bar{t})), \qquad \bar{a} \le \bar{t} \le \bar{b}.$$

(a) If $g' \ge 0$, $g(\bar{a}) = a$ and $g(\bar{b}) = b$, then g is called an *orientation-preserving change of parameter.* Prove that for such a g, $\boldsymbol{\gamma}\circ g$ runs through the same points as $\boldsymbol{\gamma}$ and in the same order (although the speed is generally different, since $\bar{\gamma}' = g'\gamma'$ by the chain rule). (Hint: Use the one-variable Intermediate Value theorem.)

(b) If $g' \leq 0$, $g(\bar{a}) = b$ and $g(\bar{b}) = a$, then g is an *orientation-reversing* change of parameter. Prove that for such a g, $\gamma \circ g$ runs through the same points as γ but in the *opposite* order.

(c) Prove that if g is an orientation-preserving change of parameter, and $\mathbf{F}$ is continuous along γ, then $\int_{\gamma\circ g} \mathbf{F} = \int_\gamma \mathbf{F}$.

(d) Prove that if g is orientation-reversing, then $\int_{\gamma\circ g} \mathbf{F} = -\int_\gamma \mathbf{F}$.

(*Remark 1:* The moral of (c) and (d) is that $\int_\gamma \mathbf{F}$ depends on $\mathbf{F}$, on the points through which γ passes, and on the order (reversing the order reverses the sign of the integral), but *not* on the speed of γ. *Remark 2:* If the new curve $\gamma\circ g$ is parametrized by arc length s, we have the curve $\mathbf{G}$ discussed in §2.3. Here, $g' > 0$, so by part (c)

$$\int_\gamma \mathbf{F} = \int_{\mathbf{G}} \mathbf{F} = \int_{\bar{a}}^{\bar{b}} \mathbf{F}(\mathbf{G}(s))\cdot\mathbf{G}'(s)\,ds.$$

Since $\mathbf{G}'(s) = \mathbf{T}(s) =$ the unit tangent vector, we arrive again at the notation $\int_\gamma \mathbf{F}\cdot\mathbf{T}\,ds$ suggested in the text.)

14. (*Conservation of energy.*) The *kinetic energy* of a particle of mass m is defined to be $\frac{1}{2}m\,|\gamma'|^2$, where γ' is the velocity. Assuming Newton's law $\mathbf{F} = m\gamma''$, prove that the work done by the force $\mathbf{F}$ in moving the particle along the curve γ equals the increase in kinetic energy. (Hint: $(|\gamma'|^2)' = 2\gamma'\cdot\gamma''$.)

15. Suppose that $\mathbf{F} = (M,N)$ is defined on a set S, and $\int_\gamma \mathbf{F} = 0$ whenever γ is a *closed* connected chain lying in S.

(a) Prove that when γ is any connected chain in S, then $\int_\gamma \mathbf{F}$ depends only on the endpoints of γ. (Hint: See Problem 10.)

(b) Prove that $\mathbf{F}$ is exact in S.

16. The *divergence* of a flow $\mathbf{F} = (M,N)$ is defined to be $M_x + N_y$. Show that if the rate of flow across every closed chain γ is zero, then the divergence is zero. (Hint: If $\int_\gamma -N\,dx + M\,dy = 0$ for every closed chain γ, then $(-N,M)$ is exact, by Problem 15.)

17. (*Winding numbers.*) Suppose that γ is a closed connected chain that does not pass through the origin, i.e. for every t, $\gamma(t) \neq (0,0)$. The *winding number of γ about the origin* is defined to be

$$\frac{1}{2\pi}\int_\gamma \frac{-y}{x^2+y^2}\,dx + \frac{x}{x^2+y^2}\,dy.$$

Compute the winding numbers of the following chains about the origin. In each case sketch the chain, and note that the winding number gives the net number of times that the chain encircles the origin counterclockwise.

(a) $\boldsymbol{\gamma}^1(t) = (r\cos t,\, r\sin t), \quad 0 \le t \le 2\pi$
(b) $\boldsymbol{\gamma}^2(t) = (r\cos(-t),\, r\sin(-t)), \quad 0 \le t \le 2\pi$
(c) $\boldsymbol{\gamma}^3(t) = (r\cos t,\, r\sin t), \quad -2\pi \le t \le 2\pi$
(d) $\boldsymbol{\gamma}^4(t) = (2r - r\cos t,\, r\sin t), \quad 0 \le t \le 2\pi$
(Hint: Prove that

$$\left(\frac{-y}{x^2+y^2}, \frac{x}{x^2+y^2}\right) = \nabla\left(\arctan\frac{y}{x}\right)$$

in a rectangle containing $\boldsymbol{\gamma}^4$.)
(e) $\boldsymbol{\gamma}$ is the chain consisting of $\boldsymbol{\gamma}^3$ and $\boldsymbol{\gamma}^4$
(f) $\boldsymbol{\gamma}$ is a chain running clockwise around the square

$$\{(x,y): |x| \le 1 \text{ and } |y| \le 1\}.$$

18. (a) Prove that the vector field

$$\left(\frac{-y}{x^2+y^2}, \frac{x}{x^2+y^2}\right)$$

is exact in the set $S = \{(x,y): y \ne 0, \text{ or } x > 0\}$, consisting of the plane with the left half of the x axis removed. In other words, there is a differentiable function f defined in S with

$$\nabla f = \left(\frac{-y}{x^2+y^2}, \frac{x}{x^2+y^2}\right).$$

(Hint: Imitate the proof of Theorem 4, as in §4.2, Problem 7(e).)

(b) Prove that if $\boldsymbol{\gamma}$ is a closed chain not passing through the left half of the x axis (the set $\{(x,y): y = 0 \text{ and } x \le 0\}$), then the winding number of $\boldsymbol{\gamma}$ about the origin is zero. (See the previous problem for the definition of winding number.)

19. The vector field

$$\left(\frac{-y}{x^2+y^2}, \frac{x}{x^2+y^2}\right)$$

is *not* the gradient of any function defined in all of $\{\mathbf{P}: |\mathbf{P}| > 0\}$; nevertheless, it can reasonably be denoted $\nabla\theta$, where θ is the angular polar coordinate. The angle θ in polar coordinates is traditionally called the *argument*, and the integral $\int_{\boldsymbol{\gamma}} \nabla\theta$ is called the *change in argument along* $\boldsymbol{\gamma}$. This problem justifies the name "change in argument," and draws some conclusions about winding numbers. (See also Problem 17(d), and note that $\tan\theta = y/x$.)

(a) If $\boldsymbol{\gamma}$ is a differentiable curve defined on the interval $[a,b]$, set

$$\varphi(s) = \int_a^s [(\nabla\theta)\circ\boldsymbol{\gamma}]\cdot\boldsymbol{\gamma}',$$

that is, $\varphi(s)$ is the integral of $\nabla\theta$ along the part of the curve where $a \leq t \leq s$. Prove that the derivative of

$$\exp\left[-i\varphi(s)\right]\left(\frac{\gamma_1(s) + i\gamma_2(s)}{|\gamma(s)|}\right)$$

is identically zero. (This is a long but straightforward calculation, so do it carefully. The notation is simplified if you set $x = \gamma_1(s)$, $y = \gamma_2(s)$, $r = \sqrt{x^2 + y^2}$, denote the derivatives by $x' = \gamma_1'(s)$, $y' = \gamma_2'(s)$, and notice that $r' = xx'/r + yy'/r$.)

(b) With $\varphi(s)$ as above, let θ_1 denote an angular coordinate for $\boldsymbol{\gamma}(a)$, that is, $\gamma_1(a) + i\gamma_2(a) = |\boldsymbol{\gamma}(a)|e^{i\theta_1}$. Prove that

$$\exp\left\{-i[\varphi(s) + \theta_1]\right\}\left(\frac{\gamma_1(s) + i\gamma_2(s)}{|\boldsymbol{\gamma}(s)|}\right) \equiv 1,$$

hence $\theta_1 + \varphi(s)$ is an angular coordinate for $\boldsymbol{\gamma}(s)$. (This has the interpretation that $\varphi(s)$ gives the net change in angular coordinate (argument) as t varies from a to s, hence in particular that $\varphi(b) = \int_\gamma \nabla\theta$ is the change in argument along $\boldsymbol{\gamma}$.)

(c) Let $\boldsymbol{\gamma}$ be any connected chain of differentiable curves $\boldsymbol{\gamma}^1, \ldots, \boldsymbol{\gamma}^n$, and let θ_1 be an argument for the beginning, $\boldsymbol{\gamma}^1(a_1)$. Prove that $\theta_1 + \int_\gamma \nabla\theta$ is an argument for the end of the chain $\boldsymbol{\gamma}^n(b_n)$.

(d) Prove that if $\boldsymbol{\gamma}$ is a *closed* connected chain, then

$$\frac{1}{2\pi}\int_\gamma \nabla\theta$$

is an integer. (This integer is called the *winding number* of $\boldsymbol{\gamma}$ about the origin.)

4.4 GREEN'S THEOREM

The formula

$$\int_\gamma \nabla f = f(\boldsymbol{\gamma}(b)) - f(\boldsymbol{\gamma}(a)) \tag{1}$$

is a sort of fundamental theorem of calculus for line integrals, expressing the integral of the "derivative" of f as the difference of the values of f at the endpoints of the curve of integration.

There is an analogous formula for double integrals, called *Green's theorem:*

$$\iint_S (N_x - M_y)\, dx\, dy = \int_\gamma M\, dx + N\, dy. \tag{2}$$

In formula (2), S is a set in the plane, and $\boldsymbol{\gamma}$ is a closed connected chain running counterclockwise around the boundary of S, as in Fig. 22.

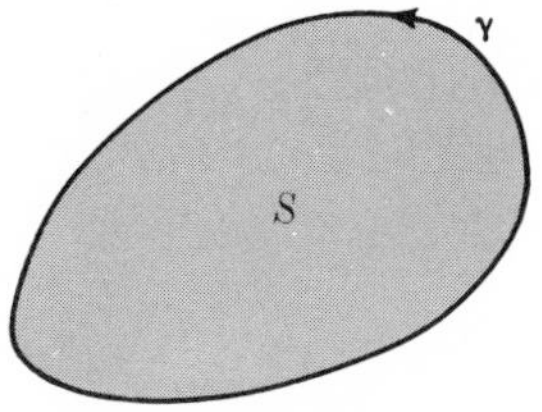

FIGURE 4.22

The following table gives the precise analogy between (1), (2), and the fundamental theorem of calculus; each formula says that the integral of the "derivative" of some function over some domain equals the integral of the function itself over the "oriented boundary" of the domain.

Function	Derivative	Domain of Integration	Oriented Boundary	Formula
f	f'	interval $[a, b]$	b taken "+" a taken "−"	$\int_a^b f' = f(b) - f(a)$
f	∇f	curve $\boldsymbol{\gamma}$	$\boldsymbol{\gamma}(b)$ taken "+" $\boldsymbol{\gamma}(a)$ taken "−"	(1) above
(M, N)	$N_x - M_y$	plane set S	a curve $\boldsymbol{\gamma}$ running counterclockwise around S	(2) above

Before proving Green's theorem, we have to translate "$\boldsymbol{\gamma}$ runs counterclockwise around the boundary of S" into a precise mathematical statement. This is deceptively difficult, and has given rise to concepts which, alas, require a longer development than our time and space allow here. (See the references listed in §4.1.) In view of this, we will work a few examples in which the connection between $\boldsymbol{\gamma}$ and S is intuitively clear, and then give Green's theorem in a form which, though inelegant, has two virtues: it covers a reasonable range of examples, and can be proved with the tools at our disposal.

Example 1. $M(x,y) = -y$, $N(x,y) = x$, and $S = \{\mathbf{P}: |\mathbf{P}| \leq r\}$. Clearly (Fig. 23), the curve

$$\boldsymbol{\gamma}(t) = (r \cos t, r \sin t), \qquad -\pi \leq t \leq \pi,$$

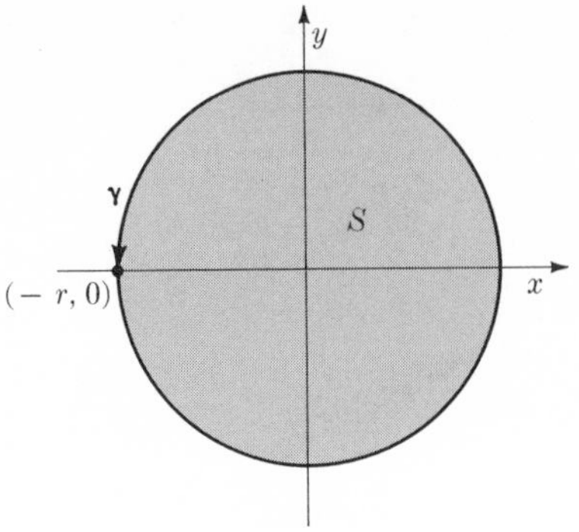

FIGURE 4.23

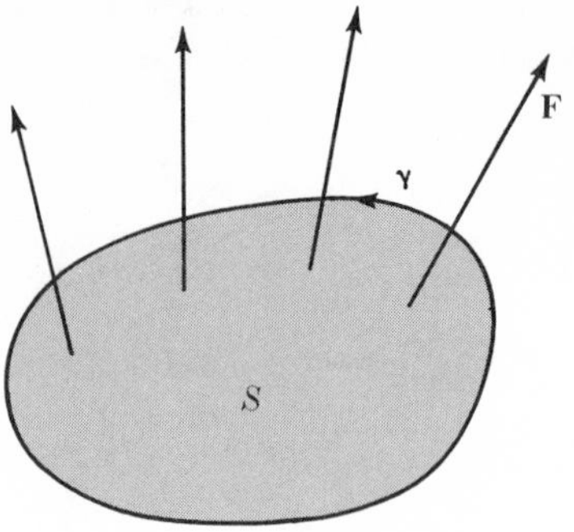

FIGURE 4.24

runs counterclockwise around the boundary of S. We have

$$\iint_S (N_x - M_y) = \iint_S 2 = 2\cdot (\text{area of } S) = 2\pi r^2,$$

since $M_y = -1$, $N_x = 1$, and S is a circle of radius r. On the other hand,

$$\int_\gamma (-y)\,dx + x\,dy = \int_{-\pi}^{\pi} (-r \sin t)(-r \sin t)\,dt + (r \cos t)(r \cos t)\,dt$$

$$= \int_{-\pi}^{\pi} r^2\,dt = 2\pi r^2.$$

Thus Green's theorem (2) is verified in this example.

Example 2. Applying Green's theorem to a plane flow, we can show that the rate of flow out of S equals the integral over S of a certain function, called the *divergence* of the flow. Recall that for a velocity field $\mathbf{F} = (M,N)$ the rate of flow from left to right across $\boldsymbol{\gamma}$ is $\int_\gamma (-N\,dx + M\,dy)$. When $\boldsymbol{\gamma}$ runs counterclockwise around the boundary of S, as in Fig. 24, then S "lies to the left of gamma"; hence this line integral gives the rate of flow *out* of S. According to Green's theorem, the rate can be expressed by an integral over S,

$$\int_\gamma (-N\,dx + M\,dy) = \iint_S (M_x + N_y).$$

The expression $M_x + N_y$ is the divergence of the flow $\mathbf{F} = (M,N)$, denoted div $\mathbf{F}$ or $\boldsymbol{\nabla}\cdot\mathbf{F}$. (Think of $\boldsymbol{\nabla}$ as the vector $(\partial/\partial x, \partial/\partial y)$, so

$$\boldsymbol{\nabla}\cdot\mathbf{F} = \frac{\partial}{\partial x} M + \frac{\partial}{\partial y} N = M_x + N_y\,.)$$

The divergence $(\boldsymbol{\nabla}\cdot\mathbf{F})(\mathbf{P})$ measures the rate of flow out from the point $\mathbf{P}$; by Green's theorem, integrating the divergence over S gives the total rate of flow out of S.

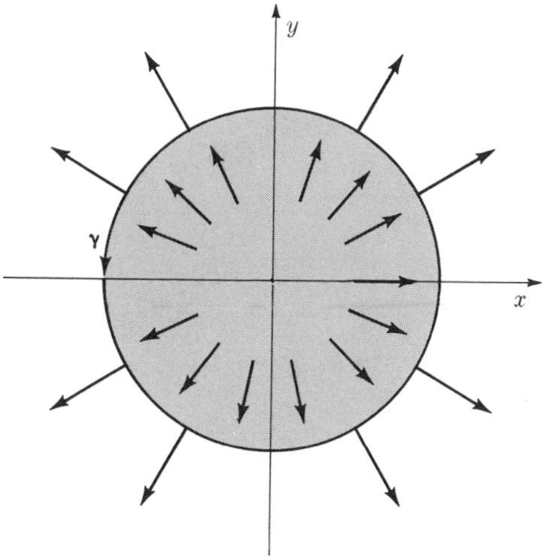

FIGURE 4.25 $\mathbf{F}(x,y) = (x,y)$

We can interpret Example 1 in connection with the flow $\mathbf{F}(x,y) = (x,y)$ in Fig. 25. Obviously, there is a positive rate of flow out of the disk of radius r, which is given by the integral $\int_\gamma (-y\,dx + x\,dy)$, where $\boldsymbol{\gamma}$ is the curve in Fig. 25 and Example 1; thus the outward rate of flow, computed by this boundary integral, is $2\pi r^2$. On the other hand, the *divergence* of the flow is $\partial x/\partial x + \partial y/\partial y = 2$ (recall that the divergence of $\mathbf{F} = (M,N)$ is defined as $M_x + N_y$.) Computing the outward rate of flow as the integral of the divergence thus gives $\iint_D 2 = 2\pi r^2$, in agreement with the boundary integral.

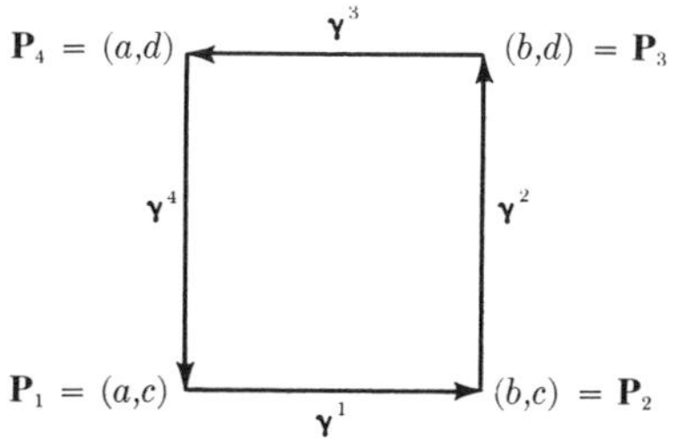

FIGURE 4.26

Example 3. $M(x,y) = xy$, $N(x,y) = x^2$, $S = \{(x,y): a \le x \le b, c \le y \le d\}$. Here the boundary of S is a chain consisting of the four straight line segments from $\mathbf{P}_1$ to $\mathbf{P}_2$, $\mathbf{P}_2$ to $\mathbf{P}_3$, $\mathbf{P}_3$ to $\mathbf{P}_4$, and $\mathbf{P}_4$ to $\mathbf{P}_1$ (see Fig. 26), with any convenient parametrization. The integral over S is

$$\iint_S (N_x - M_y) = \int_a^b \int_c^d x\,dy\,dx = \frac{1}{2}(d-c)(b^2-a^2), \qquad (3)$$

and the integral over the boundary of S is

$$\begin{aligned}\int_{\gamma} xy\,dx + x^2\,dy &= \int_{\gamma^1} (xy\,dx + x^2\,dy) + \cdots + \int_{\gamma^4} (xy\,dx + x^2\,dy)\\ &= \int_a^b tc\,dt + \int_c^d b^2\,dt + \int_{-b}^{-a} [(-t)d]\,dt + \int_{-d}^{-c} a^2\,dt\\ &= \tfrac{1}{2}c(b^2 - a^2) + (d-c)b^2 + \tfrac{1}{2}d(a^2 - b^2) + a^2(d-c). \qquad (4)\end{aligned}$$

In the next to last line we used the parametrizations

$$\begin{aligned}\boldsymbol{\gamma}^1(t) &= (t,c), & a \le t \le b\\ \boldsymbol{\gamma}^2(t) &= (b,t), & c \le t \le d\\ \boldsymbol{\gamma}^3(t) &= (-t,d), & -b \le t \le -a\\ \boldsymbol{\gamma}^4(t) &= (a,-t), & -d \le t \le -c.\end{aligned}$$

At first glance, the results in (3) and (4) appear different, but a little algebra shows them to be the same; thus Green's theorem is verified in this example.

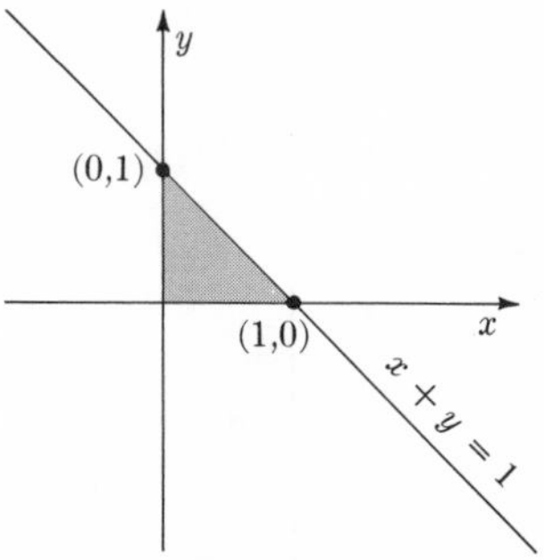

FIGURE 4.27

Example 4. $M(x,y) = y$, $N(x,y) = x$, S is the triangle

$$\{(x,y): 0 \le x \le 1, 0 \le y \le 1, x + y \le 1\}$$

in Fig. 27. In this case, $N_x - M_y = 1 - 1 = 0$, so

$$\iint_S (N_x - M_y) = 0. \qquad (5)$$

On the other hand, it is clear that the boundary of S is a closed connected chain, no matter how it is parametrized; and by Theorem 4, the vector field (M,N) is exact, so

$$\int_\gamma M\,dx + N\,dy = 0, \tag{6}$$

by the Corollary of Theorem 5. Since (5) and (6) agree, Green's theorem is verified in this example.

We come now to the formulation and proof of Green's theorem. Any formulation must state (i) what functions M and N are allowed, (ii) what regions S are allowed, and (iii) when a connected chain runs counterclockwise around S. We shall make the following hypotheses:

(i) M, N, M_y, and N_x are assumed continuous at all points of S. (This is a very natural restriction.)

(ii) S can be described both in the form

$$S = \{(x,y): a \le x \le b,\ \varphi_1(x) \le y \le \varphi_2(x)\}$$

and

$$S = \{(x,y): \psi_1(y) \le x \le \psi_2(y),\ c \le y \le d\},$$

where the φ's and ψ's are continuous, $\varphi_1 \le \varphi_2$, and $\psi_1 \le \psi_2$. (This is a rather special sort of domain, but our limited development of double integrals allows nothing more general.)

(iii) The question of the boundary is more complicated. For this, we introduce the following concept: Given a real-valued function φ defined on an interval $[a,b]$ and a connected chain $\boldsymbol{\gamma}$, we say that $\boldsymbol{\gamma}$ *runs from left to right along the graph of* φ if each point on $\boldsymbol{\gamma}$ lies in the graph of φ, and $\boldsymbol{\gamma}$ begins at $(a, \varphi(a))$ and ends at $(b, \varphi(b))$. (See Fig. 28.) Under these conditions a simple change of variables (Problem 12, §4.3) proves that

$$\int_\gamma M\,dx = \int_a^b M(x,\varphi(x))\,dx. \tag{7}$$

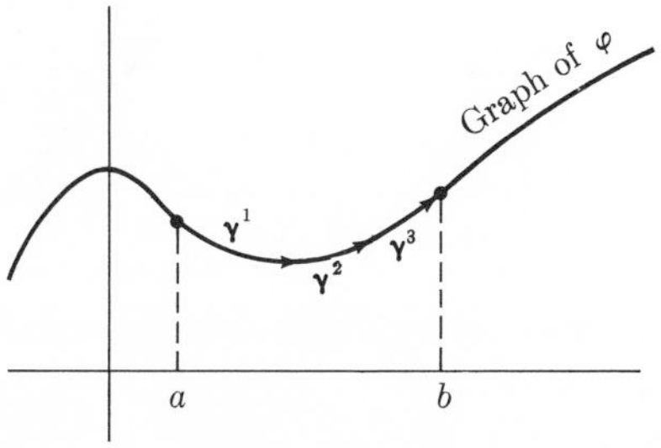

FIGURE 4.28

On the other hand, if $\boldsymbol{\gamma}$ runs from right to left, i.e. $\boldsymbol{\gamma}$ begins at $(b,\varphi(b))$ and ends at $(a,\varphi(a))$, we have

$$\int_{\gamma} M\,dx = -\int_{a}^{b} M(x,\varphi(x))\,dx. \tag{8}$$

Analogously, $\boldsymbol{\gamma}$ *runs from top to bottom along the set* $\{(x,y): x = \psi(y), c \leq y \leq d\}$ if each point on $\boldsymbol{\gamma}$ lies in that set, and $\boldsymbol{\gamma}$ begins at $(d,\psi(d))$ and ends at $(c,\psi(c))$. In this case,

$$\int_{\gamma} N\,dy = -\int_{c}^{d} N(\psi(y),y)\,dy; \tag{9}$$

and if $\boldsymbol{\gamma}$ runs from bottom to top, then

$$\int_{\gamma} N\,dy = \int_{c}^{d} N(\psi(y),y)\,dy. \tag{10}$$

Finally (Fig. 29), we say that a *connected chain* $\boldsymbol{\gamma} = \boldsymbol{\gamma}^1, \ldots, \boldsymbol{\gamma}^8$ *runs counterclockwise around the boundary of the set* S in (ii) above if the chain $\boldsymbol{\gamma}^1, \boldsymbol{\gamma}^2, \boldsymbol{\gamma}^3$ runs from left to right along the graph of φ_1; $\boldsymbol{\gamma}^3, \boldsymbol{\gamma}^4, \boldsymbol{\gamma}^5$ runs from bottom to top along $\{(x,y): x = \psi_2(y)\}$; $\boldsymbol{\gamma}^5, \boldsymbol{\gamma}^6, \boldsymbol{\gamma}^7$ runs from right to left along the graph of φ_2, and $\boldsymbol{\gamma}^7, \boldsymbol{\gamma}^8, \boldsymbol{\gamma}^1$ runs from top to bottom along $\{(x,y): x = \psi_1(y)\}$.

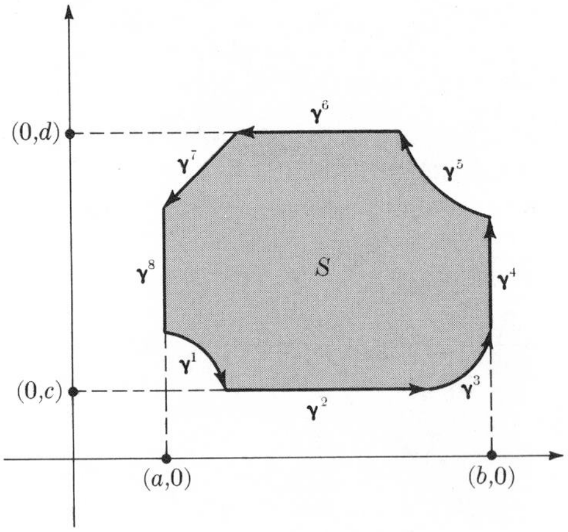

FIGURE 4.29

With the above notions defined, we can at last prove a version of Green's theorem:

Theorem 6. *If* M, N, S, *and* $\boldsymbol{\gamma}$ *satisfy conditions* (i)–(iii) *above, then*

$$\iint_S N_x - M_y \, dx \, dy = \int_\gamma M \, dx + N \, dy.$$

Proof. By Theorem 2 and the fundamental theorem of calculus,

$$-\iint_S M_y \, dx \, dy = -\int_a^b \left[\int_{\varphi_1(x)}^{\varphi_2(x)} M_y(x,y) \, dy \right] dx = -\int_a^b [M(x,y)]_{\varphi_1(x)}^{\varphi_2(x)} \, dx$$

$$= -\int_a^b M(x,\varphi_2(x)) \, dx + \int_a^b M(x,\varphi_1(x)) \, dx.$$

Using the assumptions (iii) on the chain $\boldsymbol{\gamma}^1, \ldots, \boldsymbol{\gamma}^8$, and formulas (7) and (8), we get

$$-\iint_S M_y \, dx \, dy = \int_{\gamma^5} M \, dx + \int_{\gamma^6} M \, dx + \int_{\gamma^7} M \, dx$$

$$+ \int_{\gamma^1} M \, dx + \int_{\gamma^2} M \, dx + \int_{\gamma^3} M \, dx. \tag{11}$$

Further, since $\boldsymbol{\gamma}^4$ lies in the line where $x = b$, the first component $\gamma_1{}^4$ of $\boldsymbol{\gamma}^4$ is constant, so its derivative $(\gamma_1{}^4)'$ is zero, and

$$\int_{\gamma^4} M \, dx = \int_{a_4}^{b_4} M(\gamma_1{}^4(t), \gamma_2{}^4(t))(\gamma_1{}^4)'(t) \, dt = 0.$$

Similarly, $\int_{\gamma^8} M \, dx = 0$, and adding these results to (11) yields

$$-\iint_S M_y \, dx \, dy = \sum_{j=1}^{8} \int_{\gamma^j} M \, dx = \int_\gamma M \, dx. \tag{12}$$

In a completely analogous way, beginning with the formula

$$\iint_S N_x \, dx \, dy = \int_c^d \left[\int_{\psi_1(y)}^{\psi_2(y)} N_x(x,y) \, dx \right] dy$$

$$= \int_c^d N(\psi_2(y),y) \, dy - \int_c^d N(\psi_1(y),y) \, dy,$$

we get $\iint_S N_x \, dx \, dy = \int_\gamma N \, dy$. Combining this with (12) proves the theorem.

We conclude with some examples showing how to pick the curves $\boldsymbol{\gamma}^1, \ldots, \boldsymbol{\gamma}^8$ in Theorem 6.

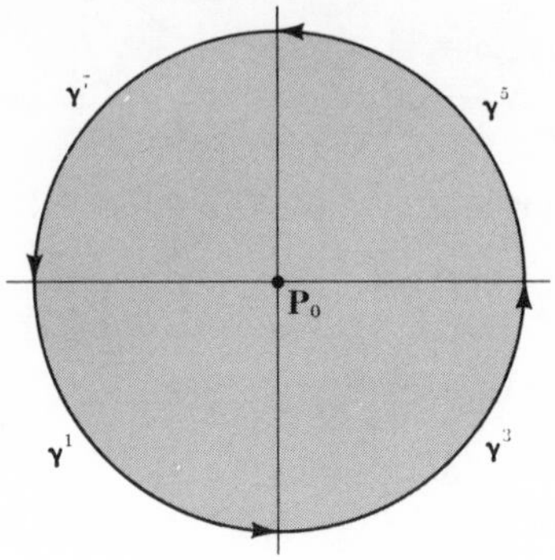

FIGURE 4.30

Example 5. To apply Theorem 6 to a disk $D = \{\mathbf{P}: |\,\mathbf{P} - \mathbf{P}_0\,| \leq r\}$ we begin with the "intuitively obvious" boundary curve

$$\boldsymbol{\gamma}(t) = \mathbf{P}_0 + (r \cos t, r \sin t), \qquad -\pi \leq t \leq \pi,$$

and break it up into four pieces, as in Fig. 30. Thus $\boldsymbol{\gamma}^1(t)$ is defined for $-\pi \leq t \leq -\pi/2$, $\boldsymbol{\gamma}^3(t)$ for $-\pi/2 \leq t \leq 0$, etc. The curves $\boldsymbol{\gamma}^2$, $\boldsymbol{\gamma}^4$, $\boldsymbol{\gamma}^6$, $\boldsymbol{\gamma}^8$ referred to in Theorem 6 reduce to a single point, and contribute nothing to the boundary integral. Thus if M, N, M_y, and N_x are continuous in D, we have

$$\iint_D (N_x - M_y)\,dx\,dy = \int_\gamma M\,dx + N\,dy.$$

Example 6. In applying Theorem 6 to a rectangle

$$R = \{(x,y): a \leq x \leq b, c \leq y \leq d\},$$

the boundary $\boldsymbol{\gamma}$ consists of the four straight line curves $\boldsymbol{\gamma}^2$, $\boldsymbol{\gamma}^4$, $\boldsymbol{\gamma}^6$, $\boldsymbol{\gamma}^8$ (Fig. 31); each of the others reduces to a single point, and contributes nothing to the boundary integral. Thus, with the usual hypotheses on $\mathbf{F} = (M,N)$,

$$\iint_R (N_x - M_y)\,dx\,dy = \int_{\gamma 2} \mathbf{F} + \int_{\gamma 4} \mathbf{F} + \int_{\gamma 6} \mathbf{F} + \int_{\gamma 8} \mathbf{F}.$$

Example 7. For the set S in Fig. 32, $\boldsymbol{\gamma}^1$, $\boldsymbol{\gamma}^2$, $\boldsymbol{\gamma}^5$, and $\boldsymbol{\gamma}^8$ can be easily parametrized, and each of the other four curves reduces to a point; thus with the usual hypotheses on $\mathbf{F} = (M,N)$, we find

$$\iint_S (N_x - M_y)\,dx\,dy = \int_{\gamma 1} \mathbf{F} + \int_{\gamma 2} \mathbf{F} + \int_{\gamma 5} \mathbf{F} + \int_{\gamma 8} \mathbf{F}.$$

Example 8. For the triangle T in Fig. 33 we can take

$$\boldsymbol{\gamma}^1(t) = \mathbf{P}_1 + t(\mathbf{P}_2 - \mathbf{P}_1), \qquad 0 \le t \le 1$$

$$\boldsymbol{\gamma}^5(t) = \mathbf{P}_2 + t(\mathbf{P}_3 - \mathbf{P}_2)$$

$$\boldsymbol{\gamma}^7(t) = \mathbf{P}_3 + t(\mathbf{P}_1 - \mathbf{P}_3).$$

Each of the other five curves reduces to a point, and contributes nothing to the boundary integral; thus, with the usual hypotheses on $\mathbf{F} = (M, N)$,

$$\iint_T (N_x - M_y) = \int_{\gamma 1} \mathbf{F} + \int_{\gamma 5} \mathbf{F} + \int_{\gamma 7} \mathbf{F}.$$

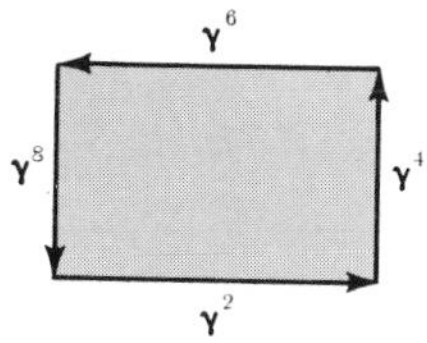

FIGURE 4.31

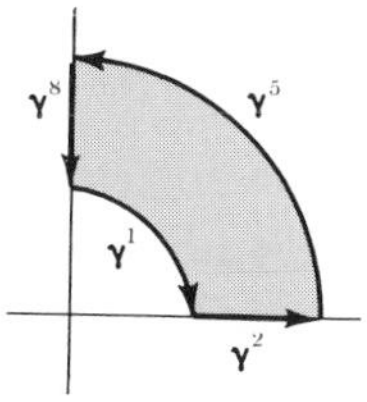

FIGURE 4.32

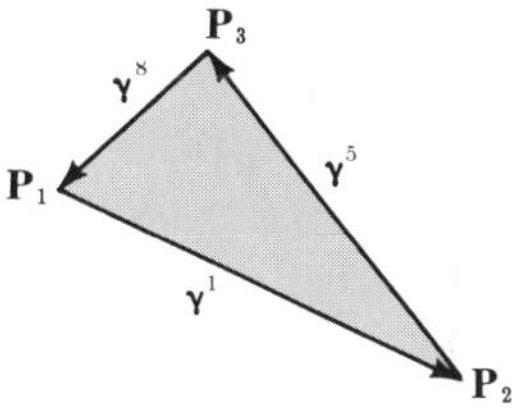

FIGURE 4.33

PROBLEMS

The first three problems are routine applications of Green's theorem. Problem 4 suggests an extension to a new type of region S, and Problem 5 fills in a detail of the proof of Theorem 6. Problems 6–11 concern applications of Green's theorem to the study of Laplace's equation $f_{xx} + f_{yy} = 0$. Problem 12 develops the theory of the planimeter.

1. Compute the rate of flow out of S both by a line integral

$$\int_\gamma -N\,dx + M\,dy$$

and by the double integral of the divergence $\iint_S (M_x + N_y)\,dx\,dy$. Sketch the flow $\mathbf{F} = (M,N)$ to see if your answer seems reasonable.

(a) $M = -y$, $N = x$, $S = \{\mathbf{P}: |\mathbf{P}| < r\}$ ($\mathbf{F}$ is a rotation.)
(b) $M = x$, $N = y$, $S = \{(x,y): a \le x \le b,\ c \le y \le d\}$
(c) $M = 1$, $N = 0$, $S = \{(x,y): x \ge 0,\ y \ge 0,\ x + y \le 1\}$
(d) $M = x$, $N = 0$, $S = \{(x,y): |x| \le 1,\ |y| \le 1\}$
(e) $M = x$, $N = 0$, $S = \{(x,y): 0 \le x \le 1,\ 0 \le y \le 1\}$
(f) $M = 0$, $N = x$, $S = \{(x,y): 0 \le x \le 1,\ 0 \le y \le 1\}$

2. Show that the area of S is given by any of the line integrals

$$\int_\gamma x\,dy, \qquad -\int_\gamma y\,dx, \qquad \frac{1}{2}\int_\gamma (x\,dy - y\,dx),$$

where $\boldsymbol{\gamma}$ denotes a chain running counterclockwise around the boundary of S.

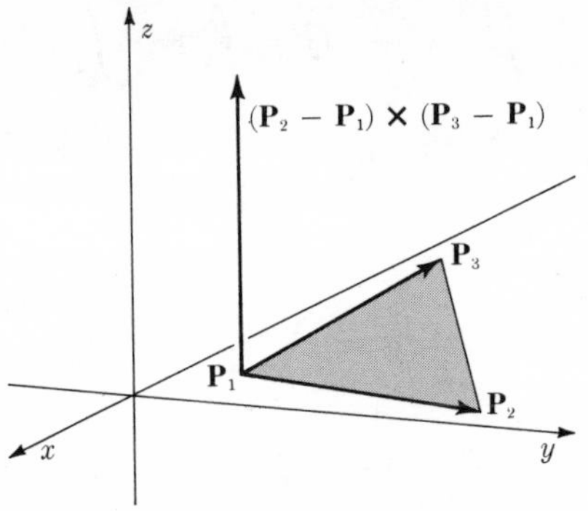

FIGURE 4.34

3. (a) Use $-\int_\gamma y\,dx$ to show that the area of the triangle S with vertices (x_1,y_1), (x_2,y_2), (x_3,y_3) is

$$\pm\frac{(x_2 - x_1)(y_2 + y_1) + (x_3 - x_2)(y_3 + y_2) + (x_1 - x_3)(y_1 + y_3)}{2}$$

(See Problem 1(e), §4.3, to evaluate the integrals on line segments.)

(b) Check the answer in part (a) by computing half the length of the cross product $|(\mathbf{P}_2 - \mathbf{P}_1) \times (\mathbf{P}_3 - \mathbf{P}_1)|$, where $\mathbf{P}_1 = (x_1,y_1,0)$, $\mathbf{P}_2 = (x_2,y_2,0)$, $\mathbf{P}_3 = (x_3,y_3,0)$. (See Fig. 34).

4. Figure 35 shows an annulus S divided into four regions S_1, S_2, S_3, S_4, to each of which Theorem 6 applies. Prove Green's theorem for the annulus

$$\sum_{j=1}^{8} \int_{\gamma^j} (M\,dx + N\,dy) = \sum_{j=1}^{4} \iint_{S_j} (N_x - M_y)\,dx\,dy.$$

(Notice that the sum on the right amounts to an integral over S, and the sum on the left adds up to $\int_\gamma (M\,dx + N\,dy)$, where $\boldsymbol{\gamma}$ runs around the boundary of S (intuitively speaking). In treating the radial curves $\boldsymbol{\gamma}^9, \ldots, \boldsymbol{\gamma}^{12}$ it may help to review Problem 10, §4.3.)

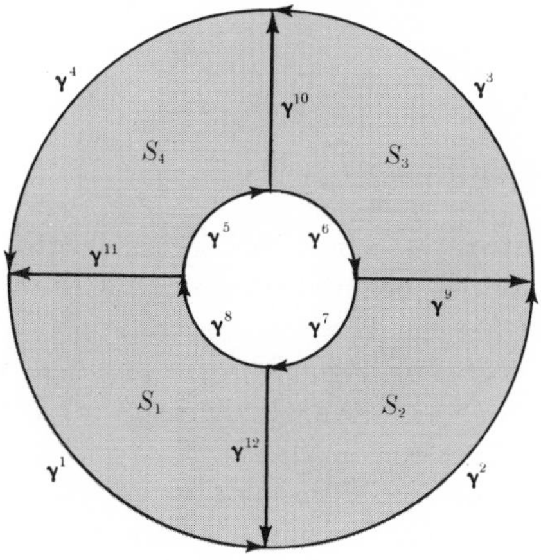

FIGURE 4.35

5. (a) Prove formula (7). (Hint: $a = \gamma_1^1(a_1)$, $\gamma_1^1(b_1) = \gamma_1^2(a_2)$, $\gamma_1^2(b_2) = \gamma_1^3(a_3)$, $\ldots$, $\gamma_1^n(b_n) = b$, so for any continuous function f,

$$\int_a^b f = \int_{\gamma_1^1(a_1)}^{\gamma_1^1(b_1)} f + \int_{\gamma_1^2(a_2)}^{\gamma_1^2(b_2)} f + \cdots + \int_{\gamma_1^n(a_n)}^{\gamma_1^n(b_n)} f.)$$

(b) Prove formula (8).

6. Suppose that $\mathbf{F} = (M,N)$ is an "incompressible flow," in the sense that $\int_\gamma (-N\,dx + M\,dy) = 0$ for every closed chain $\boldsymbol{\gamma}$. Problem 16 of the previous section proved that $\mathbf{F}$ has zero divergence, $M_x + N_y \equiv 0$.

(a) Assume now the weaker condition that $\int_\gamma (-N\,dx + M\,dy) = 0$ *for every* $\boldsymbol{\gamma}$ *which is the oriented boundary of a disk D.* Prove again that $M_x + N_y = 0$. (Use Green's theorem and Problem 7, §4.1, and assume that M_x and N_y are continuous.)

(b) Suppose that $\mathbf{F} = \nabla f$, and $\mathbf{F}$ is an incompressible flow. Prove that f satisfies Laplace's equation $f_{xx} + f_{yy} = 0$. (When $f(x,y)$ is the temperature at (x,y), then ∇f is parallel to the velocity field for the flow of heat; when the temperature does not change with time (so-called "steady state temperature distribution"), then heat cannot flow out of any rectangle, hence the flow is "incompressible" in the sense of part (a), hence $f_{xx} + f_{yy} = 0$.)

7. Suppose that S and $\boldsymbol{\gamma}$ satisfy the conditions of Theorem (6), and that $f, g, f_x, f_{xx}, f_y, f_{yy}, g_x$, and g_y are all continuous on S. Prove *Green's formula*

$$\iint_S (g\Delta f + \nabla g\cdot\nabla f) = \int_\gamma (-gf_y\,dx + gf_x\,dy), \tag{13}$$

where Δf denotes the *Laplacian* $f_{xx} + f_{yy}$.

8. (a) Suppose that the curve $\boldsymbol{\gamma}$ has arc length as parameter; thus $\boldsymbol{\gamma}'(s) = \mathbf{T}(s)$ is a unit vector tangent to the curve. If $\mathbf{T}(s) = (\gamma_1'(s), \gamma_2'(s))$, let $\mathbf{N}(s) = (\gamma_2'(s), -\gamma_1'(s))$. Prove that $\mathbf{N}(s)$ is a unit vector orthogonal to the curve at $\boldsymbol{\gamma}(s)$. (See §2.3.)

(b) With $\mathbf{T}$ and $\mathbf{N}$ as above, choose θ so that $\mathbf{T} = (\cos\theta, \sin\theta)$; show that $\mathbf{N} = (\cos(\theta - \pi/2), \sin(\theta - \pi/2))$, i.e. $\mathbf{N}$ is obtained by rotating $\mathbf{T}$ clockwise through an angle of $\pi/2$. (Hence, intuitively, if $\boldsymbol{\gamma}$ runs counterclockwise around S, then $\mathbf{N}$ is a unit normal pointing out of S.)

(c) Show that with $\boldsymbol{\gamma}$ as above, $\int_\gamma - gf_y\,dx + gf_x\,dy = \int_a^b g(\nabla f\cdot\mathbf{N})\,ds$. (The expression $\nabla f\cdot\mathbf{N}$ is the directional derivative of f in the direction of the normal $\mathbf{N}$ pointing out of S, called the "outer normal derivative of f," denoted $\partial f/\partial n$. Thus Green's formula (13) says that

$$\iint_S (g\Delta f + \nabla g\cdot\nabla f) = \int_\gamma g\frac{\partial f}{\partial n}\,ds.)$$

9. Prove the following. (See Problems 7 and 8.)

(a) $$\iint_S f\,\Delta g + \nabla f\cdot\nabla g = \int_\gamma f\frac{\partial g}{\partial n}\,ds \tag{14}$$

(b) $$\iint_S (f\,\Delta g - g\,\Delta f) = \int_\gamma \left(f\frac{\partial g}{\partial n} - g\frac{\partial f}{\partial n}\right) ds \tag{15}$$

10. Suppose that f, S, and $\boldsymbol{\gamma}$ satisfy the conditions in Problem 7, that $\Delta f \equiv 0$, and that $f = 0$ at each point on the boundary $\boldsymbol{\gamma}$ of S.

(a) Prove that $\nabla f \equiv 0$ in S. (Hint: Apply (13) with $f = g$, and apply Problem 8, §4.1.)

(b) Prove that $f \equiv 0$ in S. (In the language of temperature distributions: *If a steady state temperature distribution is zero on the boundary of S, then it is zero at every point in S.* Hint: See Problem 15, §3.3.)

11. Suppose that f, S, and $\boldsymbol{\gamma}$ satisfy the conditions in Problem 10, except that "$f \equiv 0$ on $\boldsymbol{\gamma}$" is replaced by "$\partial f/\partial n \equiv 0$ on $\boldsymbol{\gamma}$" (see Problem 8). Prove that f is constant on S.

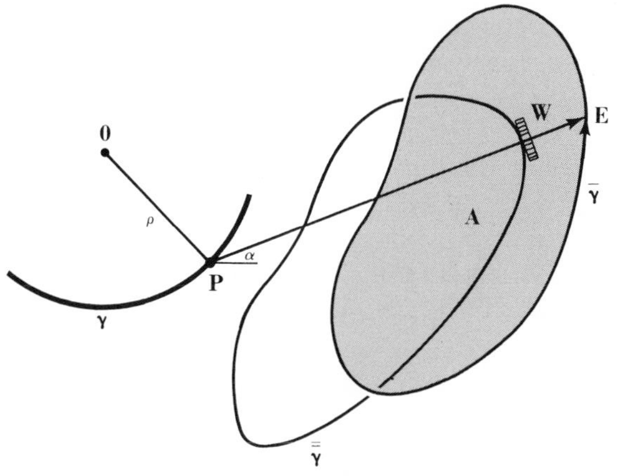

FIGURE 4.36

12. Figure 36 shows a *planimeter*, an ingenious device for measuring plane areas. An arm of radius ρ is pivoted at a fixed point **0**, and on the free end **P** of this arm is pivoted a second arm, of radius R. On the second arm, at distance r from the pivot **P**, there is a little knurled wheel W. The planimeter measures an area A by recording the net turning of the wheel W as the free end **E** of the second arm is moved around the boundary of A. This problem shows why the turning of W is proportional to the area of A.

As **E** is moved around the boundary of A, it traces a closed curve $\bar{\boldsymbol{\gamma}}$, and by Problem 2, $A = \frac{1}{2}\int_{\bar{\gamma}} (x\,dy - y\,dx)$. At the same time, the pivot **P** traces a closed curve $\boldsymbol{\gamma}$ lying entirely on the circle of radius ρ about **0**, and the wheel W is dragged over a closed curve $\bar{\bar{\boldsymbol{\gamma}}}$, as in Fig. 36. Let α be the angle between the arm **PE** and the x axis. Then $\mathbf{U}_1 = (\cos\alpha, \sin\alpha)$ is parallel to the arm **PE**, and $\mathbf{U}_2 = (-\sin\alpha, \cos\alpha)$ is perpendicular to it. Since the little knurled wheel is unaffected by motion parallel to the arm **PE**, but responds to motion perpendicular to **PE**, it turns at a rate proportional to $\mathbf{U}_2 \cdot \bar{\bar{\boldsymbol{\gamma}}}'$. Thus if $[a,b]$ is the interval on which $\boldsymbol{\gamma}$ is defined, the net turning of the wheel is

$$c\int_a^b \mathbf{U}_2 \cdot \bar{\bar{\boldsymbol{\gamma}}}' \tag{16}$$

where c is a constant of proportionality. The steps below show that if the end **E** is drawn around the boundary A so that the planimeter returns to its original position, and neither arm swings all the way around in a full circle, then $A = R\int_a^b \mathbf{U}_2 \cdot \bar{\bar{\boldsymbol{\gamma}}}'$. Thus A is proportional to the turning of the wheel, and the planimeter is justified.

(a) Suppose that $\boldsymbol{\gamma}(t)$, $\overline{\boldsymbol{\gamma}}(t)$, $\overline{\overline{\boldsymbol{\gamma}}}(t)$, and $\alpha(t)$ are respectively the position of **P**, position of **E**, position of W, and angle α at time t, and that t varies from a to b as **E** is drawn around the area A. Show that $\overline{\boldsymbol{\gamma}} = \boldsymbol{\gamma} + (R\cos\alpha, R\sin\alpha)$, $\overline{\overline{\boldsymbol{\gamma}}} = \boldsymbol{\gamma} + (r\cos\alpha, r\sin\alpha)$.

(b) If the second arm returns to its original position, and $-\pi < \alpha < \pi$ throughout the motion, and α is a differentiable function of t, then $\int_a^b \alpha' = 0$. Why?

(c) Under the conditions of part (b), show that the integral (16) giving the turning of the wheel reduces to $c\int_a^b (-\sin\alpha\gamma_1' + \cos\alpha\gamma_2')$.

(d) Show that $A = \frac{1}{2}\int_{\bar{\gamma}} (x\,dy - y\,dx)$ can be "reduced" to

$$\frac{1}{2}\int_\gamma (x\,dy - y\,dx) + \frac{R^2}{2}\int_a^b \alpha'$$

$$+ \frac{R}{2}\int_a^b [\gamma_1(\sin\alpha)' - \gamma_1'\sin\alpha - \gamma_2(\cos\alpha)' + \gamma_2'\cos\alpha].$$

(e) If the first arm returns to its original position without swinging all the way around **0**, then $\int_\gamma (x\,dy - y\,dx) = 0$. Why?

(f) In the expression in part (d), show that

$$\int_a^b \gamma_1(\sin\alpha)' = -\int_a^b \gamma_1'\sin\alpha$$

and

$$\int_a^b -\gamma_2(\cos\alpha)' = \int_a^b \gamma_2'\cos\alpha.$$

(g) Combining parts (b)–(f), show that (16) equals $\dfrac{c}{R}A$.

4.5 CHANGE OF VARIABLE

Green's theorem can be ingeniously applied to the problem of change of variable in double integrals. The most important case involves polar coordinates.* Suppose a region S of the plane is described in terms of polar coordinates as

$$S = \{(x,y) : x = r\cos\theta,\ y = r\sin\theta,\ r_1 \le r \le r_2,\ \theta_1 \le \theta \le \theta_2\}, \quad (1)$$

where $0 \le r_1 < r_2$ and $\theta_1 \le \theta_2$ (Fig. 37(a)). Then we have the formula

---

* Recall that r and θ are polar coordinates of a point $\mathbf{P} = (x,y)$ if and only if $x = r\cos\theta$ and $y = r\sin\theta$. When $r > 0$, then $r = |\mathbf{P}|$ and θ is the angle between **P** and the positive x axis.

$$\iint_S f = \int_{\theta_1}^{\theta_2} \left[\int_{r_1}^{r_2} f(r\cos\theta, r\sin\theta) r\,dr \right] d\theta \tag{2}$$

for every function f continuous on S. The point is that it is often easier to compute the double integral on the right in (2) than to compute the integral on the left in the usual way as

$$\int \left[\int_{\varphi_1}^{\varphi_2} f\,dy \right] dx \quad \text{or} \quad \int \left[\int_{\psi_1}^{\psi_2} f\,dx \right] dy. \tag{3}$$

For example, taking $f = 1$ in (2), we find easily that

$$\text{Area of } S = \iint_S 1 = \int_{\theta_1}^{\theta_2} \left[\int_{r_1}^{r_2} r\,dr \right] d\theta$$

$$= \int_{\theta_1}^{\theta_2} \frac{1}{2}(r_2^2 - r_1^2)\,d\theta = \frac{1}{2}(\theta_2 - \theta_1)(r_2^2 - r_1^2)$$

which is the formula for the area of an annular sector S of radii r_1 and r_2 and angle $\theta_2 - \theta_1$. By contrast, it is a chore to set up and evaluate $\iint_S 1$ in either of the forms (3).

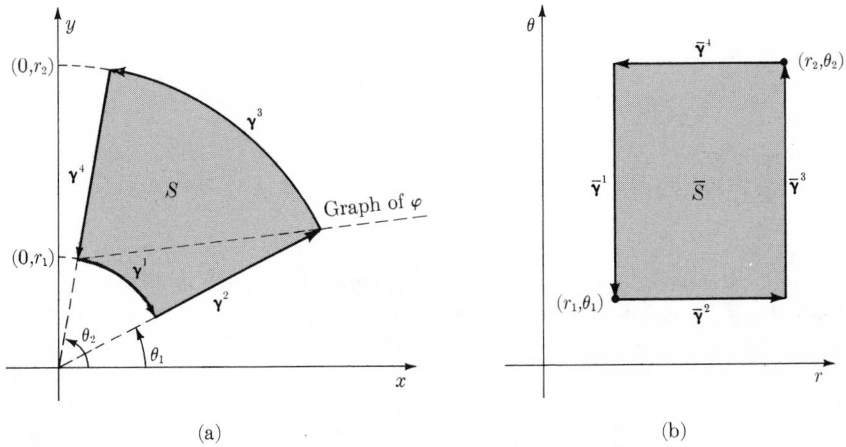

FIGURE 4.37

To understand formula (2), visualize two planes, an xy plane and an $r\theta$ plane. The function f is defined in a region S of the xy plane; according to (2), its integral can be found by integrating a *different* function, call it $\bar{f}$, over the rectangle $\bar{S}$ in the $r\theta$ plane shown in Fig. 37(b). Precisely,

$$\bar{f}(r,\theta) = rf(r\cos\theta, r\sin\theta),$$
$$\bar{S} = \{(r,\theta) : r_1 \le r \le r_2, \theta_1 \le \theta \le \theta_2\}.$$

Suppose that $f \geq 0$. Then, intuitively, $\iint_S f$ is the volume between S and the graph of f, as shown in Fig. 38. This volume can be approximated by dividing S into small sections, using radial and circular lines, as in Fig. 39. Denote the radial dimension of such a section by Δr, and the

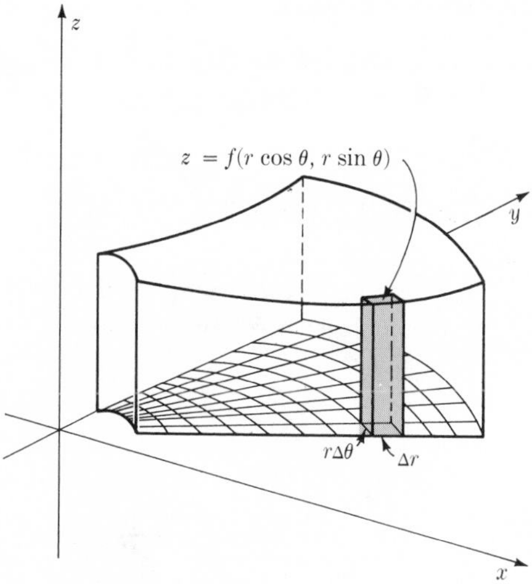

FIGURE 4.38

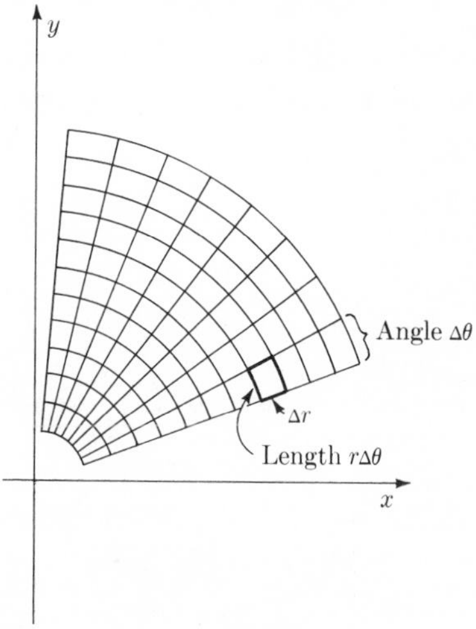

FIGURE 4.39

angular dimension by $\Delta\theta$. The area of such a section is $(r\Delta\theta)(\Delta r)$, so the volume lying over that section is approximately $f(r\cos\theta, r\sin\theta)r\Delta\theta\,\Delta r$. Since the whole volume is the sum of these parts, we find

$$\iint_S f \underset{\text{approx}}{=} \sum \overbrace{\underbrace{f(r\cos\theta, r\sin\theta)}_{\substack{\text{height of}\\ \text{column over } \bar{S}}}\, r}^{\substack{\text{height of}\\ \text{column over } S}} \overbrace{\underbrace{\Delta\theta\,\Delta r}_{\substack{\text{area of}\\ \text{base in } \bar{S}}}}^{\substack{\text{area of}\\ \text{base in } S}}. \tag{4}$$

Now, the radial and circular lines subdividing S correspond to a rectangular grid of lines subdividing $\bar{S}$ into small rectangles of area $\Delta r\,\Delta\theta$ (Fig. 40). Thus the sum (4) approximates the volume between $\bar{S}$ and the graph of $f(r\cos\theta, r\sin\theta)r$, and this volume is precisely the integral on the right in (2). Thus the factor r by which f is multiplied here is, intuitively, the

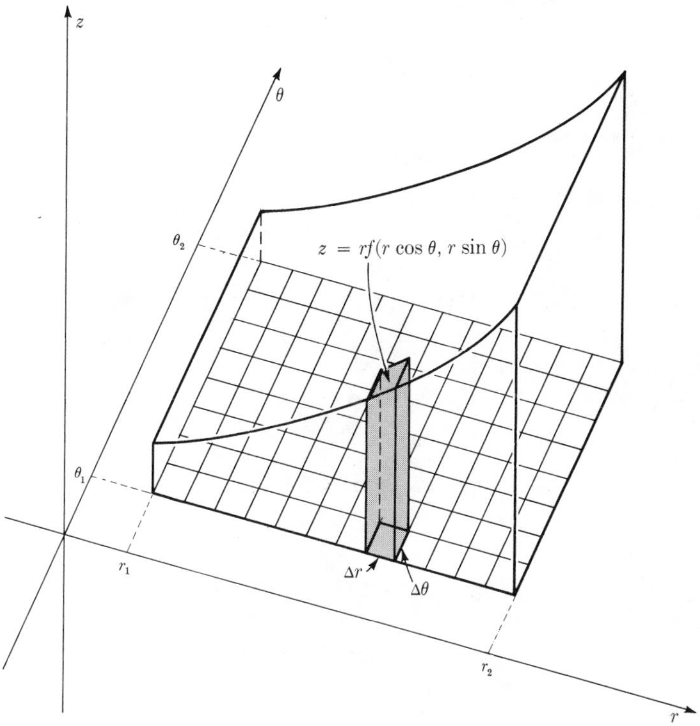

FIGURE 4.40

ratio of the area of a small piece of the S region to the corresponding small piece of the $\bar{S}$ region. This ratio is called the "magnification factor" in transforming from $\bar{S}$ to S.

In proving (2) we will apply Green's theorem to write $\iint_S f$ as a line integral around the boundary of S, transform this into a line integral around the boundary of $\bar{S}$ (using the change of variable formula for single integrals), and finally apply Green's theorem again to obtain an integral over $\bar{S}$. Suppose for simplicity that $0 \leq \theta_1 < \theta_2 \leq \pi/2$. Then Theorem 6 applies if we take the four curves $\boldsymbol{\gamma}^1$, $\boldsymbol{\gamma}^2$, $\boldsymbol{\gamma}^3$, $\boldsymbol{\gamma}^4$ in Fig. 37 as the boundary of S, and the corresponding curves $\bar{\boldsymbol{\gamma}}^1$, $\bar{\boldsymbol{\gamma}}^2$, $\bar{\boldsymbol{\gamma}}^3$, $\bar{\boldsymbol{\gamma}}^4$ as the boundary of $\bar{S}$. (This fits the terminology in (iii), §4.4, except that the curves are numbered differently, and those that reduce to a point are left out.) Let φ denote the function whose graph is the dotted line in Fig. 37(a), and define

$$M(x,y) = -\int_{\varphi(x)}^{y} f(x,t)\,dt, \qquad N(x,y) = 0.$$

Then $N_x - M_y = f$, so by Green's theorem,

$$\iint_S f = \iint_S (N_x - M_y) = \sum_{j=1}^{4} \int_{\gamma^j} M\,dx. \tag{5}$$

It is easy to check that

$$\int_{\gamma^1} M\,dx = \int_{\theta_2}^{\theta_1} M(r_1 \cos\theta, r_1 \sin\theta)(-r_1 \sin\theta)\,d\theta = \int_{\bar\gamma^1} \bar M\,dr + \bar N\,d\theta$$

$$\int_{\gamma^2} M\,dx = \int_{r_1}^{r_2} M(r\cos\theta_1, r\sin\theta_1)\cos\theta_1\,dr = \int_{\bar\gamma^2} \bar M\,dr + \bar N\,d\theta$$

$$\int_{\gamma^3} M\,dx = \int_{\theta_1}^{\theta_2} M(r_2 \cos\theta, r_2 \sin\theta)(-r_2 \sin\theta)\,d\theta = \int_{\bar\gamma^3} \bar M\,dr + \bar N\,d\theta$$

$$\int_{\gamma^4} M\,dx = \int_{r_2}^{r_1} M(r\cos\theta_2, r\sin\theta_2)(\cos\theta_2)\,dr = \int_{\bar\gamma^4} \bar M\,dr + \bar N\,d\theta$$

where

$$\bar M(r,\theta) = M(r\cos\theta, r\sin\theta)\cos\theta \tag{6}$$

$$\bar N(r,\theta) = -M(r\cos\theta, r\sin\theta) r \sin\theta. \tag{7}$$

(See Problem 2.) Applying (5) and Green's theorem, we get

$$\iint_S f = \sum_{j=1}^{4} \int_{\gamma^j} M\,dx = \sum_{j=1}^{4} \int_{\bar\gamma^j} \bar M\,dr + \bar N\,d\theta = \iint_{\bar S} (\bar N_r - \bar M_\theta). \tag{8}$$

Applying the chain rule in (6) and (7),

$$\bar M_\theta = -M\sin\theta + [M_x\cdot(-r\sin\theta) + M_y\cdot(r\cos\theta)](\cos\theta)$$
$$\bar N_r = -M\sin\theta - [M_x\cdot(\cos\theta) + M_y\cdot(\sin\theta)](r\sin\theta);$$

hence $\bar N_r - \bar M_\theta = -M_y\cdot r = f\cdot r$. (It is understood that f, like M, M_x, and M_y, is to be evaluated at the point $(r\cos\theta, r\sin\theta)$.) Thus from (8)

$$\iint_S f = \iint_{\bar S} f\cdot r = \int_c^d \left[\int_a^b f(r\cos\theta, r\sin\theta) r\,dr\right] d\theta,$$

and formula (2) is proved.

If you check the details of this proof, you will find that f has to be differentiable, not just continuous (see Problem 12). This is a weakness in the method of proof; actually, formula (2) remains valid for every continuous function f.

As we have already suggested, Theorem 6 is just a special case of a much more general result, various forms of which can be found in the references in §4.1. To illustrate what is gained by proving the general version, we show how it leads to a general rule for change of variables in a double integral. Many of the terms we use will, of necessity, not be precisely defined, but only suggested by pictures.

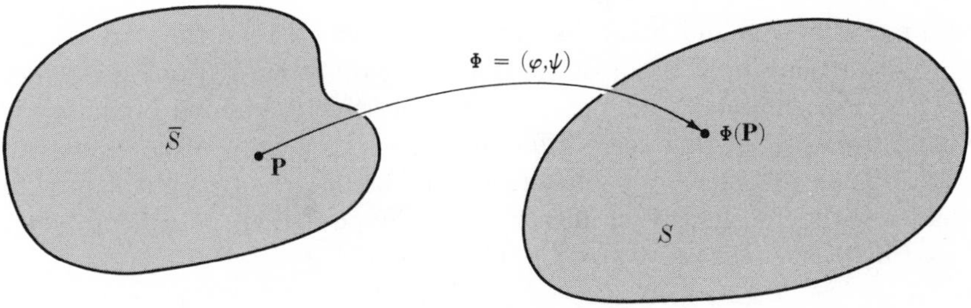

FIGURE 4.41

Suppose $\bar{S}$ is a region in the plane, and φ and ψ are two differentiable real-valued functions on $\bar{S}$. Then the *pair* of functions (φ,ψ) assigns to each point $\mathbf{P}$ in $\bar{S}$ a point $(\varphi(\mathbf{P}),\psi(\mathbf{P}))$ in the plane, in other words, (φ,ψ) is a function from $\bar{S}$ to R^2, as suggested in Fig. 41. Denote this function by $\mathbf{\Phi}$; thus $\mathbf{\Phi}(\mathbf{P}) = (\varphi(\mathbf{P}),\psi(\mathbf{P}))$. Let S be the set of all points in the range of $\mathbf{\Phi}$,

$$S = \{\mathbf{Q}: \mathbf{Q} = \mathbf{\Phi}(\mathbf{P}) \text{ for some } \mathbf{P} \text{ in } \bar{S}\}.$$

The function $\mathbf{\Phi}$ is called *one-to-one* if each point $\mathbf{Q}$ in S comes from just one point $\mathbf{P}$ in $\bar{S}$. We denote points $\mathbf{P}$ in $\bar{S}$ by (u,v) (in other words, "$\bar{S}$ lies in the uv plane"), and the derivatives of φ and ψ are denoted $\partial\varphi/\partial u$, etc. The rule for change of variable states that *if (φ,ψ) is a differentiable one-to-one map of $\bar{S}$ onto S, then*

$$\iint_S f = \iint_{\bar{S}} f(\varphi(u,v),\psi(u,v)) \left|\frac{\partial(\varphi,\psi)}{\partial(u,v)}\right| du\,dv, \tag{9}$$

where $\partial(\varphi,\psi)/\partial(u,v)$ is the *Jacobian* of (φ,ψ), defined by

$$\frac{\partial(\varphi,\psi)}{\partial(u,v)} = \begin{vmatrix} \varphi_u & \psi_u \\ \varphi_v & \psi_v \end{vmatrix} = \frac{\partial\varphi}{\partial u}\frac{\partial\psi}{\partial v} - \frac{\partial\psi}{\partial u}\frac{\partial\varphi}{\partial v}. \tag{10}$$

Thus the absolute value of the Jacobian (10) is the "magnification factor" in transforming from $\bar{S}$ to S. For example, if

$$\varphi(u,v) = u \cos v$$

$$\psi(u,v) = u \sin v,$$

then

$$\frac{\partial(\varphi,\psi)}{\partial(u,v)} = \begin{vmatrix} \cos v & \sin v \\ -u \sin u & u \cos v \end{vmatrix} = u;$$

hence (9) gives the same result as (2),

$$\iint_S f = \iint_{\bar{S}} f(u \cos v, u \sin v)\ |u|\ du\, dv,$$

except that now S and $\bar{S}$ can be much more general than they are in (2).

We can outline a proof of (9) following the same reasoning that led to (2). For simplicity, suppose that the positively oriented boundary of $\bar{S}$ is formed by a single closed differentiable curve $\bar{\boldsymbol{\gamma}}$ defined on an interval $[a,b]$. Then the curve $\boldsymbol{\gamma} = \boldsymbol{\Phi}\circ\bar{\boldsymbol{\gamma}}$ forms the boundary of S, but it may be oriented either positively or negatively. Suppose there is a vector field $\mathbf{F} = (M,0)$ such that $-M_y = f$. Then

$$\iint_S f = -\iint_S M_y = \pm\int_\gamma M\, dx = \pm\int_a^b (M\circ\boldsymbol{\gamma})\gamma_1{}'.$$

(The $\pm$ sign arises because $\boldsymbol{\gamma}$ may be oriented either positively or negatively.) Since $\boldsymbol{\gamma} = \boldsymbol{\Phi}\circ\bar{\boldsymbol{\gamma}} = (\varphi\circ\bar{\boldsymbol{\gamma}}, \psi\circ\bar{\boldsymbol{\gamma}})$, we have $\gamma_1 = \varphi\circ\bar{\boldsymbol{\gamma}}$, hence $\gamma_1{}' = (\boldsymbol{\nabla}\varphi\circ\bar{\boldsymbol{\gamma}})\cdot\bar{\boldsymbol{\gamma}}'$, and

$$\iint_S f = \pm\int_a^b [(M\circ\boldsymbol{\Phi}\circ\bar{\boldsymbol{\gamma}})\ \boldsymbol{\nabla}\varphi\circ\bar{\boldsymbol{\gamma}}]\cdot\bar{\boldsymbol{\gamma}}'$$

$$= \pm\int_{\bar{\gamma}} (M\circ\boldsymbol{\Phi})\ \boldsymbol{\nabla}\varphi\circ\bar{\boldsymbol{\gamma}}$$

$$= \pm\int_{\bar{\gamma}} M(\varphi,\psi)\frac{\partial\varphi}{\partial u}\, du + M(\varphi,\psi)\frac{\partial\varphi}{\partial v}\, dv$$

$$= \pm\iint_{\bar{S}}\left[\frac{\partial}{\partial u}\left(M(\varphi,\psi)\frac{\partial\varphi}{\partial v}\right) - \frac{\partial}{\partial v}\left(M(\varphi,\psi)\frac{\partial\varphi}{\partial u}\right)\right] du\, dv$$

$$= \pm\iint_{\bar{S}}\left\{\left[\left(M_x(\varphi,\psi)\frac{\partial\varphi}{\partial u} + M_y(\varphi,\psi)\frac{\partial\psi}{\partial u}\right)\frac{\partial\varphi}{\partial v} + M(\varphi,\psi)\frac{\partial^2\varphi}{\partial u\partial v}\right]\right.$$

$$\left. -\left[\left(M_x(\varphi,\psi)\frac{\partial\varphi}{\partial v} + M_y(\varphi,\psi)\frac{\partial\psi}{\partial v}\right)\frac{\partial\varphi}{\partial u} + M(\varphi,\psi)\frac{\partial^2\varphi}{\partial v\partial u}\right]\right\} du\, dv$$

$$= \pm\iint_{\bar{S}}\left\{-M_y(\varphi,\psi)\left(\frac{\partial\varphi}{\partial u}\frac{\partial\psi}{\partial v} - \frac{\partial\varphi}{\partial v}\frac{\partial\psi}{\partial u}\right)\right\} du\, dv$$

$$= \pm\iint_{\bar{S}} f(\varphi,\psi)\frac{\partial(\varphi,\psi)}{\partial(u,v)}\, du\, dv.$$

Now we have to choose the + or the − sign. If $f = 1$, we get

$$\iint_S 1 = \iint_{\bar{S}} \pm \frac{\partial(\varphi,\psi)}{\partial(u,v)}\, du\, dv.$$

Since the left-hand side is not negative, neither is the right, so we must have the sign that makes

$$\pm \frac{\partial(\varphi,\psi)}{\partial(u,v)} \geq 0,$$

in other words, we have $|\partial(\varphi,\psi)/\partial(u,v)|$, and we arrive at (9).

Formula (9) should be compared to the rule for change of variable in a single integral,

$$\int_{\varphi(a)}^{\varphi(b)} f(x)\, dx = \int_a^b f(\varphi(u))\varphi'(u)\, du. \tag{10}$$

Imagine φ mapping the u axis into the x axis, as in Fig. 42. If $\varphi' \geq 0$, then φ maps the interval $\bar{S} = [a,b]$ onto $S = [\varphi(a),\varphi(b)]$; but if $\varphi' \leq 0$, it maps onto $S = [\varphi(b),\varphi(a)]$, as in Fig. 42(b). In the first case, $\varphi' = |\varphi'|$, so by (10)

$$\int_S f = \int_{\varphi(a)}^{\varphi(b)} f = \int_a^b f(\varphi(u))\varphi'(u)\, du = \int_a^b f(\varphi(u))\, |\varphi'(u)|\, du.$$

In the second case, $\varphi' = -|\varphi'|$, so

$$\int_S f = \int_{\varphi(b)}^{\varphi(a)} f = -\int_{\varphi(a)}^{\varphi(b)} f = -\int_a^b f(\varphi(u))\varphi'(u)\, du$$

$$= \int_a^b f(\varphi(u))\, |\varphi'(u)|\, du.$$

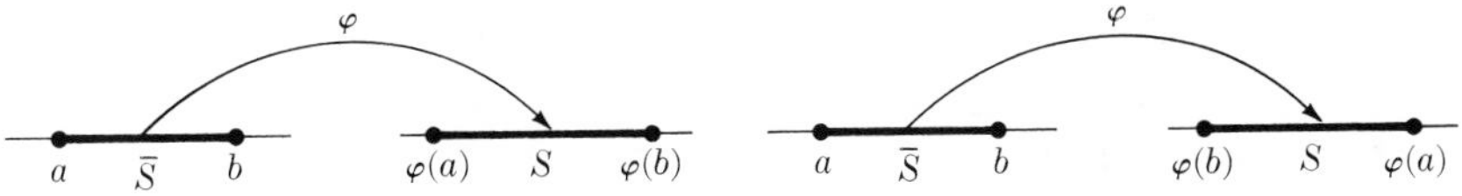

(a) $\varphi' \geq 0$ FIGURE 4.42 (b) $\varphi' \leq 0$

Hence in either case,

$$\int_S f = \int_{\bar{S}} f(\varphi(u))\,|\varphi'(u)|\,du.$$

This formula is the one-variable version of (9); the derivative $\varphi' = d\varphi/du$ corresponds to the Jacobian $\partial(\varphi,\psi)/\partial(u,v)$ in two variables. Just as $\varphi' \le 0$ corresponds to the fact that φ reverses the endpoints of the interval, $\partial(\varphi,\psi)/\partial(u,v) \le 0$ means that (φ,ψ) reverses the direction of the boundary curve.

PROBLEMS

1. Evaluate the following integrals in polar coordinates, using formula (2).

(a) $\displaystyle\int_0^1 \int_0^{\sqrt{1-y^2}} x\,dx\,dy$ (Sketch the set S over which you integrate.)

(b) $\displaystyle\iint_S \frac{xy}{x^2+y^2}\,dx\,dy$, where S is the annulus $\{\mathbf{P}: r_1 \le |\mathbf{P}| \le r_2\}$

(c) $\displaystyle\int_0^R \int_0^{\sqrt{R^2-x^2}} \exp(x^2+y^2)\,dy\,dx$ (It is not practical to evaluate the integral explicitly *without* changing to polar coordinates.)

2. This problem evaluates an important "improper integral,"

$$\int_0^\infty \exp(-x^2)\,dx = \lim_{R\to\infty} \int_0^R \exp(-x^2)\,dx = \frac{\sqrt{\pi}}{2}.$$

(a) Prove that $\displaystyle\int_0^R \int_0^{\sqrt{R^2-x^2}} \exp(-x^2-y^2)\,dy\,dx = \frac{\pi}{4}(1-e^{-R^2})$.

(b) Show that

$$\left(\int_0^R \exp(-x^2)\,dx\right)^2 = \int_0^R \int_0^R \exp(-x^2-y^2)\,dy\,dx.$$

(Hint: $\exp(-x^2-y^2) = \exp(-x^2)\exp(-y^2)$.)

(c) Prove that $0 \le$

$$\int_0^R \int_0^R \exp(-x^2-y^2)\,dy\,dx - \int_0^R \int_0^{\sqrt{R^2-x^2}} \exp(-x^2-y^2)\,dy\,dx$$

$$\le R^2 \exp(-R^2).$$

(Notice that the difference in question is the integral of $e^{-x^2-y^2}$ over the set S in Fig. 43 and that $\exp(-x^2-y^2) \le \exp(-R^2)$ on S.)

(d) Using parts (a)–(c), show that

$$\lim_{R\to\infty}\left(\int_0^R e^{-x^2}\,dx\right)^2 = \frac{\pi}{4}.$$

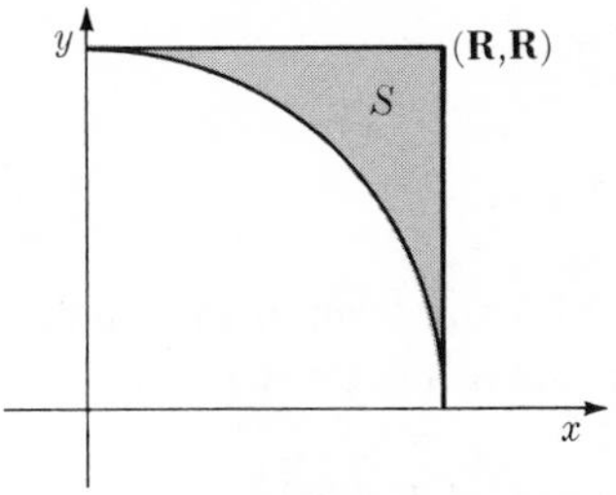

FIGURE 4.43

3. Let $\varphi(u,v) = u + v$, $\psi(u,v) = u - v$, and $\mathbf{\Phi} = (\varphi,\psi)$.

(a) Show that $\dfrac{\partial(\varphi,\psi)}{\partial(u,v)} = -2$.

(b) Let $\bar{S} = \{(u,v) : u^2 + v^2 \le 1\}$. Show that $\mathbf{\Phi}$ carries $\bar{S}$ one-to-one onto the set $S = \{(x,y) : x^2 + y^2 \le 2\}$.

(c) The curve $\boldsymbol{\gamma}(t) = (\cos t, \sin t)$, $0 \le t \le 2\pi$, forms a positively oriented boundary of $\bar{S}$. Show that $\mathbf{\Phi}\circ\boldsymbol{\gamma}$ is the *negatively* oriented boundary of S. (*Hint:* $\cos t + \sin t = \sqrt{2}\cos(\pi/4 - t)$, and there is a similar formula for $\cos t - \sin t$. *Note:* The switch in orientation is expected, since the Jacobian in part (a) is negative.)

(d) Without using (9), check by comparing areas that $\iint_S dx\,dy = 2\iint_{\bar{S}} du\,dv$, with S and $\bar{S}$ as in part (b).

(e) Show that the result in part (d) agrees with (9).

4. (a) The formula

$$\int_0^1\int_{v-1}^{1-v} 2f(u+v,\, u-v)\,du\,dv = \int_{-1}^1\int_{-1}^x f(x,y)\,dy\,dx$$

is a special case of (9). What choices of φ, ψ, S, and $\bar{S}$ reduce (9) to this?

(b) Use Part (a) to evaluate

$$\int_{-1}^1\int_{-1}^x \frac{1}{x-y-2}\,dy\,dx.$$

5. In the proof of the change of variable formula (2), show that

$$\int_{\gamma^1} M\,dx = \int_{\bar{\gamma}^1} \bar{M}\,dr + \bar{N}\,d\theta.$$

6. In proving (2), we neglected to show that the functions $M, \bar{M}, \bar{N}, M_x$, etc. are continuous. This problem fills the gap, on the assumption that f, f_x, and f_y are continuous and bounded on an open set containing S.

(a) Prove that $M(x,y) = \int_y^{\varphi(x)} f(x,t)\,dt$ is continuous. (Note that

$$M(x,y) - M(x_0,y_0)$$
$$= \left[\int_{y_0}^{\varphi(x)} f(x,t)\,dt - \int_{y_0}^{\varphi(x_0)} f(x_0,t)\,dt\right] + \int_y^{y_0} f(x,t)\,dt;$$

Use Theorem 1 for the term in square brackets, and use the boundedness of f for the other term.)

(b) Prove that $M_x(x,y) = \int_y^{\varphi(x)} f_x(x,t)\,dt + \varphi'(x)f(x,\varphi(x))$ and is continuous. (See §4.1, Problem 6.)

(c) Conclude from parts (a), (b) and a theorem on the composition of continuous functions that $\bar{M}$ and $\bar{N}$ are continuous and have continuous first partial derivatives.

7. The planimeter in Problem 12 of the previous section can be analyzed in a slightly different way. Let β denote the angle made by the first arm and the x axis. Then if $\boldsymbol{\gamma}$ denotes the same curve as in Problem 12 above, we have $\boldsymbol{\gamma}(t) = (\rho \cos \beta(t), \rho \sin \beta(t))$, and the turning of the wheel is proportional to

$$\int_a^b (-\gamma_1' \sin \alpha + \gamma_2' \cos \alpha) = \rho \int_a^b (\sin \alpha \sin \beta + \cos \alpha \cos \beta)\beta'. \qquad (*)$$

(See part (c) of Problem 12, §4.4.)

(a) Since α and β are functions of t, we have a curve $\mathbf{\Gamma}(t) = (\alpha(t),\beta(t))$ in the $\alpha\beta$ plane. Show that (*) is $\int_{\Gamma} \cos(\beta - \alpha)\,d\beta$.

(b) Suppose $\mathbf{\Gamma}$ forms the positively oriented boundary of a region $\bar{S}$ in the $\alpha\beta$ plane; show that (*) equals $\rho \iint_{\bar{S}} \sin(\beta - \alpha)\,d\alpha\,d\beta$.

(c) For any given α and β, the coordinates of the endpoint $\mathbf{E}$ of the planimeter are

$$x = \rho \cos \beta + R \cos \alpha = \varphi(\alpha,\beta)$$
$$y = \rho \sin \beta + R \sin \alpha = \psi(\alpha,\beta).$$

Suppose that $\mathbf{\Phi} = (\varphi,\psi)$ defines a one-to-one function from $\bar{S}$ onto the region S in the xy plane whose area A we are computing. Suppose further that $\sin(\beta - \alpha) \geq 0$ in $\bar{S}$. Show that

$$\rho \iint_{\bar{S}} \sin(\beta - \alpha)\,d\alpha\,d\beta = \frac{1}{R} \iint_S dx\,dy = \frac{1}{R} A.$$

Chapter V

Functions of n Variables

The elementary theory of functions of n variables is so similar to the two-variable theory that the first few sections of this chapter are practically a review of Chapter IV:

§5.1 Continuity, partial derivatives, and gradients

§5.2 The implicit function theorem

§5.3 Taylor expansions

§5.4 Vector fields and line integrals in R^3.

These four sections give the basic outline, omitting the many proofs that are virtually the same as those already given in the case of two variables. The last four sections introduce new material:

§5.5 Surface integrals and Stokes' theorem

§5.6 Triple integrals

§5.7 The divergence theorem

§5.8 A very brief introduction to differential forms.

Here, again, the topics are covered in outline, partly because of the similarity to Chapter IV, but primarily because a thorough discussion is beyond the scope of this book. For a thorough discussion, see the references listed at the end of §4.1.

5.1 CONTINUITY, PARTIAL DERIVATIVES, AND GRADIENTS

The *domain* of a function f of n variables is a set in R^n, and f assigns to each point $\mathbf{X}$ in its domain a real number $f(\mathbf{X})$. The *range* of f is the set of values assumed by f, that is, the set $\{y: y = f(\mathbf{X}) \text{ for some } \mathbf{X}\}$. The graph of f is the set

$$\{(\mathbf{X},y) : \mathbf{X} \text{ is in the domain of } f \text{ and } y = f(\mathbf{X})\}.$$

Here, $\mathbf{X}$ denotes a point $(x_1, \ldots, x_n)$ in R^n, y is a real number, and $(\mathbf{X},y)$ is the point $(x_1, \ldots, x_n, y)$ in R^{n+1}. When $n = 3$, the graph lies in R^4 and cannot be visualized very well. However, the *level surfaces*

$$\{\mathbf{X}: f(\mathbf{X}) = c\}$$

are sets in R^3, and are sometimes rather easy to visualize. For example, if

$$f(x_1,x_2,x_3) = x_1^2 + x_2^2 + 2x_3^2,$$

then the level surface where $f = c$ is an *ellipsoid* for $c > 0$ (see Fig. 1).

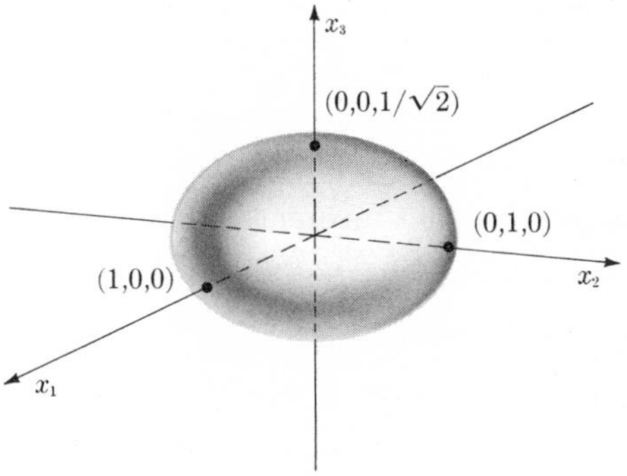

FIGURE 5.1

A function f is *continuous* at $\mathbf{X}_0$ if (i) $f(\mathbf{X}_0)$ is defined, and (ii) for every $\epsilon > 0$, there is $\delta > 0$ such that for all $\mathbf{X}$ in the domain of f,

$$|\mathbf{X} - \mathbf{X}_0| < \delta \Rightarrow |f(\mathbf{X}) - f(\mathbf{X}_0)| < \epsilon.$$

A function f has *limit* L at $\mathbf{X}_0$ if, for every $\epsilon > 0$, there is $\delta > 0$ such that

$$0 < |\mathbf{X} - \mathbf{X}_0| < \delta \Rightarrow f(\mathbf{X}) \text{ is defined and } |f(\mathbf{X}) - L| < \epsilon.$$

In treating continuity it is useful to consider the more general concept of *vector function*, that is, a function $\mathbf{F}$ whose domain is a set S in R^n, and which assigns to each point $\mathbf{X}$ in S a point $\mathbf{F}(\mathbf{X})$ in R^m. We have already studied various special cases in some detail:

$n = 1, m = 1$	(real-valued functions of one variable)
$n = 1$, m general	(m-dimensional vector functions of one variable, curves, §2.1)
$n = 2, m = 1$	(real functions of two variables, Chapter III)
$n = 2, m = 2$	(vector fields in the plane, §4.2; change of variable in double integrals, §4.5).

A vector function $\mathbf{F}$ is *continuous* at $\mathbf{X}_0$ if (i) $\mathbf{F}(\mathbf{X}_0)$ is defined and (ii) for every $\epsilon > 0$, there is $\delta > 0$ such that for all $\mathbf{X}$ in the domain of $\mathbf{F}$,

$$|\mathbf{X} - \mathbf{X}_0| < \delta \quad \Rightarrow \quad |\mathbf{F}(\mathbf{X}) - \mathbf{F}(\mathbf{X}_0)| < \epsilon.$$

A vector function $\mathbf{F}$ has m components $f_1, \ldots, f_m$, real-valued functions of n variables, such that $\mathbf{F}(\mathbf{X}) = (f_1(\mathbf{X}), \ldots, f_m(\mathbf{X}))$. It is easy to prove that $\mathbf{F}$ is continuous at $\mathbf{X}_0$ if and only if each component f_j is continuous at $\mathbf{X}_0$ (Problem 13).

Let S be a set in R^n, and T be a set in R^m. Given a vector-valued function $\mathbf{F}: S \to R^m$ and another function $\mathbf{G}: T \to R^l$, we can form the composition $\mathbf{G}\circ\mathbf{F}(\mathbf{X}) = \mathbf{G}(\mathbf{F}(\mathbf{X}))$, Fig. 2. It can be proved (exactly as in the case of one variable) that *if $\mathbf{F}$ is continuous at $\mathbf{X}_0$ and $\mathbf{G}$ is continuous at $\mathbf{F}(\mathbf{X}_0)$, then $\mathbf{G}\circ\mathbf{F}$ is continuous at $\mathbf{X}_0$*.

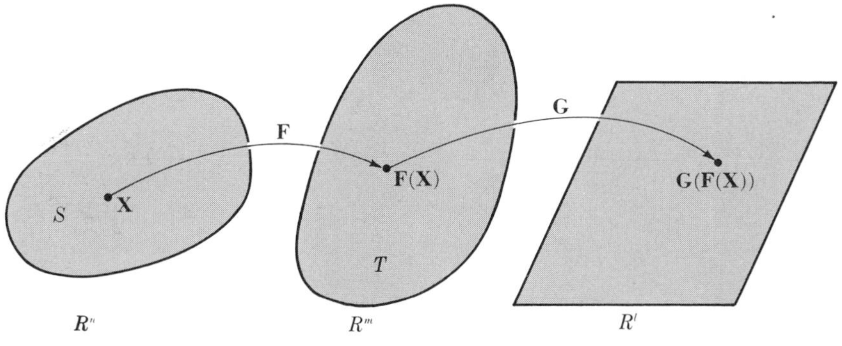

FIGURE 5.2

A set S in R^n is *open* if for every point $\mathbf{X}_0$ in S there is an open ball of positive radius centered at $\mathbf{X}_0$ and contained entirely in S. Intuitively, an open set (like an open interval) is one that contains none of its boundary points. When the domain of a function $\mathbf{F}$ is an open set, then continuity can be expressed in terms of limits: $\mathbf{F}$ is continuous at $\mathbf{X}_0$ if and only if

$$\lim_{\mathbf{X}\to\mathbf{X}_0} |\mathbf{F}(\mathbf{X}) - \mathbf{F}(\mathbf{X}_0)| = 0.$$

Let f be a real-valued function of one variable. The *partial derivatives* of f, denoted by $D_1 f, \ldots, D_n f$, are defined by

$$D_j f(\mathbf{X}) = \lim_{h \to 0} \frac{f(x_1, \ldots, x_j + h, x_{j+1}, \ldots, x_n) - f(x_1, \ldots, x_j, \ldots, x_n)}{h}.$$

Thus, to compute $D_j f$, hold all variables except x_j fixed, and differentiate with respect to x_j in the usual way. This derivative is also denoted

$$\frac{\partial f}{\partial x_j} \quad \text{or} \quad f_{x_j}.$$

For example, if

$$f(x_1,x_2,x_3) = x_1^2 + x_2^2 + 2x_3^2,$$

then

$$D_1 f(x_1,x_2,x_3) = f_{x_1} = \frac{\partial f}{\partial x_1} = 2x_1$$

$$D_2 f(x_1,x_2,x_3) = f_{x_2} = \frac{\partial f}{\partial x_2} = 2x_2$$

$$D_3 f(x_1,x_2,x_3) = f_{x_3} = \frac{\partial f}{\partial x_3} = 4x_3.$$

When the partial derivatives are continuous in an open set, then "mixed partials" may be taken in any order; for example,

$$D_jD_k f = D_kD_j f, \qquad D_1^2D_3 f = D_1D_3D_1 f = D_3D_1^2 f, \qquad \text{etc.}$$

This follows from the corresponding result for functions of two variables (Theorem 10, §3.6), since $D_jD_k f$ and $D_kD_j f$ are computed by holding constant all but the two variables x_j and x_k.

In the case of three variables, it is customary to write $\mathbf{P} = (x,y,z)$ instead of $\mathbf{X} = (x_1,x_2,x_3)$, and f_y or $\partial f/\partial y$ instead of $D_2 f$, etc. Thus if $g(x,y,z) = xe^{yz}$, then

$$g_x = e^{yz}, \qquad g_y = xze^{yz}, \qquad \frac{\partial g}{\partial z} = xye^{yz}.$$

The concept of *differentiability* of f requires more than the mere existence of the partial derivatives; it is based on the relation between f and an appropriate polynomial of first degree, i.e. a function g of the form

$$g(\mathbf{X}) = \mathbf{X} \cdot \mathbf{M} + c;$$

here, c is a constant and $\mathbf{M}$ is a given vector in R^n, called the *slope* of g. Given a point $\mathbf{X}_0$, a slope vector $\mathbf{M}$, and a constant d, there is a unique first degree polynomial g with slope $\mathbf{M}$ such that $g(\mathbf{X}_0) = d$, namely

$$g(\mathbf{X}) = d + (\mathbf{X} - \mathbf{X}_0) \cdot \mathbf{M}. \tag{1}$$

The graph of g is a hyperplane in R^{n+1}; equation (1) gives the hyperplane of prescribed slope $\mathbf{M}$ passing through a given point $(\mathbf{X}_0, d)$ in R^{n+1}.

From this brief digression on first degree polynomials, we return to the concept of differentiability. A function f is *differentiable at* $\mathbf{X}_0$ if and only if there is a first degree polynomial

$$g(\mathbf{X}) = f(\mathbf{X}_0) + (\mathbf{X} - \mathbf{X}_0)\cdot\mathbf{M}$$

such that

$$\lim_{\mathbf{X}\to\mathbf{X}_0} \frac{f(\mathbf{X}) - g(\mathbf{X})}{|\mathbf{X} - \mathbf{X}_0|} = 0. \tag{3}$$

When f is differentiable at $\mathbf{X}_0$, then the partial derivatives $D_1 f(\mathbf{X}_0), \ldots, D_n f(\mathbf{X}_0)$ all exist, and the vector $\mathbf{M}$ in (2) is the *gradient*

$$\nabla f(\mathbf{X}_0) = (D_1 f(\mathbf{X}_0), \ldots, D_n f(\mathbf{X}_0)).$$

Conversely, when the first partials all exist in an open ball about $\mathbf{X}_0$ *and are continuous* at $\mathbf{X}_0$, then f is differentiable at $\mathbf{X}_0$. When the first partials exist and are continuous, f is called *continuously differentiable.*

If f is differentiable at $\mathbf{X}_0$, and $\boldsymbol{\gamma}$ is a curve in R^n with $\boldsymbol{\gamma}(t_0) = \mathbf{X}_0$, and $\boldsymbol{\gamma}'(t_0)$ exists, then the *chain rule* holds:

$$(f\circ\boldsymbol{\gamma})'(t_0) = \nabla f(\boldsymbol{\gamma}(t_0))\cdot\boldsymbol{\gamma}'(t_0), \tag{4}$$

or in Leibniz notation

$$\frac{df\circ\boldsymbol{\gamma}}{dt} = \sum_1^n \frac{\partial f}{\partial x_j}\frac{dx_j}{dt}. \tag{5}$$

If we take the particular curve $\boldsymbol{\gamma}(t) = \mathbf{X}_0 + t\mathbf{U}$, with $\mathbf{U}$ a unit vector, then at time zero $\boldsymbol{\gamma}$ moves through the point $\mathbf{X}_0$ in the direction $\mathbf{U}$ (Fig. 3); the derivative of $f\circ\boldsymbol{\gamma}$,

$$(f\circ\boldsymbol{\gamma})'(0) = \nabla f(\mathbf{X}_0)\cdot\mathbf{U},$$

is called the *directional derivative* of f in the direction $\mathbf{U}$. This is maximum when $\mathbf{U}$ points in the direction $\nabla f(\mathbf{X}_0)$, and zero when $\mathbf{U}$ is orthogonal to $\nabla f(\mathbf{X}_0)$.

If $\boldsymbol{\gamma}$ is any curve lying in a level surface

$$\{\mathbf{X}: f(\mathbf{X}) = c\}, \tag{6}$$

then $f\circ\boldsymbol{\gamma} \equiv c$, so $(f\circ\boldsymbol{\gamma})' \equiv 0$. Since $(f\circ\boldsymbol{\gamma})' = (\nabla f\circ\boldsymbol{\gamma})\cdot\boldsymbol{\gamma}'$, it follows that ∇f is orthogonal to $\boldsymbol{\gamma}'$, in other words, *the gradient at each point of the level surface* (6) *is orthogonal to every curve lying in that surface* (Fig. 4). Because of this, we say simply that the gradient is orthogonal to the level surface (just as in two dimensions the gradient is orthogonal to the level line, or contour line). Further, when $\mathbf{X}_0$ is on the level surface (6) and $\nabla f(\mathbf{X}_0) \neq \mathbf{0}$,

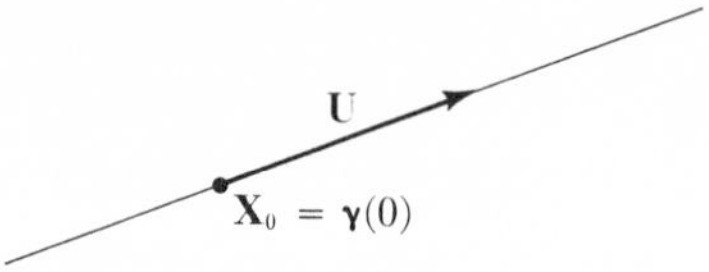

FIGURE 5.3

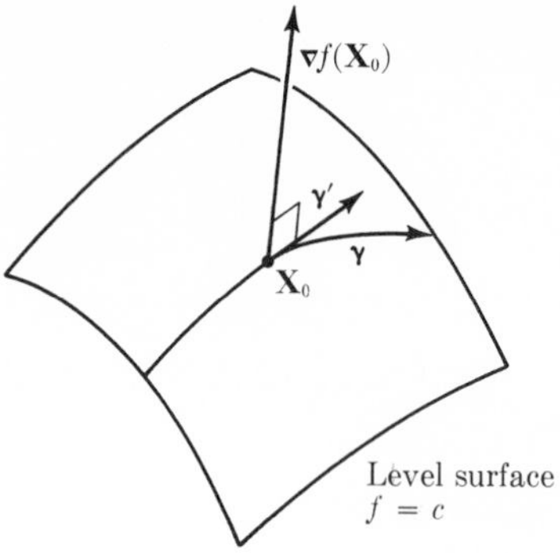

FIGURE 5.4

we define the *tangent plane* to the surface at $\mathbf{X}_0$ to be the plane with equation

$$(\mathbf{X} - \mathbf{X}_0) \cdot \nabla f(\mathbf{X}_0) = 0.$$

When $n = 2$, the level "surface" is actually a curve, and the tangent "plane" is actually a line; when $n = 3$, the tangent plane is a genuine two-dimensional plane in R^3, and when $n > 3$, it is an $(n - 1)$-dimensional object called a "hyperplane."

In the case $n = 3$, a possible conflict appears between the definition of tangent plane to the level surface of a function of three variables given here and the definition of tangent plane to the graph of a function of two variables given in the previous chapter. What if a level surface is also a graph? Do the definitions then agree? They do, and it is easy to prove this by the chain rule. (See Example 2 below.)

The chain rule (4) or (5) applies to partial derivatives as well. Suppose that f is a continuously differentiable function of n variables, and that $\varphi_1, \ldots, \varphi_n$ are continuously differentiable functions of m variables. Then the composite function

$$F(x_1, \ldots, x_m) = f(\varphi_1(x_1, \ldots, x_m), \ldots, \varphi_n(x_1, \ldots, x_m))$$

has continuous partial derivatives given by

$$D_1F = D_1f(\varphi_1, \ldots, \varphi_n)D_1\varphi_1 + D_2f(\varphi_1, \ldots, \varphi_n)D_1\varphi_2 + \cdots + D_nf(\varphi_1, \ldots, \varphi_n)D_1\varphi_n$$

$$\vdots$$

$$D_mF = D_1f(\varphi_1, \ldots, \varphi_n)D_m\varphi_1 + \cdots + D_nf(\varphi_1, \ldots, \varphi_n)D_m\varphi_n\,.$$

These formulas may look more familiar in Leibniz notation, as in §3.4.

If we represent the situation by a scheme such as

$$\begin{array}{ccccc} (x_1, \ldots, x_m) & \rightarrow & (y_1, \ldots, y_n) & \rightarrow & z \\ y_j = \varphi_j(x_1, \ldots, x_m), & & z = f(y_1, \ldots, y_n) & = & F(x_1, \ldots, x_m) \end{array} \tag{7}$$

then the derivatives of the composite function F are given by

$$\frac{\partial z}{\partial x_1} = \frac{\partial z}{\partial y_1}\frac{\partial y_1}{\partial x_1} + \frac{\partial z}{\partial y_2}\frac{\partial y_2}{\partial x_1} + \cdots + \frac{\partial z}{\partial y_n}\frac{\partial y_n}{\partial x_1}$$

$$\vdots$$

$$\frac{\partial z}{\partial x_m} = \frac{\partial z}{\partial y_1}\frac{\partial y_1}{\partial x_m} + \quad \cdots \quad + \frac{\partial z}{\partial y_n}\frac{\partial y_n}{\partial x_m}.$$

Example 1. Find the equation of the tangent plane to the hyperboloid

$$x^2 + y^2 - z^2 = 1 \tag{8}$$

at the point $\mathbf{P}_0 = (1,1,-1)$. (See Fig. 5.)

First solution. Equation (8) defines a level surface for the function $f(x,y,z) = x^2 + y^2 - z^2$, so the gradient $\nabla f = (2x,2y,-2z)$ is normal to the tangent plane. Substituting $(1,1,-1)$ for (x,y,z) gives the normal $\mathbf{N} = (2,2,2)$, so the tangent plane has the equation $\mathbf{N} \cdot (\mathbf{P} - \mathbf{P}_0) = 0$, or

$$2(x-1) + 2(y-1) + 2(z+1) = 0,$$

or

$$x + y + z = 1.$$

Second solution. Near the point $(1,1,-1)$, equation (8) determines z as a function of x and y,

$$z = \varphi(x,y) = -\sqrt{x^2 + y^2 - 1}$$

(*not* $z = \sqrt{x^2 + y^2 - 1}$). According to the previous chapter, the tangent plane has the equation

$$\begin{aligned} z &= \varphi(\mathbf{P}_0) + (\mathbf{P} - \mathbf{P}_0) \cdot \nabla\varphi(\mathbf{P}_0) \\ &= \varphi(1,1) + (x-1)\varphi_x(1,1) + (y-1)\varphi_y(1,1) \\ &= -1 + (x-1)(-1) + (y-1)(-1), \end{aligned}$$

or

$$(z+1) + (x-1) + (y-1) = 0.$$

This is the same plane found in the first solution.

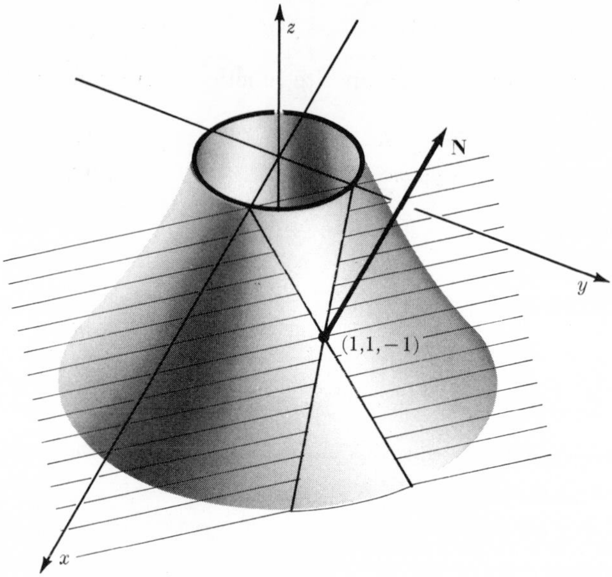

FIGURE 5.5 Graph and tangent plane shown only for $z \leq 0$

Example 2. Suppose that the level surface $\{(x,y,z): f(x,y,z) = c\}$ contains the graph of a differentiable function φ. Let $\mathbf{P}_0 = (x_0,y_0,z_0)$ be a point on the graph, and suppose that f has continuous derivatives and $\nabla f(\mathbf{P}_0) \neq \mathbf{0}$. Prove that the tangent plane to the graph of φ at $\mathbf{P}_0$ has the equation

$$(\mathbf{P} - \mathbf{P}_0)\cdot\nabla f(\mathbf{P}_0) = 0.$$

Solution. Since the graph of φ lies in the level surface of f, we have

$$f(x,y,\varphi(x,y)) \equiv c.$$

Differentiating this with respect to x by the chain rule,

$$D_1 f(x,y,\varphi(x,y)) + D_3 f(x,y,\varphi(x,y)) \frac{\partial \varphi}{\partial x} \equiv 0,$$

and differentiating with respect to y,

$$D_2 f(x,y,\varphi(x,y)) + D_3 f(x,y,\varphi(x,y)) \frac{\partial \varphi}{\partial y} \equiv 0. \tag{10}$$

Since $\nabla f(\mathbf{P}_0) \neq \mathbf{0}$, it follows that $D_3 f(\mathbf{P}_0) \neq 0$; (for if $D_3 f(\mathbf{P}_0) = 0$, then

$D_1 f(\mathbf{P}_0) = 0$ by (9), and $D_2 f(\mathbf{P}_0) = 0$ by (10)). Hence we can solve (9) and (10) to find

$$\frac{\partial \varphi}{\partial x} = -\frac{D_1 f}{D_3 f}, \quad \frac{\partial \varphi}{\partial y} = -\frac{D_2 f}{D_3 f}. \tag{11}$$

By §3.3, the tangent plane to the graph of φ at the point $\mathbf{P}_0 = (x_0,y_0,z_0)$ has the equation

$$(z - z_0) - (x - x_0)\frac{\partial \varphi}{\partial x}(x_0,y_0) - (y - y_0)\frac{\partial \varphi}{\partial y}(x_0,y_0) = 0. \tag{12}$$

Substituting the expressions from (11) and multiplying by $D_3 f$ reduces (12) to the form $(\mathbf{P} - \mathbf{P}_0)\cdot\nabla f(\mathbf{P}_0) = 0$, and the problem is solved.

Example 3. Suppose that the temperature at the point (x,y,z) is

$$T(x,y,z) = xy + yz + zx.$$

A particle travels along the curve

$$\boldsymbol{\gamma}(t) = (t, 3t^2, 2\cos t).$$

What is the rate of change of temperature observed by the particle at time t?

First solution. The temperature observed at the point $\boldsymbol{\gamma}(t)$ is $T(\boldsymbol{\gamma}(t))$, so we compute the derivative $(T\circ\boldsymbol{\gamma})'(t) = \nabla T(\boldsymbol{\gamma}(t))\cdot\boldsymbol{\gamma}'(t)$. We have

$$\nabla T(x,y,z) = (T_x,T_y,T_z) = (y + z, x + z, x + y),$$

so

$$\nabla T(\boldsymbol{\gamma}(t)) = (3t^2 + 2\cos t, t + 2\cos t, t + 3t^2).$$

Further,

$$\boldsymbol{\gamma}'(t) = (1, 6t, -2\sin t),$$

so

$$\begin{aligned}(T\circ\boldsymbol{\gamma})'(t) &= (3t^2 + 2\cos t)\cdot 1 + (t + 2\cos t)\cdot 6t + (t + 3t^2)(-2\sin t)\\ &= 9t^2 + (12t + 2)\cos t - 2(t + 3t^2)\sin t.\end{aligned}$$

Second solution. At time t the particle is at the point with coordinates

$$x = t, \qquad y = 3t^2, \qquad z = 2\cos t,$$

so the temperature observed is

$$xy + yz + zx = 3t^3 + 6t^2\cos t + 2t\cos t,$$

and the rate of change is

$$9t^2 + (12t + 2)\cos t - (6t^2 + 2t)\sin t.$$

Example 4. Suppose that the "electrical potential" at the point (x,y,z) is $E(x,y,z) = x^2 + y^2 - 2z^2$. According to the principles of electrodynamics, a positively charged particle is accelerated in the direction of maximum decrease of potential. What is the direction of acceleration at the point $(1,3,2)$?

Solution. The maximum decrease of E is the maximum increase of $-E$, so the charged particle moves in the direction $\nabla(-E) = -\nabla E$. We find that

$$-\nabla E = (-2x,-2y,4z),$$

and the value at (1,3,2) is

$$(-2,-6,8);$$

hence the direction of acceleration is parallel to $(-2,-6,8)$, or parallel to $(-1,-3,4)$.

PROBLEMS

1. Let $f(x,y,z) = e^{xy}\cos(yz)$, and compute the following derivatives.
   (a) f_x
   (b) $D_1^2 f$
   (c) f_{xy}
   (d) $D_2D_1 f$
   (e) $D_2D_1D_3 f$
   (f) $D_1D_2D_3 f$

2. Show that each of the following functions satisfies Laplace's equation $f_{xx} + f_{yy} + f_{zz} = 0$. (This equation is satisfied by electrical potentials, and by steady-state temperature distributions.)
   (a) $x^2 - 2y^2 + z^2$
   (b) $(x^2 + y^2 + z^2)^{-1/2}$
   (c) $2x^3 - 3(y^2 + z^2)x$
   (d) $e^{5x+12y}\sin 13z$
   (e) $e^{3y+4z}\cos 5x$
   (f) $\cos 3x \sin 4y e^{5z}$

3. Find an equation of the plane tangent to the given surface at the given point.
   (a) $x^2 + y^2 + 2z^2 = 1$, at (1,0,0)
   (b) $e^{xy}\cos(yz) = 1$, at (1,0,1)
   (c) $x^2 + y^3 - z^4 = -16$, at $(1,-1,2)$

4. Find an equation of the hyperplane tangent to the given "surface" at the given point.
   (a) $x_1^2 + x_2^2 = 2$, at (1,1)
   (b) $x_1^2 + x_2^2 + x_3^2 + x_4^2 = 4$, at (1,1,1,1)
   (c) $x_1^2 + x_2^2 - x_3^2 - x_4^2 = 0$, at $(1,1,1,-1)$

5. Suppose that the temperature T at the point (x,y,z) is given by $T(x,y,z) = xyz$.
   (a) Starting at (1,2,3), in what direction should you move to achieve the maximum rate of increase of temperature?
   (b) Starting at $(1,-3,1)$, in what direction should you move to achieve the maximum rate of cooling?

6. Suppose that ∇f is orthogonal to a differentiable curve γ at every point on γ. Prove that f is *constant* on γ, in other words, that γ lies in a single level surface of f.

7. (a) Prove that the graph of any function f of two variables is automatically a level surface of a function F of three variables. (Hint: All you have to do is write $z = f(x,y)$ in the form $F(x,y,z) = 0$.)
   (b) Show that not every level surface is a graph.

8. Suppose that f is a function of three variables having continuous partial derivatives, and define a new function

$$F(r,\theta,z) = f(r\cos\theta, r\sin\theta, z).$$

   (a) Find F_r, F_θ, and F_z in terms of $D_1 f$, $D_2 f$, $D_3 f$.
   (b) Show that

$$D_1^2 f + D_2^2 f + D_3^2 f = F_{rr} + \frac{1}{r} F_r + \frac{1}{r^2} F_{\theta\theta} + F_{zz}.$$

   (The variables r, θ, and z are called *cylindrical coordinates* of (x,y,z) when $x = r\cos\theta$, $y = r\sin\theta$, $z = z$. See Fig. 6. The formula in part (b) shows how to write Laplace's equation in cylindrical coordinates.)

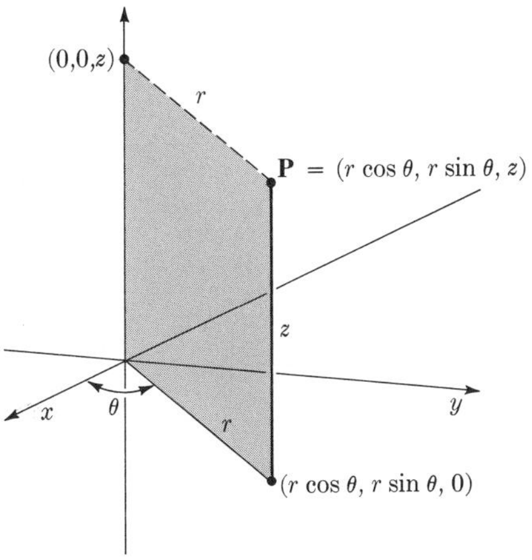

FIGURE 5.6

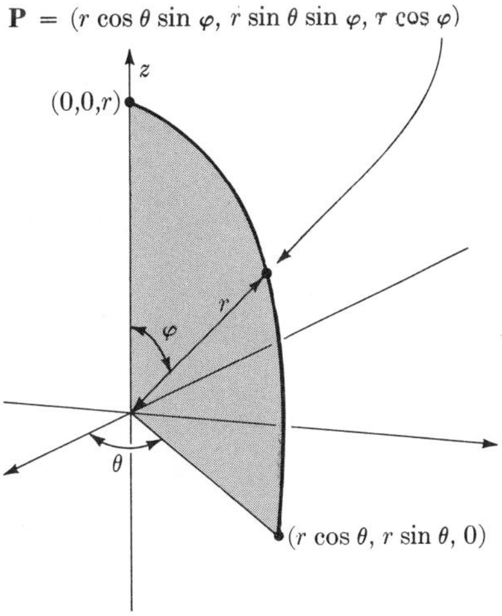

FIGURE 5.7

9. Suppose that f is a function of three variables having continuous partial derivatives, and set

$$F(r,\theta,\varphi) = f(r\cos\theta\sin\varphi, r\sin\theta\sin\varphi, r\cos\varphi).$$

(See Fig. 7; r, θ, and φ are the *spherical coordinates* of (x,y,z) when $x = r\cos\theta\sin\varphi$, $y = r\sin\theta\sin\varphi$, $z = r\cos\varphi$.)

(a) Show that for $r \sin \varphi \neq 0$,

$$D_1^2f + D_2^2f + D_3^2f = F_{rr} + \frac{2}{r}F_r + \frac{1}{r^2}F_{\varphi\varphi} + \frac{\cot \varphi}{r^2}F_\varphi + \frac{1}{r^2 \sin^2 \varphi}F_{\theta\theta}.$$

(b) Show that if $f(x,y,z) = g(\sqrt{x^2+y^2+z^2})$, where $g(r)$ has continuous second derivatives for $r > 0$, then

$$D_1^2f + D_2^2f + D_3^2f = g''(r) + \frac{2}{r}g'(r) \quad \text{with } r = \sqrt{x^2+y^2+z^2}.$$

(c) Show that $g(\sqrt{x^2+y^2+z^2})$ satisfies $f_{xx} + f_{yy} + f_{zz} = 0$ (Laplace's equation) if and only if $g(r) = A/r + B$ for some constants A and B.

10. Prove the chain rule

$$(f \circ \boldsymbol{\gamma})' = \sum_1^n \gamma_j'(D_jf)\circ\boldsymbol{\gamma}$$

or

$$\frac{df}{dt} = \sum_1^n \frac{df}{dx_j}\frac{dx_j}{dt}.$$

11. Prove that if f has continuous first partial derivatives at $\mathbf{P}_0 = (x_0,y_0,z_0)$, then f is differentiable at $\mathbf{P}_0$. (Hint: $f(x,y,z) - f(x_0,y_0,z_0) = f(x,y,z) - f(x_0,y,z) + f(x_0,y,z) - f(x_0,y_0,z) + f(x_0,y_0,z) - f(x_0,y_0,z_0)$.)

12. Prove the theorem on continuity of a composite function: *If* $\mathbf{F}$ *is continuous at* $\mathbf{X}_0$ *and* $\mathbf{G}$ *is continuous at* $\mathbf{F}(\mathbf{X}_0)$, *then* $\mathbf{G}\circ\mathbf{F}$ *is continuous at* $\mathbf{X}_0$.

13. Suppose that $f_1, \ldots, f_m$ are the components of a vector-valued function $\mathbf{F}$.

(a) Prove that if $\mathbf{F}$ is continuous at $\mathbf{X}_0$, then so are $f_1, \ldots, f_m$. (Hint: See the proof of Theorem 2, §2.1.)

(b) Prove that if $f_1, \ldots, f_m$ are all continuous at $\mathbf{X}_0$, then so is $\mathbf{F}$.

5.2 THE IMPLICIT FUNCTION THEOREM

Section 3.5 proved that under certain natural hypotheses an equation

$$f(x,y) = c \tag{1}$$

determines y as a function of x, locally, near any point (x_0,y_0) on the contour line defined by (1). In other words, near (x_0,y_0) the contour line can be represented as the graph of a function of one variable.

There is a similar *implicit function theorem* which states that under certain natural hypotheses, the equation

$$f(x_1, \ldots, x_n) = c \tag{2}$$

determines x_n as a function of $x_1, \ldots, x_{n-1}$, locally, near any point $\mathbf{X}_0$ on the level surface (2). To simplify the notation, we take $\mathbf{X}_0 = \mathbf{0}$; then the theorem reads as follows:

Suppose that $f(\mathbf{0}) = c$, and $D_n f(\mathbf{0}) \neq 0$, and f has continuous first partial derivatives in an open set containing the origin. Then there is a cylinder

$$C = \{\mathbf{X}: x_1^2 + \cdots + x_{n-1}^2 < \delta^2 \text{ and } |x_n| < \epsilon\}$$

and there is a function φ with continuous first derivatives defined in the ball

$$B = \{(x_1, \ldots, x_{n-1}): \sum_1^{n-1} x_j^2 < \delta^2\}$$

such that for $\mathbf{X}$ in C,

$$f(\mathbf{X}) = c \quad \Leftrightarrow \quad x_n = \varphi(x_1, \ldots, x_{n-1}).$$

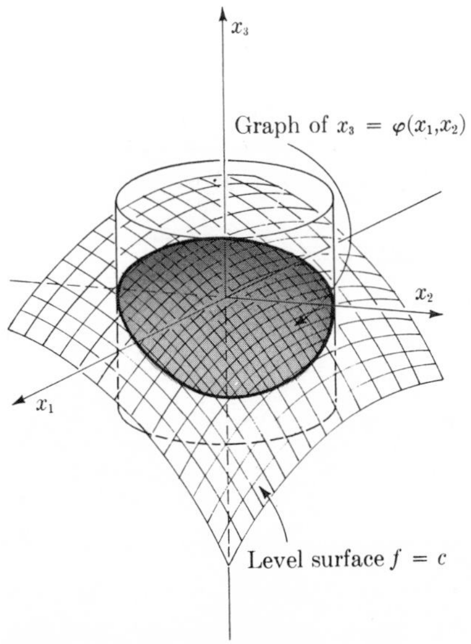

FIGURE 5.8 The cylinder has height 2ϵ and radius δ

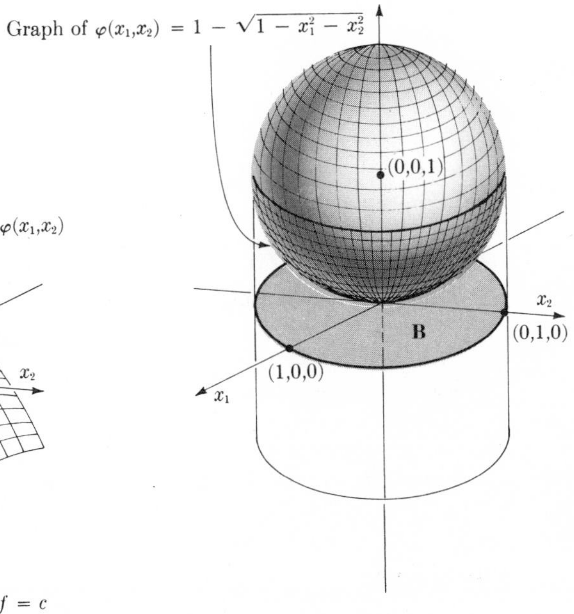

FIGURE 5.9

Figure 8 illustrates the situation with $n = 3$. A simple example is the equation

$$f(x_1,x_2,x_3) = x_1^2 + x_2^2 + (x_3 - 1)^2 = 1,$$

which is satisfied with $x_1 = x_2 = x_3 = 0$. Since $D_3 f(\mathbf{0}) = -2 \neq 0$, the implicit function theorem applies. It is easy to see (from Fig. 9) that the biggest possible B in this case is the unit ball

$$B = \{(x_1,x_2) : x_1^2 + x_2^2 < 1\},$$

that $\varphi(x_1,x_2) = 1 - \sqrt{1 - x_1^2 - x_2^2}$, and that

$$C = \{(x_1,x_2,x_3) : x_1^2 + x_2^2 < 1 \text{ and } |x_3| < 1\}.$$

Of course, we don't usually bother to apply the implicit function theorem when the function φ can be written down so easily; the real point is that an equation like

$$z + \cos(xyz) e^{x^2+y^2+z^2} = 1 \tag{3}$$

defines z as a function of x and y (at least near the origin), although it is not possible to solve (3) explicitly for z.

Example 1. Let $f(x,y,z) = xe^{x+y+z}$. The point $\mathbf{P}_0 = (1,0,-1)$ lies on the level surface $f = 1$. The gradient is $\nabla f = e^{x+y+z}(1 + x,x,x)$; hence $\nabla f(\mathbf{P}_0) = (2,1,1)$. Since

$$\frac{\partial f}{\partial z}(\mathbf{P}_0) = 1 \neq 0,$$

the equation $f = 1$ defines z locally as a function $\varphi(x,y)$; similarly,

$$\frac{\partial f}{\partial x}(\mathbf{P}_0) \neq 0 \qquad \text{and} \qquad \frac{\partial f}{\partial y}(\mathbf{P}_0) \neq 0,$$

so $f = 1$ defines x locally as a function $\psi(y,z)$, or y as a function $\eta(x,z)$. We will deduce some of the properties of $\psi(y,z)$. First of all, since $\mathbf{P}_0 = (1,0,-1)$ is on the level surface $f = 1$, it must be on the graph of ψ, that is, $1 = \psi(0,-1)$. Further, differentiating the identity

$$\psi(y,z)e^{\psi(y,z)+y+z} = 1$$

with respect to y, we get

$$\psi_y e^{\psi+y+z} + \psi e^{\psi+y+z}(\psi_y + 1) = 0,$$

whence $\psi_y = -\psi/(1 + \psi)$, and in particular $\psi_y(0,-1) = -1/2$.

PROBLEMS

1. Let $f(x,y,z) = z + \cos(xyz)e^{x^2+y^2+z^2}$.

(a) Prove that there is a cylinder

$$C = \{(x,y,z) : x^2 + y^2 < \delta^2 \text{ and } |z| < \epsilon\}$$

and there is a function $\varphi(x,y)$ defined for $x^2 + y^2 < \delta^2$ such that for (x,y,z) in C,

$$f(x,y,z) = 1 \quad \Leftrightarrow \quad z = \varphi(x,y).$$

(Simply check that the implicit function theorem applies.)

(b) Show that $\varphi(0,0) = 0$.

(c) Show that $\varphi_x(0,0) = 0$ and $\varphi_y(0,0) = 0$. (Hint: Differentiate $\varphi + \cos(xy\varphi)e^{x^2+y^2+\varphi^2} = 1$.)

(d) Show that $\varphi(x,y) = \varphi(y,x)$.

2. (a) Show that the equation

$$x \sin(x + y + z) = 0$$

determines x as a function $\psi(y,z)$, locally, near the point $(2,-1,-1)$.

(b) Show that $\psi(-1,-1) = 2$.

(c) Show that $\psi_z(-1,-1) = -1$.

(d) Find $\psi_y(-1,-1)$.

(e) Show that there is a function φ of one variable such that $\psi(y,z) = \varphi(y + z)$ when y and z are in the domain of ψ.

3. Let φ be a differentiable function of two variables, and set $f(x,y,z) = [z - \varphi(x,y)]^2$.

(a) Prove that $f = 0 \quad \Leftrightarrow \quad z = \varphi(x,y)$.

(b) Prove that at every point $\mathbf{P}_0$ where $f(\mathbf{P}_0) = 0$ we have $\nabla f(\mathbf{P}_0) = \mathbf{0}$.

(c) Reconcile parts (a) and (b) with the implicit function theorem.

4. Prove the implicit function theorem in R^3: *If f has continuous first partial derivatives at $\mathbf{P}_0 = (x_0,y_0,z_0)$, and $D_3 f(\mathbf{P}_0) \neq 0$, then there is a cylinder*

$$C = \{(x,y,z) : (x - x_0)^2 + (y - y_0)^2 < \delta^2 \text{ and } |z - z_0| < \epsilon\}$$

and a differentiable function φ such that for (x,y,z) in C,

$$f(x,y,z) = f(x_0,y_0,z_0) \quad \Leftrightarrow \quad z = \varphi(x,y).$$

(Hint: Review the proof of the implicit function theorem in §3.5.)

5. The implicit function theorem shows when *one* equation $f(x,y,z) = c$ can determine z as a function of x and y. This problem shows when *two* equations

$$f(x,y,z) = c$$

$$g(x,y,z) = d$$

can determine y and z both as functions of x; thus the two equations together define a curve (Fig. 10).

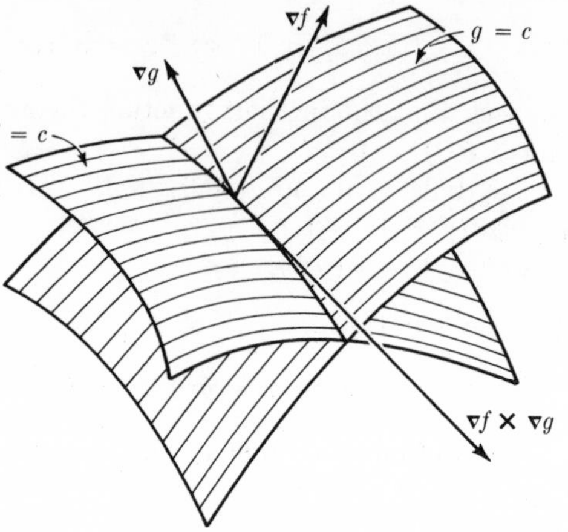

FIGURE 5.10

Suppose that f and g have continuous first partial derivatives at $\mathbf{P}_0 = (x_0,y_0,z_0)$, and the first component of $\nabla f(\mathbf{P}_0) \times \nabla g(\mathbf{P}_0)$ is not zero.

(a) Prove that either $f_z(\mathbf{P}_0) \neq 0$ or $g_z(\mathbf{P}_0) \neq 0$.

(b) Supposing $f_z(\mathbf{P}_0) \neq 0$, show that there is a differentiable function φ and a cylinder C of height 2ϵ centered at $\mathbf{P}_0$ in which

$$f(x,y,z) = f(\mathbf{P}_0) \quad \Leftrightarrow \quad z = \varphi(x,y).$$

(c) Using the result in part (b), show that for points in the cylinder C, the two equations

$$\begin{aligned} f(x,y,z) &= f(\mathbf{P}_0) \\ g(x,y,z) &= g(\mathbf{P}_0) \end{aligned} \tag{4}$$

are equivalent to the equations

$$G(x,y) = g(\mathbf{P}_0), \qquad z = \varphi(x,y)$$

where $G(x,y) = g(x,y,\varphi(x,y))$.

(d) Assuming $f_z(\mathbf{P}_0) \neq 0$ and the first component of $\nabla f(\mathbf{P}_0) \times \nabla g(\mathbf{P}_0)$ is not zero, prove that $G_y(x_0,y_0) \neq 0$.

(e) Prove that there is a rectangle

$$R = \{(x,y,z)\colon |x - x_0| < \delta_1 \text{ and } |y - y_0| < \epsilon_1\}$$

in which the equation $G(x,y) = g(\mathbf{P}_0)$ is equivalent to $y = \psi(x)$, where ψ is a differentiable function.

(f) Prove that for $|x - x_0| < \delta_1$, $|y - y_0| < \epsilon_1$, and $|z - z_0| < \epsilon$, the two equations (4) are equivalent to

$$y = \psi(x)$$

$$z = \varphi(x,\psi(x))$$

or

$$y = \psi_1(x), \qquad z = \psi_2(x). \tag{5}$$

(g) The two equations (5) define a curve, given parametrically by

$$x = t, \qquad y = \psi_1(t), \qquad z = \psi_2(t).$$

Prove that $\nabla f(\mathbf{P}_0) \times \nabla g(\mathbf{P}_0)$ is tangent to this curve at time $t = x_0$.

(h) Suppose that the *third* component of $\nabla f(\mathbf{P}_0) \times \nabla g(\mathbf{P}_0)$ is not zero; draw a conclusion analogous to the one in part (f) above.

6. Suppose $\mathbf{P}_0 = (x_0,y_0,z_0)$ lies on the level surface $S = \{\mathbf{P}: f(\mathbf{P}) = c\}$, and $g(\mathbf{P}_0) \geq g(\mathbf{P})$ for all $\mathbf{P}$ on the surface S. Assuming that f and g have continuous derivatives, and that $\nabla f(\mathbf{P}_0) \neq \mathbf{0}$, prove that there is a "Lagrange multiplier" λ such that $\nabla g(\mathbf{P}_0) = \lambda \nabla f(\mathbf{P}_0)$. (Hint: See the discussion of Lagrange multipliers in §3.5.)

7. Find the minimum of $g(x,y,z) = x^2 + y^2 + z^2$ on the surface defined by $xyz = 1$. (You are finding the point on the surface that is closest to the origin. Use Lagrange multipliers, Problem 6, and assume that a minimum exists.)

8. Suppose that $\mathbf{P}_0 = (x_0,y_0,z_0)$ lies in the set

$$C = \{\mathbf{P}: f(\mathbf{P}) = c \text{ and } g(\mathbf{P}) = d\},$$

and suppose that h is a function such that $h(\mathbf{P}_0) \geq h(\mathbf{P})$ for every $\mathbf{P}$ in C. Prove that $\nabla h(\mathbf{P}_0) \cdot (\nabla f(\mathbf{P}_0) \times \nabla g(\mathbf{P}_0)) = 0$. (Hint: Use Problem 5. Geometrically, the condition $\nabla h \cdot (\nabla f \times \nabla g) = 0$ says that ∇h is orthogonal to the curve C at the given point.)

9. Find the maximum of $h(x,y,z) = x^2 + y^2 + z^2$ on the intersection of the two surfaces $xyz = 1$, $x^2 + y^2 + 2z^2 = 4$. (Hint 1: Assume that a maximum exists. Hint 2: The intersection of the two surfaces is the set of points (x,y,z) such that

$$f(x,y,z) = xyz = 1 \tag{6}$$

and

$$g(x,y,z) = x^2 + y^2 + 2z^2 = 4. \tag{7}$$

By Problem 8, you are looking for points $\mathbf{P}_0$ that satisfy (6), (7), and the equation $\nabla h \cdot (\nabla f \times \nabla g) = 0$. There are four such points, and two of them maximize h.)

5.3 TAYLOR EXPANSIONS

The Taylor expansion in n variables approximates $f(\mathbf{A} + \mathbf{H})$ by a polynomial in $\mathbf{H}$; the approximation is best when $\mathbf{H}$ is small, or when the degree of the polynomial is large. To obtain a simple expression for the approximating polynomial, we introduce the "vector operator"

$$\nabla = (D_1, \ldots, D_n)$$

and the dot product $\mathbf{H}\cdot\nabla$, defined by

$$(\mathbf{H}\cdot\nabla f)(\mathbf{X}) = \sum_{j=1}^{n} h_j D_j f(\mathbf{X}). \tag{1}$$

Then the kth *degree Taylor polynomial* of f at the point $\mathbf{A}$ is defined to be

$$f_k(\mathbf{A},\mathbf{H}) = \sum_{j=0}^{k} \frac{1}{j!} ((\mathbf{H}\cdot\nabla)^j f)\ (\mathbf{A}).$$

The first term, $\frac{1}{0!}((H\cdot\nabla)^0 f)(\mathbf{A})$, stands for $f(\mathbf{A})$, and the second term is simply (1) with $\mathbf{X} = \mathbf{A}$. In the remaining terms, the derivatives in $(\mathbf{H}\cdot\nabla)^j$ are applied to f, with $\mathbf{H}$ considered constant; thus if the second derivatives of f are continuous at $\mathbf{A}$, we have

$$\begin{aligned}((\mathbf{H}\cdot\nabla)^2 f)\ (\mathbf{A}) &= (h_1D_1 + \cdots + h_nD_n)^2 f(\mathbf{A}) \qquad (2)\\ &= \sum_{l=1}^{n}\sum_{m=1}^{n} h_l h_m D_l D_m f(\mathbf{A})\\ &= h_1^2 D_1^2 f(\mathbf{A}) + \cdots + h_n^2 D_n^2 f(\mathbf{A})\\ &\quad + 2[h_1h_2D_1D_2 f(\mathbf{A}) + h_1h_3D_1D_3 f(\mathbf{A}) + \cdots\\ &\qquad + h_{n-1}h_nD_{n-1}D_n f(\mathbf{A})],\end{aligned}$$

where the square brackets above contain all the "cross" terms that come from expanding the square on the right-hand side of (2).

Taylor's theorem says that if all the derivatives of f of order $\leq k$ are continuous in a ball of radius ϵ about $\mathbf{A}$, then for every $|\mathbf{H}| < \epsilon$ we can write

$$f(\mathbf{A} + \mathbf{H}) = f_{k-1}(\mathbf{A},\mathbf{H}) + \frac{1}{k!}(\mathbf{H}\cdot\nabla)^k f(\mathbf{A} + \theta\mathbf{H})$$

for some number θ between 0 and 1. It follows that

$$\lim_{\mathbf{H}\to 0} \frac{f(\mathbf{A} + \mathbf{H}) - f_k(\mathbf{A},\mathbf{H})}{|\mathbf{H}|^k} = 0. \tag{3}$$

In particular, taking $k = 1$, we have the first degree Taylor polynomial

$$f_1(\mathbf{A},\mathbf{H}) = f(\mathbf{A}) + \mathbf{H}\cdot\nabla f(\mathbf{A}),$$

and (3) becomes

$$\lim_{\mathbf{H}\to\mathbf{0}} \frac{f(\mathbf{A}+\mathbf{H}) - f(\mathbf{A}) - \mathbf{H}\cdot\nabla f(\mathbf{A})}{|\mathbf{H}|} = 0. \tag{4}$$

This is precisely the condition for differentiability of f at $\mathbf{A}$.

A useful tool in the study of maxima and minima is the second degree Taylor polynomial

$$\begin{aligned} f_2(\mathbf{A},\mathbf{H}) &= f(\mathbf{A}) + \mathbf{H}\cdot\nabla f(\mathbf{A}) + \tfrac{1}{2}(\mathbf{H}\cdot\nabla)^2 f(\mathbf{A}) \\ &= f(\mathbf{A}) + \sum_{j=1}^{n} h_j D_j f(\mathbf{A}) + \frac{1}{2}\sum_{l=1}^{n}\sum_{m=1}^{n} h_l h_m D_l D_m f(\mathbf{A}). \end{aligned} \tag{5}$$

$\mathbf{A}$ is a *critical point* for f if $\nabla f(\mathbf{A}) = \mathbf{0}$; at a critical point, we have

$$f_2(\mathbf{A},\mathbf{H}) = f(\mathbf{A}) + \frac{1}{2}\sum_{l=1}^{n}\sum_{m=1}^{n} h_l h_m D_l D_m f(\mathbf{A}).$$

Just as with two variables, it is generally possible to determine whether a critical point $\mathbf{A}$ is a local maximum, minimum, or saddle point by studying the "quadratic form"

$$\sum_{l=1}^{n}\sum_{m=1}^{n} h_l h_m D_l D_m f(\mathbf{A});$$

however, when $n > 2$, the general study of quadratic forms requires concepts from linear algebra, and we will have to restrict ourselves to particularly simple cases.

Example 1. Let

$$f(x_1,x_2,x_3) = x_1^2 + 2x_2^2 + 3x_3^2 - \cos(x_1 + x_3) + \sin(x_1x_2x_3).$$

Find the Taylor polynomial $f_2(\mathbf{0},\mathbf{H})$ about the point $\mathbf{A} = \mathbf{0}$. *Solution.* You can check that $f(\mathbf{0}) = -1$, $\nabla f(\mathbf{0}) = \mathbf{0}$, $D_1^2 f(\mathbf{0}) = 3$, $D_2^2 f(\mathbf{0}) = 4$, $D_3^2 f(\mathbf{0}) = 7$, $D_1D_2 f(\mathbf{0}) = \mathbf{0}$, $D_1D_3 f(\mathbf{0}) = 1$, $D_2D_3 f(\mathbf{0}) = 0$. Hence

$$\begin{aligned} f_2(\mathbf{H}) &= f(\mathbf{0}) + \mathbf{H}\cdot\nabla f(\mathbf{0}) + \tfrac{1}{2}\big((h_1D_1 + h_2D_2 + h_3D_3)^2 f\big)(\mathbf{0}) \\ &= f(\mathbf{0}) + 0 + \tfrac{1}{2}(h_1^2D_1^2 f + h_2^2D_2^2 f + h_3^3D_3^2 f)(\mathbf{0}) \\ &\qquad + \tfrac{1}{2}\cdot 2(h_1h_2D_1D_2 f + h_1h_3D_1D_3 f + h_2h_3D_2D_3 f)(\mathbf{0}) \\ &= -1 + \tfrac{1}{2}(3h_1^2 + 4h_2^2 + 7h_3^2) + 1(h_1h_3) \\ &= -1 + \tfrac{3}{2}h_1^2 + 2h_2^2 + \tfrac{7}{2}h_3^2 + h_1h_3\,. \end{aligned} \tag{6}$$

Example 2. The function f in Example 1 has $\mathbf{0}$ as a critical point. Examine this point to see whether it is a local maximum or minimum.

Solution. From (6) it seems likely that $f_2(\mathbf{0},\mathbf{H}) > -1$ if $\mathbf{H} \neq \mathbf{0}$. This can be proved by writing $f_2(\mathbf{0},\mathbf{H})$ in the form

$$-1 + h_1^2 + 2h_2^2 + 3h_3^2 + \tfrac{1}{2}(h_1 + h_3)^2$$

(which is suggested by the definition of f in Example 1). From this it is clear that

$$f_2(\mathbf{0},\mathbf{H}) \geq -1 + h_1^2 + h_2^2 + h_3^2 = -1 + |\mathbf{H}|^2; \tag{7}$$

hence the *Taylor polynomial* f_2 has an absolute minimum at $\mathbf{0}$.

Using (3) and (7), we will show that f itself has a *local* minimum at $\mathbf{0}$. First of all, (3) implies that there is a number $\delta > 0$ such that

$$0 < |\mathbf{H}| < \delta \;\Rightarrow\; \frac{|f(\mathbf{H}) - f_2(\mathbf{0},\mathbf{H})|}{|\mathbf{H}|^2} < 1 \;\Rightarrow\; |f(\mathbf{H}) - f_2(\mathbf{0},\mathbf{H})| < |\mathbf{H}|^2. \tag{8}$$

Hence for $0 < |\mathbf{H}| < \delta$ we have

$$\begin{aligned} f(\mathbf{H}) &\geq f_2(\mathbf{0},\mathbf{H}) - |\,\mathbf{H}\,| \\ &> -1 + |\mathbf{H}|^2 - |\mathbf{H}|^2 = -1 \qquad \text{(by (7))}; \end{aligned}$$

thus

$$0 < |\mathbf{H}| < \delta \;\Rightarrow\; f(\mathbf{H}) > -1 = f(\mathbf{0}),$$

and $\mathbf{0}$ is a local minimum point of f.

PROBLEMS

1. Let $f(x_1,x_2,x_3) = x_1e^{x_2+x_3}$, and find the Taylor polynomial $f_k(\mathbf{A},\mathbf{H})$ when
(a) $\mathbf{A} = \mathbf{0}$, $k = 1$;
(b) $\mathbf{A} = (1,-1,1)$, $k = 2$;
(c) $\mathbf{A} = (0,0,1)$, $k = 3$.

2. (a) Suppose that f is differentiable at $\mathbf{A}$, and has a local maximum at $\mathbf{A}$; i.e. there is a number $\delta > 0$ such that

$$|\mathbf{H}| < \delta \;\Rightarrow\; f(\mathbf{A} + \mathbf{H}) \leq f(\mathbf{A}).$$

Prove that $\nabla f(\mathbf{A}) = \mathbf{0}$.

(b) Prove that the function in Problem 1 has no local maximum or minimum.

3. Prove that if f has continuous partial derivatives of order $\leq k$ in the ball of radius ϵ about $\mathbf{A}$, then for $|\mathbf{H}| < \epsilon$

$$\begin{aligned} f(\mathbf{A} + \mathbf{H}) = {} & \sum_0^{k-1} \frac{1}{j!}(\mathbf{H}\cdot\nabla)^j f(\mathbf{A}) \\ & + \frac{1}{k!}(\mathbf{H}\cdot\nabla)^k f(\mathbf{A} + \theta\mathbf{H}), \qquad 0 < \theta < 1, \end{aligned}$$

and alternatively

$$f(\mathbf{A} + \mathbf{H}) = \sum_0^{k-1} \frac{1}{j!} (\mathbf{H}\cdot\nabla)^j f(\mathbf{A})$$
$$+ \frac{1}{(k-1)!} \int_0^1 (\mathbf{H}\cdot\nabla)^k f(\mathbf{A} + t\mathbf{H}) (1-t)^{k-1}\, dt.$$

4. Prove that f is a polynomial of degree $< k$ if and only if all the kth order derivatives of f are identically zero.

5. Prove that if f is a homogeneous polynomial of degree k (i.e. f is a sum of monomial terms each of degree k), then

$$f(\mathbf{H}) = \frac{1}{k!} (\mathbf{H}\cdot\nabla)^k f(\mathbf{0}).$$

6. (a) Prove that if f is homogeneous of degree k (i.e. $f(t\mathbf{X}) = t^k f(\mathbf{X})$ for every $\mathbf{X} \neq \mathbf{0}$ and every $t > 0$), and f is differentiable for $\mathbf{X} \neq \mathbf{0}$, then $D_1 f, \ldots, D_n f$ are all homogeneous of degree $k - 1$.

(b) Suppose that f is homogeneous of degree k, and has kth order partial derivatives which are continuous at $\mathbf{0}$. Prove that the kth order derivatives are constant. (See Problem 7(c), §3.4.)

(c) For the f in part (b), prove that f is a *homogeneous polynomial* of degree k.

5.4 VECTOR FIELDS AND LINE INTEGRALS IN R^3

A vector field $\mathbf{F}$ over a set V in R^3 assigns to each point $\mathbf{X}$ in V a vector $\mathbf{F}(\mathbf{X})$ in R^3. The three components of this vector are denoted $f_1(\mathbf{X})$, $f_2(\mathbf{X}), f_3(\mathbf{X})$. Obviously, a single vector function $\mathbf{F}$ is equivalent to three real-valued functions f_1, f_2, f_3.

In physics, vector fields generally stand for *forces* or *flows*. Mathematically, vector fields can arise as gradients. If the vector field $\mathbf{F} = (f_1, f_2, f_3)$ happens to be the gradient of a function f, i.e. if $f_1 = f_x, f_2 = f_y$, and $f_3 = f_z$, then $\mathbf{F}$ is called *exact*. If $\mathbf{F}$ is exact and f_1, f_2, f_3 have continuous partial derivatives, we find that these components must satisfy certain relations, for example,

$$\frac{\partial f_1}{\partial y} = \frac{\partial}{\partial y}\left(\frac{\partial f}{\partial x}\right) = \frac{\partial}{\partial x}\left(\frac{\partial f}{\partial y}\right) = \frac{\partial f_2}{\partial x}.$$

Working out similar expressions for the other components and other partial derivatives, we find that

if **F** *is exact and has continuous derivatives, then*

$$\frac{\partial f_1}{\partial y} = \frac{\partial f_2}{\partial x}, \qquad \frac{\partial f_1}{\partial z} = \frac{\partial f_3}{\partial x}, \qquad \frac{\partial f_2}{\partial z} = \frac{\partial f_3}{\partial y}. \tag{1}$$

A vector field **F** which satisfies the conditions (1) is called *closed.* We have just shown that "exact" implies "closed"; on the other hand, the example in (2) below shows that a vector field can be closed but *not* exact.

Given a vector field **F** and a differentiable curve

$$\boldsymbol{\gamma}: [a,b] \to R^3,$$

the line integral of **F** over $\boldsymbol{\gamma}$ is defined by

$$\int_\gamma \mathbf{F} = \int_a^b (\mathbf{F}\circ\boldsymbol{\gamma})\cdot\boldsymbol{\gamma}'.$$

If $\boldsymbol{\gamma}$ is a chain of curves $\boldsymbol{\gamma}^1, \ldots, \boldsymbol{\gamma}^n$, then

$$\int_\gamma \mathbf{F} = \sum_{j=1}^{n} \int_{\gamma^j} \mathbf{F}.$$

In physics, when **F** is a force, then $\int_\gamma \mathbf{F}$ is the work done by **F** in moving a particle along the curve $\boldsymbol{\gamma}$. When **F** is a flow, $\int_\gamma \mathbf{F}$ has no special meaning; for flows, we integrate not over curves but over surfaces, as discussed in the next section.

Line integrals help to clarify the difference between closed and exact vector fields. By the same reasoning as in §4.3, you can prove:

(I) If **F** is exact in V, i.e. if there is a function f in V such that $\mathbf{F} = \nabla f$, then $\int_\gamma \mathbf{F} = f(\mathbf{P}_2) - f(\mathbf{P}_1)$ for every connected chain $\boldsymbol{\gamma}$ lying in V, beginning at $\mathbf{P}_1$ and ending at $\mathbf{P}_2$. In particular, when $\boldsymbol{\gamma}$ is a closed chain (i.e. when $\mathbf{P}_2 = \mathbf{P}_1$), then $\int_\gamma \mathbf{F} = 0$.

(II) Conversely, if $\int_\gamma \mathbf{F}$ depends only on the endpoints of $\boldsymbol{\gamma}$ for every connected chain $\boldsymbol{\gamma}$ lying in V, then **F** is exact in V.

From (I) we find, for example, that the vector field

$$\mathbf{F}(x,y,z) = \left(\frac{-y}{x^2+y^2}, \frac{x}{x^2+y^2}, z\right), \qquad x^2 + y^2 \neq 0, \tag{2}$$

is *not* exact, since $\int_\gamma \mathbf{F} = 2\pi$ when $\boldsymbol{\gamma}$ is the closed curve

$$\boldsymbol{\gamma}(t) = (\cos t, \sin t, 0), \qquad 0 \le t \le 2\pi.$$

This vector field *is* closed, however, since the equations (1) are satisfied.

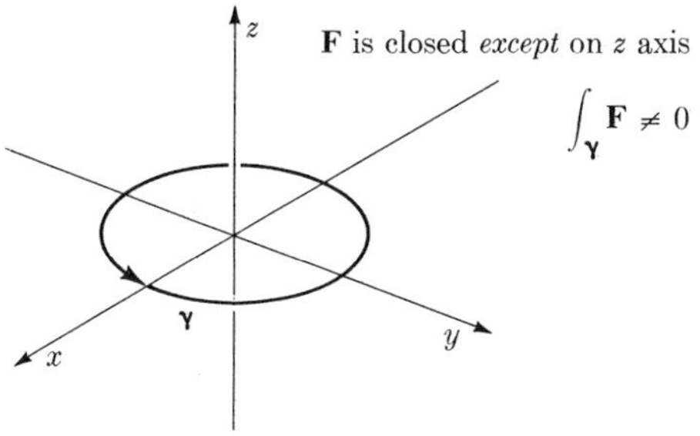

FIGURE 5.11

The reason for this discrepancy between "closed" and "exact" lies in the shape of the region V where the vector field $\mathbf{F}$ is defined. The vector field (2) is defined everywhere *except along the z axis*; it is no coincidence that the curve $\boldsymbol{\gamma}$ on which $\int_\gamma \mathbf{F} \neq 0$ encircles the set where $\mathbf{F}$ is *not* defined (Fig. 11). By contrast:

(III) When a closed vector field $\mathbf{F}$ is defined everywhere in R^3, then $\mathbf{F}$ is exact in R^3.

Proof. For any point $\mathbf{P}$ in R^3, let $\boldsymbol{\gamma}^{\mathbf{P}}$ be the straight line path from $\mathbf{0}$ to $\mathbf{P}$,

$$\boldsymbol{\gamma}^{\mathbf{P}}(t) = t\mathbf{P}, \qquad 0 \leq t \leq 1.$$

Define a function f by

$$f(\mathbf{P}) = \int_{\gamma^{\mathbf{P}}} \mathbf{F}. \tag{3}$$

(This definition is practically forced by (1) above. If we are to have $\mathbf{F} = \nabla f$, then $f(\mathbf{P}) = f(\mathbf{0}) + \int_{\gamma^{\mathbf{P}}} \mathbf{F}$, and the constant $f(\mathbf{0})$ does not affect the gradient. Thus, if $\mathbf{F}$ is the gradient of anything at all, it is the gradient of the function f defined by (3).) For each point $\mathbf{P} = (x,y,z)$, we have $(\boldsymbol{\gamma}^{\mathbf{P}})'(t) = \mathbf{P} = (x,y,z)$; hence

$$f(x,y,z) = \int_0^1 \mathbf{F}(t\mathbf{P}) \cdot \mathbf{P}\, dt$$

$$= \int_0^1 \big(xf_1(tx,ty,tz) + yf_2(tx,ty,tz) + zf_3(tx,ty,tz)\big)\, dt, \tag{4}$$

where $\mathbf{F} = (f_1,f_2,f_3)$. Differentiate (4) with respect to x, applying Leibniz' rule and the chain rule, to obtain

$$\frac{\partial f}{\partial x} = \int_0^1 [f_1(t\mathbf{P}) + txD_1 f_1(t\mathbf{P}) + tyD_1 f_2(t\mathbf{P}) + tzD_1 f_3(t\mathbf{P})]\, dt.$$

Since $\mathbf{F}$ is closed, we can set $D_1 f_2 = D_2 f_1$ and $D_1 f_3 = D_3 f_1$; hence

$$\frac{\partial f}{\partial x} = \int_0^1 [f_1(t\mathbf{P}) + txD_1 f_1(t\mathbf{P}) + tyD_2 f_1(t\mathbf{P}) + tzD_3 f_1(t\mathbf{P})]\, dt$$

$$= \int_0^1 \frac{d}{dt}[tf_1(t\mathbf{P})]\, dt = [tf_1(t\mathbf{P})]_0^1 = f_1(\mathbf{P}),$$

as desired. Similarly, $\partial f/\partial y = f_2$ and $\partial f/\partial z = f_3$, so the claim (III) is established.

Exactly the same proof works when $\mathbf{F}$ is defined not in all of R^3 but in a more restricted set, such as a ball of radius r centered at $\mathbf{0}$, or an open rectangular solid containing $\mathbf{0}$. In fact, it works for every open set V with the following property: *Whenever* $\mathbf{P}$ *is in* V, *then* V *contains the straight line segment between* $\mathbf{0}$ *and* $\mathbf{P}$. Such a set V is called "star-shaped with respect to the origin" (Fig. 12). More generally, V is called star-shaped with respect to a point $\mathbf{P}_0$ if, whenever $\mathbf{P}$ is in V, then V contains the straight line segment from $\mathbf{P}_0$ to $\mathbf{P}$. You can easily prove:

(III′) If $\mathbf{F}$ is a closed vector field defined in a region V which is star-shaped with respect to some point $\mathbf{P}_0$, then $\mathbf{F}$ is exact in V.

FIGURE 5.12 V is star-shaped with respect to $\mathbf{0}$

For example, the "half space"

$$H = \{(x,y,z) : z > 0\}$$

is star-shaped with respect to the point $\mathbf{P}_0 = (0,0,1)$; but the set

$$S = \{(x,y,z) : x^2 + y^2 > 0\},$$

in which the vector field (2) is closed but not exact, is not star-shaped with respect to any point $\mathbf{P}_0$ (Fig. 13).

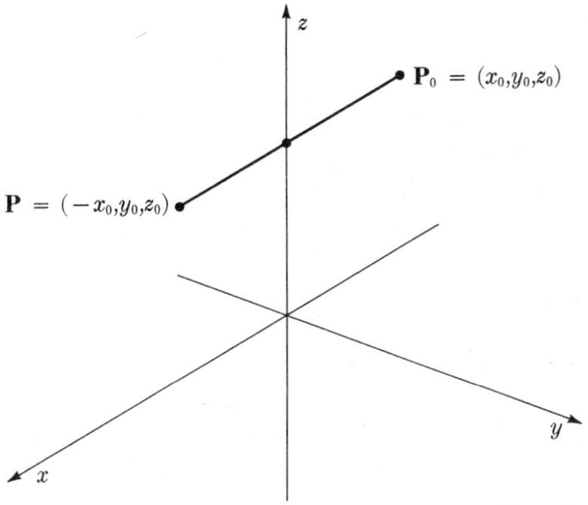

FIGURE 5.13 The segment from $\mathbf{P}_0$ to $\mathbf{P}$ does not lie entirely in $S = \{(x,y,z): x^2 + y^2 > 0\}$, so S is not star-shaped with respect to $\mathbf{P}_0$

PROBLEMS

1. Compute the line integral $\int_\gamma \mathbf{F}$ in the following cases:
   (a) $\mathbf{F}(x,y,z) = (e^x,e^y,e^z)$, $\boldsymbol{\gamma}(t) = (ta,tb,tc)$, $0 \le t \le 1$, a, b, and c constants.
   (b) $\mathbf{F}(x,y,z) = (y + z, z + x, x + y)$, $\boldsymbol{\gamma}(t) = (t^2,t^3,t^4)$, $0 \le t \le 1$.
   (c) $\mathbf{F}(\mathbf{P}) = \dfrac{\mathbf{P}}{|\mathbf{P}|^3}$, $\boldsymbol{\gamma}(t) = (ta,tb,tc)$, $r \le t \le R$.

   (Here, a, b, c, r, R are constants and $0 < r < R$.)

2. Let $\mathbf{F}(\mathbf{P}) = \dfrac{\mathbf{P}}{|\mathbf{P}|^3}$.
   (a) Show that $\mathbf{F}$ is closed, using the formulas (1).
   (b) Show that $\mathbf{F} = \nabla f$ when $f(\mathbf{P}) = -|\mathbf{P}|^{-1}$.
   (c) Show that $\displaystyle\int_\gamma \frac{\mathbf{P}}{|\mathbf{P}|^3} = \frac{1}{|\boldsymbol{\gamma}(a)|} - \frac{1}{|\boldsymbol{\gamma}(b)|}$.

(d) Compute the work done by $\mathbf{F}$ in moving a particle from (1,3,5) to $(100, 50, -80)$.
(e) Compute the work done by $\mathbf{F}$ in moving a particle from (1,3,5) "all the way to infinity."

3. Prove statement (I) in the text, namely; $\int_\gamma \nabla f = f(\mathbf{P}_2) - f(\mathbf{P}_1)$, where $\boldsymbol{\gamma}$ is a connected chain beginning at $\mathbf{P}_1$ and ending at $\mathbf{P}_2$.

4. Prove statement (II) in the text namely: If $\mathbf{F}$ is a continuous vector field in an open connected set V, and for every curve $\boldsymbol{\gamma}$ in V, $\int_\gamma \mathbf{F}$ depends only on the endpoints of $\boldsymbol{\gamma}$, then there is a function f defined in V such that $\nabla f = \mathbf{F}$.

5. Prove statement (III′) in the text. (Hint: Use the paths $\boldsymbol{\gamma}_{\mathbf{P}_0}{}^{\mathbf{P}}(t) = \mathbf{P}_0 + t(\mathbf{P} - \mathbf{P}_0)$. Alternate Hint: Consider the vector field $\mathbf{G}$ defined by $\mathbf{G}(\mathbf{P}) = \mathbf{F}(\mathbf{P} - \mathbf{P}_0)$; $\mathbf{G}$ is defined in a region which is star-shaped with respect to the origin.)

6. The *curl* of a vector field $\mathbf{F}$, denoted $\nabla \times \mathbf{F}$, is defined by

$$\nabla \times \mathbf{F} = (D_2 f_3 - D_3 f_2, D_3 f_1 - D_1 f_3, D_1 f_2 - D_2 f_1).$$

This is the cross product of the "vector" $\nabla = (D_1, D_2, D_3)$ and the vector $\mathbf{F} = (f_1, f_2, f_3)$.
(a) Show that $\mathbf{F}$ is closed if and only if $\nabla \times \mathbf{F} = \mathbf{0}$.
(b) Show that if f has continuous second derivatives, then

$$\nabla \times (\nabla f) = \mathbf{0}.$$

7. A particle of mass m moves along a curve $\boldsymbol{\gamma}$ from time a to time b, propelled by a force $\mathbf{F}$ according to Newton's law $\mathbf{F} = m\boldsymbol{\gamma}''$. At each time t, its *kinetic energy* is defined to be $\frac{1}{2}m\,|\boldsymbol{\gamma}'(t)|^2$, and its *potential energy* to be $-\int_a^{t_0} (\mathbf{F}\circ\boldsymbol{\gamma})\cdot\boldsymbol{\gamma}'$. Prove the "conservation of energy" law, namely, the sum of the kinetic energy and the potential energy is constant.

8. Suppose that $|\mathbf{F}(\mathbf{X})| \leq M$ for every point on the differentiable curve $\boldsymbol{\gamma}: [a,b] \to R^3$. Prove that $|\int_\gamma \mathbf{F}| \leq M\cdot$(length of $\boldsymbol{\gamma}$). (Hint: Use the Schwarz inequality.)

5.5 SURFACE INTEGRALS AND STOKES' THEOREM

A *parametric surface* is a continuous vector-valued function $\boldsymbol{\sigma}$ defined on some set S in R^2, and assigning to each point (u,v) in S a point $\boldsymbol{\sigma}(u,v)$ in R^3. The set S is called the *parameter domain*, and u and v are the *parameters*.

For example, the function

$$\boldsymbol{\sigma}(u,v) = (\cos u \sin v, \sin u \sin v, \cos v) \tag{1}$$

defined on the set

$$S = \{(u,v): 0 < u < \pi, 0 < v < \pi\}$$

is a parametric surface representing one half of the unit sphere (Fig. 14). The lines where u is constant and v varies are the "meridians" (the great-circle lines from the North Pole to the South Pole), and the lines where v is constant but u varies are the "parallels" (circles parallel to the equator).

If we retain formula (1) for $\boldsymbol{\sigma}$, but enlarge the parameter domain S to the rectangle

$$\bar{S} = \{(u,v): 0 \le u \le 2\pi, 0 \le v \le \pi\},$$

we get the entire sphere in Fig. 15. The points along the heavily drawn meridian are all obtained twice (once with $u = 0$ and once with $u = 2\pi$), and the North and South Poles are obtained infinitely often (with every value of u, when $v = 0$ or $v = \pi$).

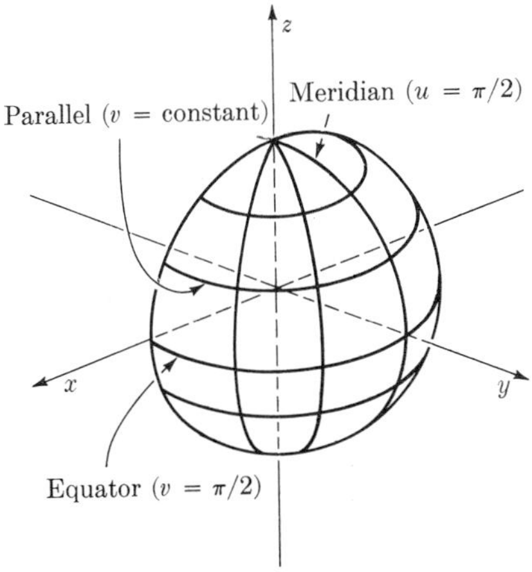

FIGURE 5.14

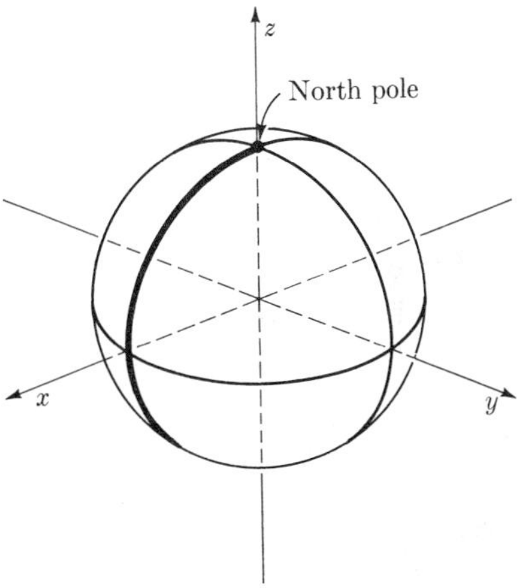

FIGURE 5.15

The graph of any function f of two variables can be considered as a parametric surface. We take the parameter domain S to be the same as the domain of f, and set

$$\boldsymbol{\sigma}(u,v) = (u,v,f(u,v)).$$

Obviously, every point $\boldsymbol{\sigma}(u,v)$ on this surface $\boldsymbol{\sigma}$ lies in the graph of f and, conversely, every point $(x,y,f(x,y))$ on the graph of f has the form $\boldsymbol{\sigma}(u,v)$

with $u = x$ and $v = y$. For example, if $f(x,y) = \sqrt{1 - x^2 - y^2}$ with domain $\{(x,y);\ x^2 + y^2 < 1\}$, we take $S = \{(u,v):\ u^2 + v^2 < 1\}$ and $\boldsymbol{\sigma}(u,v) = (u,v,\sqrt{1 - u^2 - v^2})$. This gives the upper half of the unit sphere as a parametric surface.

In any parametric surface, we can obtain a curve by fixing v and allowing u to vary; this is called a "u-curve." Similarly, fixing u and allowing v to vary produces a "v-curve." In the surface (1), the v-curves are the meridians and the u-curves are the parallels.

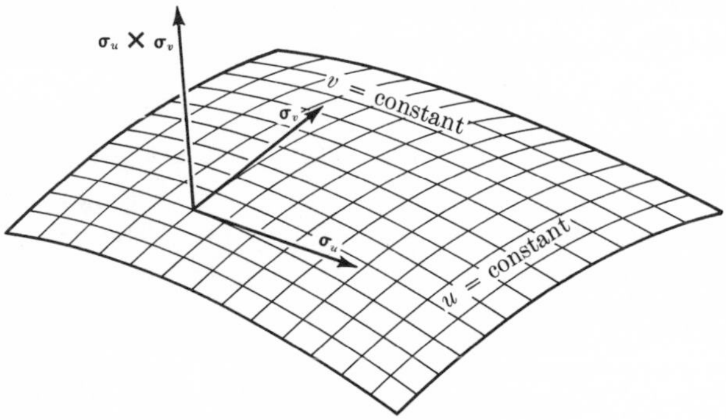

FIGURE 5.16

The derivative of a u-curve is simply the partial derivative $\boldsymbol{\sigma}_u$, obtained by taking the partial derivative of each component of $\boldsymbol{\sigma}$ with respect to u. From the general theory of curves, $\boldsymbol{\sigma}_u$ is tangent to the u-curve, and similarly $\boldsymbol{\sigma}_v$ is tangent to the v-curve, as in Fig. 16. Thus, intuitively, $\boldsymbol{\sigma}_u$ and $\boldsymbol{\sigma}_v$ should be tangent to the surface $\boldsymbol{\sigma}$, so their cross product $\boldsymbol{\sigma}_u \times \boldsymbol{\sigma}_v$ should be *normal* to $\boldsymbol{\sigma}$. This motivates the following

Definition. If $\boldsymbol{\sigma}$ is a parametric surface each of whose components is differentiable, then the vector $\boldsymbol{\sigma}_u \times \boldsymbol{\sigma}_v$ is called the *standard normal vector* to $\boldsymbol{\sigma}$, denoted $\mathbf{N}_\sigma$.

When $\boldsymbol{\sigma}$ happens to be the graph of a function f,

$$\boldsymbol{\sigma}(u,v) = (u,v,f(u,v)),$$

then $\boldsymbol{\sigma}_u = (1,0,f_u)$, $\boldsymbol{\sigma}_v = (0,1,f_v)$, and $\boldsymbol{\sigma}_u \times \boldsymbol{\sigma}_v = (-f_u,-f_v,1)$, which we recognize as a normal to the tangent plane to the graph of f; thus, the new definition of normal agrees with the old. Further, when the surface $\boldsymbol{\sigma}$ lies in the level surface of a function g of three variables, then $\mathbf{N}_\sigma$ is parallel to ∇g at every point of the surface, so the two notions of "normal vector" agree in this case too. (See Problem 12 below.)

There is a far-reaching analogy between surfaces and curves in which the normal $\mathbf{N}_\sigma = \boldsymbol{\sigma}_u \times \boldsymbol{\sigma}_v$ of a surface $\boldsymbol{\sigma}$ corresponds to the derivative $\boldsymbol{\gamma}'$ of a curve $\boldsymbol{\gamma}$. The following table lists the points of analogy, and the rest of this section explains them.

Curve $\boldsymbol{\gamma}$: $[a, b] \to R^3$	Surface $\boldsymbol{\sigma}$: $S \to R^3$
Derivative $\boldsymbol{\gamma}'$	Normal $\mathbf{N}_\sigma = \boldsymbol{\sigma}_u \times \boldsymbol{\sigma}_v$
(I) $\boldsymbol{\gamma}'$ points in positive direction along $\boldsymbol{\gamma}$	$\mathbf{N}_\sigma$ points toward positive side of surface
(II) $\int_a^b \lvert\boldsymbol{\gamma}'\rvert$ = length of curve	$\iint_S \lvert\mathbf{N}_\sigma\rvert$ = area of surface
(III) $\int_a^b (\mathbf{F}\circ\boldsymbol{\gamma}) \cdot \boldsymbol{\gamma}'$ is the *line integral* $\int_\gamma \mathbf{F}$	$\iint_S (\mathbf{F}\circ\boldsymbol{\sigma}) \cdot \mathbf{N}_\sigma$ is the *surface integral* $\iint_\sigma \mathbf{F}$
(IV) $\int_\gamma \nabla f = f(\boldsymbol{\gamma}(b)) - f(\boldsymbol{\gamma}(a))$	$\iint_\sigma \nabla \times \mathbf{F} = \int_{\bar\gamma} \mathbf{F}$, where $\bar{\boldsymbol{\gamma}}$ is the positively oriented boundary of $\boldsymbol{\sigma}$

(I) *Oriented normal.* A curved line in space can be "oriented" in either of two ways, in the sense that a particle can move in either of two directions along the line. A parametric curve $\boldsymbol{\gamma}$ chooses a particular so-called "positive" direction (the direction of increasing values of t), and the derivative $\boldsymbol{\gamma}'$ points in that direction.

Similarly, a curved surface in space generally has two sides. A parametric surface chooses a particular side, the one toward which the normal $\mathbf{N}_\sigma$ points, and this is called the positive side of the surface (Fig. 17).

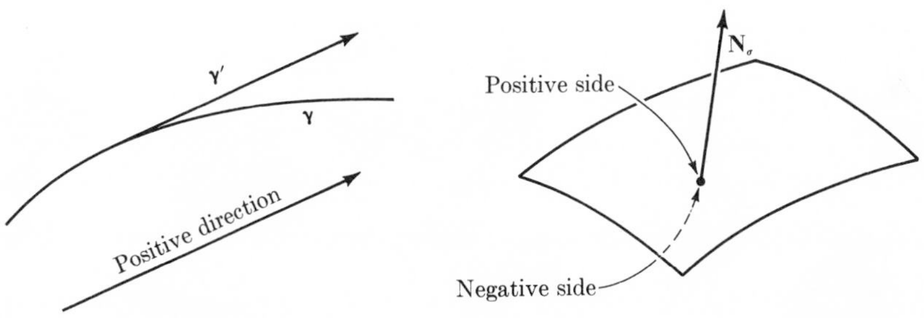

FIGURE 5.17

(II) *Surface area.* It is very difficult to give a rigorous and geometrically motivated development of the theory of surface area, so we take the easy way out and simply make a

Definition. If $\boldsymbol{\sigma}$ is a surface with parameter domain S, and the components of $\boldsymbol{\sigma}$ have continuous first partial derivatives, and $\iint_S |\boldsymbol{\sigma}_u \times \boldsymbol{\sigma}_v|$ is defined, then this integral is called the *area* of the surface $\boldsymbol{\sigma}$.

We have to show that this definition is consistent with the well-known formula in an important special case, the area of a surface of revolution. Suppose f is a real-valued function defined on an interval $[a,b]$, and f' is continuous on $[a,b]$. Then the area of the surface generated by revolving the graph of f about the x axis is given in one-variable calculus as

$$2\pi \int_a^b |f| \sqrt{1 + (f')^2}\,. \tag{2}$$

Now, we can represent the surface of revolution parametrically by

$$\boldsymbol{\sigma}(u,v) = (u, f(u)\cos v, f(u)\sin v)$$

on the parameter domain

$$S = \{(u,v) : a \le u \le b, 0 \le v \le 2\pi\}.$$

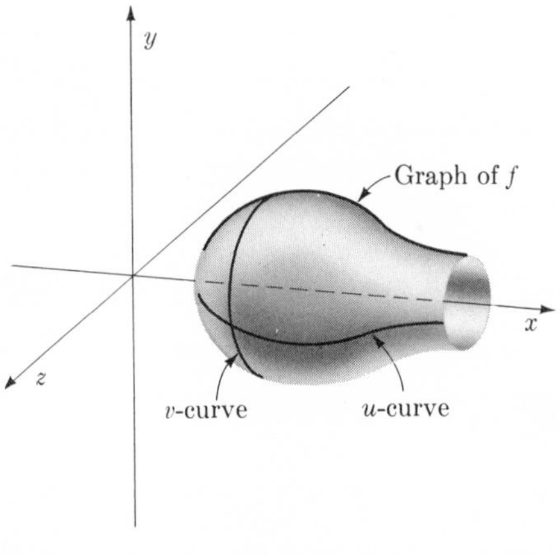

FIGURE 5.18

Each v-curve is a circle around the x axis, and each u-curve looks like the graph of f, but rotated through some angle (Fig. 18). We find

$$\begin{aligned}
\boldsymbol{\sigma}_u &= (1, f'(u) \cos v, f'(u) \sin v) \\
\boldsymbol{\sigma}_v &= (0, -f(u) \sin v, f(u) \cos v) \\
\mathbf{N}_\sigma = \boldsymbol{\sigma}_u \times \boldsymbol{\sigma}_v &= (f'(u)f(u), -f(u) \cos v, -f(u) \sin v) \\
&= f(u)\ (f'(u), -\cos v, -\sin v)
\end{aligned}$$

$$|\boldsymbol{\sigma}_u \times \boldsymbol{\sigma}_v| = |f(u)| \sqrt{1 + f'(u)^2}\,.$$

Hence the surface area is

$$\iint_S |\boldsymbol{\sigma}_u \times \boldsymbol{\sigma}_v| = \int_a^b \int_0^{2\pi} |f(u)| \sqrt{1 + f'(u)^2}\, dv\, du$$

$$= 2\pi \int_a^b |f(u)| \sqrt{1 + f'(u)^2}\, du,$$

which agrees with (2).

Another case we should check, to see whether the above definition of surface area is consistent with our earlier work, is that of a surface lying in the xy plane, i.e. the case where $\boldsymbol{\sigma}$ has the form

$$\boldsymbol{\sigma}(u,v) = (\varphi(u,v), \psi(u,v), 0)$$

for some functions φ and ψ. Here we find

$$\boldsymbol{\sigma}_u = (\varphi_u, \psi_u, 0), \qquad \boldsymbol{\sigma}_v = (\varphi_v, \psi_v, 0)$$

$$\boldsymbol{\sigma}_u \times \boldsymbol{\sigma}_v = (0, 0, \varphi_u\psi_v - \psi_u\varphi_v),$$

$$\iint_S |\boldsymbol{\sigma}_u \times \boldsymbol{\sigma}_v| = \iint_S |\varphi_u\psi_v - \psi_u\varphi_v|. \tag{3}$$

If the function $\boldsymbol{\sigma}$ is one-to-one (i.e. if each point on the surface comes from exactly one point in S), then the formula for change of variable in a double integral shows that (3) is in fact the area of the region onto which $\boldsymbol{\sigma}$ maps S. If $\boldsymbol{\sigma}$ is not one-to-one, then (3) will generally be larger than the area of the region onto which $\boldsymbol{\sigma}$ maps S, reflecting the fact that the parametric surface "covers" some points several times. (See Problem 2 below for examples of "multiple covering" of certain points by a parametric surface.)

(III) *Surface integrals.* We simply *define* surface integrals by the formula

$$\iint_\sigma \mathbf{F} = \iint_S (\mathbf{F} \circ \boldsymbol{\sigma}) \cdot \mathbf{N}_\sigma\,.$$

When $\mathbf{F}$ is a flow, then $\iint_\sigma \mathbf{F}$ is interpreted as the rate of flow across $\boldsymbol{\sigma}$ in the positive direction, i.e. from the negative side toward the positive side.

There is an analogy here with the line integral of a plane flow along a plane curve, and the explanation is similar. $\iint_S (\mathbf{F}\circ\boldsymbol{\sigma})\cdot\mathbf{N}_\sigma = \iint_S |\mathbf{F}| \cos\theta\, |\mathbf{N}_\sigma|$, where θ is the angle between the flow $\mathbf{F}$ and the normal $\mathbf{N}_\sigma$. If we look at a small part $\bar{S}$ of the parameter domain S, then $|\mathbf{F}| \cos\theta$ is approximately constant on the small part $\bar{\boldsymbol{\sigma}}$ of the surface corresponding to $\bar{S}$, so $\iint_{\bar{S}} |\mathbf{F}| \cos\theta\, |\mathbf{N}_\sigma|$ is nearly the same as $|\mathbf{F}| \cos\theta \iint_{\bar{S}} |\mathbf{N}_\sigma|$. This last expression is the *normal component of the flow* across $\bar{\boldsymbol{\sigma}}$ times the *area of* $\bar{\boldsymbol{\sigma}}$, thus giving the *rate of flow* across $\bar{\boldsymbol{\sigma}}$ (Fig. 19). Adding up these small pieces $\bar{S}$ over all of S, we get the total rate of flow through the surface $\boldsymbol{\sigma}$.

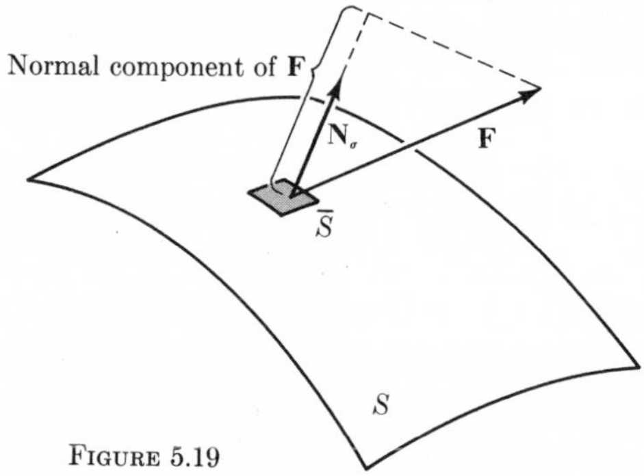

FIGURE 5.19

Example 1. Take $\boldsymbol{\sigma}(u,v) = (\cos u \sin v, \sin u \sin v, \cos v)$ and $S = \{(u,v)\colon 0 < u < \pi, 0 < v < \pi\}$ (Fig. 14). Find the normal $\mathbf{N}_\sigma$, the area of $\boldsymbol{\sigma}$, and the surface integral $\int_\sigma \mathbf{F}$, where $\mathbf{F}(x,y,z) = (0,2,0)$. *Solution.* We have

$$\boldsymbol{\sigma}_u = \frac{\partial\boldsymbol{\sigma}}{\partial u} = (-\sin u \sin v, \cos u \sin v, 0)$$

$$\boldsymbol{\sigma}_v = (\cos u \cos v, \sin u \cos v, -\sin v);$$

hence

$$\mathbf{N}_\sigma = \boldsymbol{\sigma}_u \times \boldsymbol{\sigma}_v = (-\cos u \sin^2 v, -\sin u \sin^2 v, -\sin v \cos v)$$
$$= (-\sin v)\boldsymbol{\sigma}.$$

Since $\sin v > 0$, this shows that at each point $\boldsymbol{\sigma}(u,v)$ on the surface, the vector $\mathbf{N}_\sigma$ points in the direction opposite to $\boldsymbol{\sigma}$, i.e. towards the origin. It is thus "intuitively obvious" that $\mathbf{N}_\sigma$ really is orthogonal to the hemisphere at $\boldsymbol{\sigma}(u,v)$.

The area of the hemisphere is

$$\iint_S |\mathbf{N}_\sigma| = \int_0^\pi\int_0^\pi |(-\sin v)\boldsymbol{\sigma}|\,du\,dv = \int_0^\pi\int_0^\pi \sin v\,du\,dv,$$

since $|\boldsymbol{\sigma}(u,v)| \equiv 1$ and $\sin v \geq 0$ for $0 \leq v \leq \pi$. Hence the area is

$$\pi[-\cos v]_0^\pi = 2\pi,$$

which agrees (as it should) with the traditional formula for the area of a hemisphere of radius 1.

Finally, the surface integral $\int_\sigma \mathbf{F}$, where $\mathbf{F} = (0,2,0)$, is by definition

$$\iint_S \mathbf{N}_\sigma \cdot \mathbf{F} = \int_0^\pi \int_0^\pi 2(-\sin u \sin^2 v)du\, dv = -2\pi.$$

You can see that this is reasonable by thinking of $\mathbf{F}$ as a flow, flowing constantly from left to right at the speed of two units of distance per unit of time; say 2 feet per second. In one second, the amount that has flowed through S fills the volume in Fig. 20; since the bulging cap on the right has exactly the same volume as the hollow on the left, the total volume flowing through $\boldsymbol{\sigma}$ in one second should be 2π, the volume of a cylinder of height 2 and radius 1. Finally, since the flow actually passes from the positive side of $\boldsymbol{\sigma}$ to the negative side, the rate of flow *toward* the positive side should be -2π.

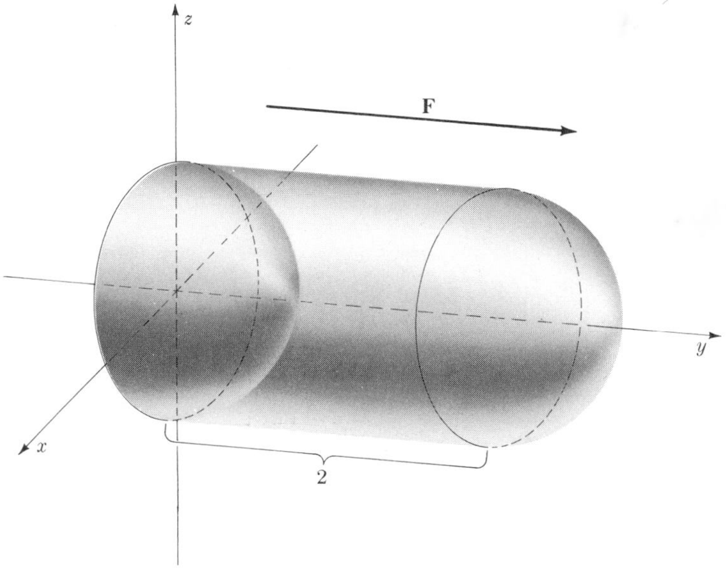

FIGURE 5.20

(IV) *Stokes' theorem.* In the preceding chapter we proved Green's theorem for certain special regions S: if the chain of curves $\boldsymbol{\gamma}$ forms the positively oriented boundary of S, then every vector field (M,N) having continuous partial derivatives in S satisfies the equation

$$\iint_S (N_x - M_y)\, dx\, dy = \int_\gamma M\, dx + N\, dy. \tag{4}$$

Now suppose that such a region S with positively oriented boundary $\boldsymbol{\gamma}$ is the parameter domain of a surface $\boldsymbol{\sigma}$. Then the composite function $\bar{\boldsymbol{\gamma}} = \boldsymbol{\sigma}\circ\boldsymbol{\gamma}$ is a curve in R^3 (or, more generally, a chain of curves); we call this composite function the *positively oriented boundary* of $\boldsymbol{\sigma}$. Stokes' theorem, like Green's theorem (4), relates the integral of a certain "derivative" of $\mathbf{F}$ over a surface $\boldsymbol{\sigma}$ to the integral of $\mathbf{F}$ itself over the boundary of $\boldsymbol{\sigma}$. The derivative in this case is the *curl* of $\mathbf{F}$,

$$\nabla \times \mathbf{F} = (D_2 f_3 - D_3 f_2\,,\, D_3 f_1 - D_1 f_3\,,\, D_1 f_2 - D_2 f_1) \tag{5}$$

which is simply the cross product of $\nabla = (D_1,D_2,D_3)$ and $\mathbf{F} = (f_1, f_2, f_3)$. Stokes' theorem says that under appropriate conditions on $\boldsymbol{\sigma}$ and $\mathbf{F}$,

$$\iint_{\sigma} \nabla \times \mathbf{F} = \int_{\bar{\gamma}} \mathbf{F}, \tag{6}$$

where $\bar{\boldsymbol{\gamma}}$ is the positively oriented boundary of $\boldsymbol{\sigma}$.

Now that all the terms have been defined, Stokes' theorem (6) follows from Green's theorem (4) by a straightforward (but long!) calculation, using the chain rule. To simplify the writing, we assume that the second and third components of $\mathbf{F}$ vanish, i.e. $\mathbf{F} = (f,0,0)$. If we write the three components of $\boldsymbol{\sigma}$ as σ_1, σ_2, and σ_3, and use Leibniz notation with the scheme

$$\begin{array}{ccccccc} t & \longrightarrow & (u,v) & \longrightarrow & (x,y,z) & \longrightarrow & w \\ u = \gamma_1(t) & & x = \sigma_1(u,v) & & w = f(x,y,z) & & \\ v = \gamma_2(t) & & y = \sigma_2(u,v) & & & & \\ & & z = \sigma_3(u,v) & & & & \end{array}$$

we get $\mathbf{F}\circ\boldsymbol{\sigma}\circ\boldsymbol{\gamma} = (w,0,0)$ and $\boldsymbol{\sigma}\circ\boldsymbol{\gamma} = (x,y,z)$; hence

$$(\boldsymbol{\sigma}\circ\boldsymbol{\gamma})' = \left(\frac{dx}{dt}, \frac{dy}{dt}, \frac{dz}{dt}\right),$$

and

$$\int_{\bar{\gamma}} \mathbf{F} = \int_a^b (\mathbf{F}\circ\boldsymbol{\sigma}\circ\boldsymbol{\gamma})\cdot(\boldsymbol{\sigma}\circ\boldsymbol{\gamma})' = \int_a^b w\frac{dx}{dt}\,dt$$

$$= \int_a^b w\left(\frac{\partial x}{\partial u}\frac{du}{dt} + \frac{\partial x}{\partial v}\frac{dv}{dt}\right)dt = \int_{\gamma}\left(w\frac{\partial x}{\partial u}\,du + w\frac{\partial x}{\partial v}\,dv\right)$$

$$= \iint_S \left(\frac{\partial}{\partial u}\left(w\frac{\partial x}{\partial v}\right) - \frac{\partial}{\partial v}\left(w\frac{\partial x}{\partial u}\right)\right)du\,dv \quad \text{(by Green's theorem)} \tag{7}$$

$$= \iint_S \left(\frac{\partial w}{\partial u}\frac{\partial x}{\partial v} - \frac{\partial w}{\partial v}\frac{\partial x}{\partial u}\right)du\,dv \quad \left(\text{since } \frac{\partial^2 x}{\partial u\partial v} = \frac{\partial^2 x}{\partial v\partial u}\right) \tag{8}$$

$$= \iint_S \left(\left(\frac{\partial w}{\partial x}\frac{\partial x}{\partial u} + \frac{\partial w}{\partial y}\frac{\partial y}{\partial u} + \frac{\partial w}{\partial z}\frac{\partial z}{\partial u} \right) \frac{\partial x}{\partial v} \right.$$

$$\left. - \left(\frac{\partial w}{\partial x}\frac{\partial x}{\partial v} + \frac{\partial w}{\partial y}\frac{\partial y}{\partial v} + \frac{\partial w}{\partial z}\frac{\partial z}{\partial v} \right) \frac{\partial x}{\partial u} \right) du\, dv \quad \text{(chain rule)}$$

$$= \iint_S \left(\frac{\partial w}{\partial z}\left(\frac{\partial z}{\partial u}\frac{\partial x}{\partial v} - \frac{\partial z}{\partial v}\frac{\partial x}{\partial u} \right) - \frac{\partial w}{\partial y}\left(\frac{\partial y}{\partial v}\frac{\partial x}{\partial u} - \frac{\partial y}{\partial u}\frac{\partial x}{\partial v} \right) \right) du\, dv. \qquad (9)$$

But $\mathbf{F} = (f,0,0)$ and $f(x,y,z) = w$, so

$$\nabla \times \mathbf{F} = \nabla \times (f,0,0) = \left(0, \frac{\partial w}{\partial z}, -\frac{\partial w}{\partial y}\right);$$

and

$$\boldsymbol{\sigma}_u \times \boldsymbol{\sigma}_v = \frac{\partial \boldsymbol{\sigma}}{\partial u} \times \frac{\partial \boldsymbol{\sigma}}{\partial v}$$

$$= \left(\frac{\partial x}{\partial u}, \frac{\partial y}{\partial u}, \frac{\partial z}{\partial u} \right) \times \left(\frac{\partial x}{\partial v}, \frac{\partial y}{\partial v}, \frac{\partial z}{\partial v} \right)$$

$$= \left(\frac{\partial y}{\partial u}\frac{\partial z}{\partial v} - \frac{\partial y}{\partial v}\frac{\partial z}{\partial u}, \frac{\partial z}{\partial u}\frac{\partial x}{\partial v} - \frac{\partial z}{\partial v}\frac{\partial x}{\partial u}, \frac{\partial x}{\partial u}\frac{\partial y}{\partial v} - \frac{\partial x}{\partial v}\frac{\partial y}{\partial u} \right),$$

so from (9) we obtain

$$\int_{\tilde{\gamma}} \mathbf{F} = \iint_S (\nabla \times \mathbf{F}) \cdot (\boldsymbol{\sigma}_u \times \boldsymbol{\sigma}_v) = \iint_{\boldsymbol{\sigma}} \nabla \times \mathbf{F},$$

which proves Stokes' theorem in the case $\mathbf{F} = (f,0,0)$. In the general case $\mathbf{F} = (f_1, f_2, f_3)$, the calculation is exactly the same but requires three times as much space, so we leave it to you.

By looking back at the calculations above, it is easy to see the conditions under which we have proved Stokes' theorem:

(i) step (7) requires that the parameter domain S with its boundary $\boldsymbol{\gamma}$ be such that Green's theorem (4) holds for every pair of functions (M,N) having continuous partial derivatives in S;

(ii) step (8) requires that the components σ_1, σ_2, σ_3 of the surface $\boldsymbol{\sigma}$ have continuous second partial derivatives, and that the components f_1, f_2, f_3 of $\mathbf{F}$ have continuous first partial derivatives at every point $\boldsymbol{\sigma}(u,v)$ on the surface $\boldsymbol{\sigma}$.

Stokes' theorem sheds some light on the line integral of a closed vector field. Since "**F** is closed" means that

$$D_1 f_2 = D_2 f_1\,, \qquad D_1 f_3 = D_3 f_1\,, \qquad D_2 f_3 = D_3 f_2\,,$$

it follows immediately from the definition of the curl $\nabla \times \mathbf{F}$ in (5) that **F** *is closed if and only if* $\nabla \times \mathbf{F} = \mathbf{0}$. Hence, *if* **F** *is closed, and the curve* $\bar{\boldsymbol{\gamma}}$ *forms the boundary of a surface* $\boldsymbol{\sigma}$ *satisfying conditions* (i) *and* (ii) *above, then the integral of* **F** *over* $\bar{\boldsymbol{\gamma}}$ *is zero:*

$$\int_{\bar{\gamma}} \mathbf{F} = \int_{\sigma} \nabla \times \mathbf{F} = \int_{\sigma} \mathbf{0} = 0.$$

Example 2. If

$$\mathbf{F}(x,y,z) = \left(\frac{-y}{x^2+y^2}, \frac{x}{x^2+y^2}, z\right), \tag{10}$$

then $\nabla \times \mathbf{F}$ exists and equals zero everywhere except along the z axis. If $\boldsymbol{\gamma}^1$ is the curve in Fig. 21 (a),

$$\boldsymbol{\gamma}^1(t) = (\sin t, 1, \cos t), \qquad 0 \le t \le 2\pi,$$

then $\boldsymbol{\gamma}^1$ forms the boundary of a disk-shaped surface

$$\boldsymbol{\sigma}(u,v) = (u,1,v)$$

on the parameter domain

$$S = \{(u,v) : u^2 + v^2 \le 1\} \tag{11}$$

with boundary

$$\boldsymbol{\gamma}(t) = (\sin t, \cos t), \qquad 0 \le t \le 2\pi. \tag{12}$$

The conditions (i) and (ii) for Stokes' theorem are satisfied, so

$$\int_{\gamma^1} \mathbf{F} = \iint_{\sigma} \nabla \times \mathbf{F} = 0.$$

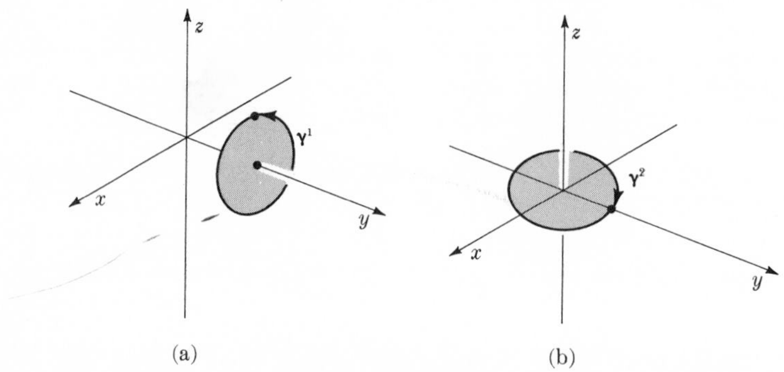

FIGURE 5.21

Example 3. Take $\mathbf{F}$ as in (10), and let $\boldsymbol{\gamma}^2$ be the curve in Fig. 21 (b),

$$\boldsymbol{\gamma}^2(t) = (\sin t, \cos t, 0), \qquad 0 \leq t \leq 2\pi.$$

Again, $\boldsymbol{\gamma}^2$ is the boundary of a surface

$$\boldsymbol{\sigma}(u,v) = (u,v,0),$$

with the parameter domain S and its boundary $\boldsymbol{\gamma}$ the same as in (11) and (12). However, Stokes' theorem does *not* apply for this $\mathbf{F}$ and $\boldsymbol{\sigma}$, since $\boldsymbol{\sigma}$ contains a point (the origin) where the derivatives of $\mathbf{F}$ do not exist. Thus, we cannot conclude from Stokes' theorem that $\int_{\gamma^2} \mathbf{F} = 0$. In fact, in §5.4 we computed $\int_{\gamma^2} \mathbf{F} = 2\pi$.

PROBLEMS

1. Let $\boldsymbol{\sigma}(u,v) = (\cos u \sin v, \ \sin u \sin v, \ \cos v)$ for $0 \leq u \leq 2\pi$ and $0 \leq v \leq \pi$. (This is the sphere in Fig. 15.)
   (a) Find $\mathbf{N}_\sigma = \boldsymbol{\sigma}_u \times \boldsymbol{\sigma}_v$.
   (b) Show that $\boldsymbol{\sigma}$ and $\mathbf{N}_\sigma$ are parallel, in fact $\mathbf{N}_\sigma = (-\sin v)\boldsymbol{\sigma}$. Explain geometrically why $\boldsymbol{\sigma}$ and $\mathbf{N}_\sigma$ should be parallel.
   (c) Compute the area of the unit sphere as $\int\int |\boldsymbol{\sigma}_u \times \boldsymbol{\sigma}_v|$.
   (d) Compute $\int\int_\sigma \mathbf{F}$ where $\mathbf{F}(x,y,z) = (1,0,0)$. Interpret $\mathbf{F}$ as a flow, and thus explain why the integral should be zero.
   (e) Compute $\int\int_\sigma \mathbf{F}$ where $\mathbf{F}(x,y,z) = (x,y,z)$. Interpret $\mathbf{F}$ as a flow, and thus explain why the integral should be -4π.

2. This problem concerns parametric representations of the sphere that do not "cover" the sphere exactly once. In each case, the formula for $\boldsymbol{\sigma}$ is the same as in Problem 1, but the parameter domain S is different. Compute the area of the surface if the parameter domain S is
   (a) $S = \{(u,v): 0 \leq u \leq 4\pi, 0 \leq v \leq \pi\}$ (This surface covers the sphere twice, so you should find the area 8π.)
   (b) $S = \{(u,v): 0 \leq u \leq 2\pi, 0 \leq v \leq 2\pi\}$
   (c) $S = \{(u,v): 0 \leq u \leq \pi, 0 \leq v \leq \pi\}$
   (d) $S = \{(u,v): 0 \leq u \leq 4\pi, 0 \leq v \leq 2\pi\}$
   In each part, try to visualize how the parametric surface $\boldsymbol{\sigma}$ wraps around the sphere.

3. Let $\mathbf{A}$ and $\mathbf{B}$ be vectors in R_3, $\mathbf{A} \times \mathbf{B} \neq \mathbf{0}$, and let $\boldsymbol{\sigma}(u,v) = \mathbf{P}_0 + u\mathbf{A} + v\mathbf{B}$, where $\mathbf{P}_0$ is some fixed vector in R^3.
   (a) Taking the parameter domain $S = \{(u,v): 0 \leq u \leq 1, 0 \leq v \leq 1\}$, $\boldsymbol{\sigma}$ defines a parallelogram (Fig. 22). Show that the area of the parallelogram is $|\mathbf{A} \times \mathbf{B}|$. (Thus our definition of area is consistent with the geometric interpretation of $|\mathbf{A} \times \mathbf{B}|$ in §1.2.)

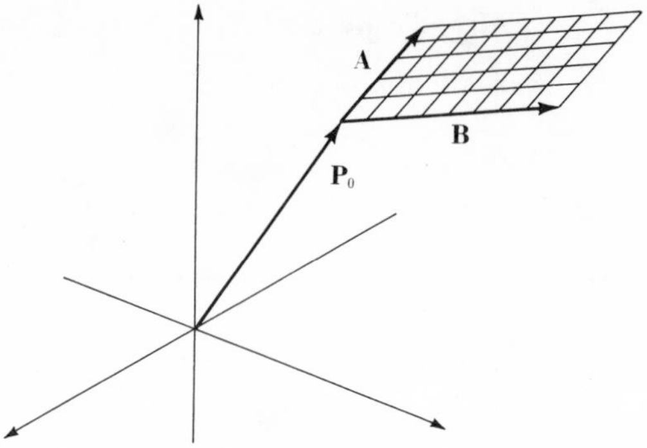

FIGURE 5.22

(b) Take the parameter domain

$$S = \{(u,v): 0 \leq u \leq 1,\ 0 \leq v \leq 1 - u\}.$$

What geometric figure does $\boldsymbol{\sigma}$ produce, and what is its area?

4. (a) Let $\boldsymbol{\sigma}$ be the parallelogram in Problem 3(a), and let $\mathbf{F}$ be any vector field which is constant along the parallelogram, that is, $\mathbf{F}(\boldsymbol{\sigma}(u,v)) \equiv \mathbf{C}$ for some constant vector $\mathbf{C}$. Show that

$$\iint_{\sigma} \mathbf{F} = (\mathbf{A} \times \mathbf{B}) \cdot \mathbf{C}.$$

(b) Show that the rate of flow through the parallelogram in part (a) is $(\mathbf{N} \cdot \mathbf{C}) \times$ (area of parallelogram), where

$$\mathbf{N} = \frac{1}{|\mathbf{A} \times \mathbf{B}|} \mathbf{A} \times \mathbf{B}$$

is the positive unit normal to the parallelogram.

5. A cone with vertex $\mathbf{V}$, altitude $\mathbf{A}$, and radius r is given by

$$\boldsymbol{\sigma}(u,v) = \mathbf{V} + u\mathbf{A} + ru(\cos v\,\mathbf{B} + \sin v\,\mathbf{C}), \quad 0 \leq u \leq 1, \ -\pi \leq v \leq \pi,$$

where $\mathbf{B}$ and $\mathbf{C}$ are unit vectors orthogonal to $\mathbf{A}$, and $\mathbf{B} \cdot \mathbf{C} = 0$ (Fig. 23).

(a) Compute the area of the cone. (Hint: $\mathbf{A} \times \mathbf{B}$, $\mathbf{A} \times \mathbf{C}$, and $\mathbf{B} \times \mathbf{C}$ are mutually orthogonal, by §1.5; use the Pythagorean formula.)

(b) Compute $\iint_{\sigma} \mathbf{A}$ and $\iint_{\sigma} \mathbf{B}$, where $\mathbf{A}$ and $\mathbf{B}$ are the constant vectors in the definition of $\boldsymbol{\sigma}$. Explain your results by interpreting $\mathbf{A}$ and $\mathbf{B}$ as constant flows.

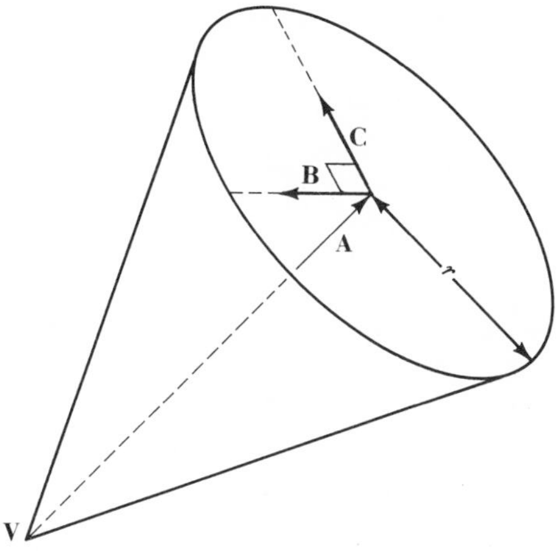

FIGURE 5.23

6. In each of the following cases, compute $\iint_\sigma \nabla \times \mathbf{F}$ by the definition of surface integral (III), and check that $\iint_\sigma \nabla \times \mathbf{F} = \int_{\bar\gamma} \mathbf{F}$, where $\bar{\boldsymbol\gamma} = \boldsymbol\sigma \circ \boldsymbol\gamma$ is the positively oriented boundary of $\boldsymbol\sigma$.

(a) $\mathbf{F}(x,y,z) = (x,y,z)$, $\boldsymbol\sigma(u,v) = (u,v,0)$, $S = \{(u,v): 0 \le u \le 1, 0 \le v \le 1\}$, $\boldsymbol\gamma$ consists of the four obvious straight line curves.

(b) $\mathbf{F}(x,y,z) = (y,z,x)$ with $\boldsymbol\sigma$, S, and $\boldsymbol\gamma$ as in part (a).

(c) $\mathbf{F}(x,y,z) = (z,x,y)$, $\boldsymbol\sigma(u,v) = (u,v,u^2 + v^2)$, $S = \{(u,v): u^2 + v^2 \le 1\}$, $\boldsymbol\gamma(t) = (\cos t, \sin t)$, $0 \le t \le 2\pi$.

7. An *ellipsoid* with semi-axes a, b, c can be represented parametrically by $\boldsymbol\sigma(u,v) = (a \cos u \sin v, b \sin u \sin v, c \cos v)$, $0 \le u \le 2\pi, 0 \le v \le \pi$. Obtain an integral for the surface area of the ellipsoid. (The integral is complicated; do not try to evaluate it.)

8. Suppose f is a function of two variables (x,y) with domain S. Represent the graph of f as a parametric surface (as in the text above), and thus deduce a formula for the surface area A of the graph,

$$A = \iint_S \sqrt{1 + |\nabla f|^2}\,.$$

(Notice the resemblance to the integral for the *length* of the graph of a function f of one variable, $\int_a^b \sqrt{1 + (f')^2}$.)

9. Use the formula in the previous problem to compute the area of the following surfaces:

(a) The graph of $f(x,y) = 3x$ with domain $\{(x,y): 0 \le x \le 1, 0 \le y \le 1\}$. (Your integral gives the area of a rectangle; check the result by computing the sides of the rectangle.)

(b) The part of the plane $\{(x,y,z): z = 3x + 4y\}$ lying over the rectangle $0 \leq x \leq 1, 0 \leq y \leq 1$. (Your integral gives the area of a parallelogram; check the result by using a cross product.)

(c) The part of the plane $\{(x,y,z): z = 3x\}$ lying over the circle $x^2 + y^2 \leq 1$ in the xy plane. (Your integral gives the area of an ellipse; check the result against the formula πab for the area of an ellipse whose longest diameter is $2a$ and shortest diameter is $2b$.)

(d) The part of the plane $\{(x,y,z): z = 3x + 4y\}$ lying over the disk $x^2 + y^2 \leq 1$ in the xy plane. (Again, check the result against the simple formula for the area of an ellipse.)

(e) The part of the "saddle" $\{(x,y,z): z = xy\}$ lying over the disk $x^2 + y^2 \leq 1$ in the xy plane. (Use polar coordinates, §4.5.)

(f) The part of the paraboloid $\{(x,y,z): z = x^2 + y^2\}$ lying over the disk $x^2 + y^2 \leq 1$ in the xy plane.

10. Show that the graphs of $f(x,y) = 2xy$ and $g(x,y) = x^2 + y^2$, when restricted to lie over the same domain S in the xy plane, always have equal surface area.

11. Suppose that $\boldsymbol{\sigma}$ is a surface lying on the unit sphere, i.e. $|\boldsymbol{\sigma}(u,v)| = 1$ for every u and v. Prove that there is a real-valued function $\lambda(u,v)$ such that $\mathbf{N}_\sigma(u,v) = \lambda(u,v)\boldsymbol{\sigma}(u,v)$. (Hint: Show that $\boldsymbol{\sigma}_u$ and $\boldsymbol{\sigma}_v$ are orthogonal to $\boldsymbol{\sigma}$, and apply §1.5. Problem 1 was a special case, and there you found $\lambda(u,v) = -\sin v$.)

12. Suppose that a surface $\boldsymbol{\sigma}$ lies in a level surface $\{\mathbf{P}: f(\mathbf{P}) = c\}$ of a differentiable function f. Prove that $\mathbf{N}_\sigma$ and ∇f are parallel. (Hint: If the level surface is defined by $f = c$, then $f \circ \boldsymbol{\sigma} \equiv c$. Differentiate this to show that ∇f is orthogonal to $\boldsymbol{\sigma}_u$ and $\boldsymbol{\sigma}_v$. It is then "geometrically obvious" that ∇f is parallel to $\boldsymbol{\sigma}_u \times \boldsymbol{\sigma}_v$; the proof uses §1.5.)

13. Suppose that $\boldsymbol{\gamma}$ is any differentiable curve lying in the parameter domain S of a surface $\boldsymbol{\sigma}$. Then $\boldsymbol{\sigma} \circ \boldsymbol{\gamma}$ is a curve lying in the surface. Show that $(\boldsymbol{\sigma} \circ \boldsymbol{\gamma})'$ is orthogonal to $\mathbf{N}_\sigma$ at every point. (Hint: By the chain rule, write $(\boldsymbol{\sigma} \circ \boldsymbol{\gamma})'$ as a combination of $\boldsymbol{\sigma}_u$ and $\boldsymbol{\sigma}_v$.)

14. Suppose that $\boldsymbol{\sigma}$ is a surface not passing through the origin $\mathbf{0}$. The *solid angle subtended by* $\boldsymbol{\sigma}$ *at* $\mathbf{0}$ is defined to be $\int\int_\sigma \boldsymbol{\Omega}$, where $\boldsymbol{\Omega}$ is the vector field $\boldsymbol{\Omega}(\mathbf{P}) = \mathbf{P}/|\mathbf{P}|^3$.

(a) Compute $\int\int_\sigma \boldsymbol{\Omega}$ when $\boldsymbol{\sigma}$ is the disk $\boldsymbol{\sigma}(u,v) = (1,u,v)$ with $u^2 + v^2 \leq 1$.

(b) Same question, with $\boldsymbol{\sigma}(u,v) = (a,u,v)$ and $u^2 + v^2 \leq R^2$. What happens as the constant $a \to 0$? $a \to \infty$? $R \to \infty$? Explain geometrically.

(c) Compute $\int\int_\sigma \boldsymbol{\Omega}$ when $\boldsymbol{\sigma}$ is the rectangle $\boldsymbol{\sigma}(u,v) = (a,u,v)$ with $|u| \leq b$ and $|v| \leq c$. What happens as $a \to \infty$? (Use a table of integrals.)

(d) Compute $\int\int_{\boldsymbol{\sigma}} \Omega$ when $\boldsymbol{\sigma}$ is the sphere in Problem 1.

(e) Compute $\int\int_{\boldsymbol{\sigma}} \Omega$ when $\boldsymbol{\sigma}$ is the sphere in Problem 2(c).

(f) Suppose that $\boldsymbol{\sigma}$ is any surface lying in a sphere of radius r about the origin, and that $\mathbf{N}_\sigma \cdot \boldsymbol{\sigma} \geq 0$ at every point. Show that $r^2 \int\int_{\boldsymbol{\sigma}} \Omega$ is the area of $\boldsymbol{\sigma}$. (Hint: $\mathbf{N}_\sigma \cdot \boldsymbol{\sigma} = r\,|\mathbf{N}_\sigma|$; see Problem 11.)

(g) Let $\boldsymbol{\sigma}$ be a given surface not passing through the origin, and define a new surface $\bar{\boldsymbol{\sigma}}$ by

$$\bar{\boldsymbol{\sigma}}(u,v) = \frac{1}{|\boldsymbol{\sigma}(u,v)|}\,\boldsymbol{\sigma}(u,v).$$

(This is the "projection" of $\boldsymbol{\sigma}$ onto the unit sphere.) Show that $\int\int_{\boldsymbol{\sigma}} \Omega = \int\int_{\bar{\boldsymbol{\sigma}}} \Omega$. (Hint:

$$\left(\frac{\boldsymbol{\sigma}}{|\boldsymbol{\sigma}|}\right)_u = \frac{\boldsymbol{\sigma}_u}{|\boldsymbol{\sigma}|} - \frac{\boldsymbol{\sigma}_u \cdot \boldsymbol{\sigma}}{|\boldsymbol{\sigma}|^3}\,\boldsymbol{\sigma}.)$$

5.6 TRIPLE INTEGRALS

The set V in Fig. 24 is bounded by the graphs of two continuous functions φ_1 and φ_2 with domain S in R^2; i.e.

$$V = \{(x,y,z) : (x,y) \text{ is in } S,\ \varphi_1(x,y) \leq z \leq \varphi_2(x,y)\}, \tag{1}$$

where $\varphi_1 \leq \varphi_2$ on S. Suppose that f is continuous on V. Then it can be proved that

$$F(x,y) = \int_{\varphi_1(x,y)}^{\varphi_2(x,y)} f(x,y,z)\,dz$$

is a continuous function on S. If, further, the set S is of the type we considered in studying double integrals in the preceding chapter, then the *triple integral* of f over V is defined by

$$\iiint_V f = \iint_S \left[\int_{\sigma_1(x,y)}^{\varphi_2(x,y)} f(x,y,z)\,dz\right] dx\,dy.$$

For example, if V is the unit ball, then we can take S to be the unit disk, and

$$\iiint_V f = \iint_S \left[\int_{-\sqrt{1-x^2-y^2}}^{\sqrt{1-x^2-y^2}} f\,dz\right] dx\,dy$$

$$= \int_{-1}^{1}\left[\int_{-\sqrt{1-y^2}}^{\sqrt{1-y^2}}\left[\int_{-\sqrt{1-x^2-y^2}}^{\sqrt{1-x^2-y^2}} f\,dz\right] dx\right] dy.$$

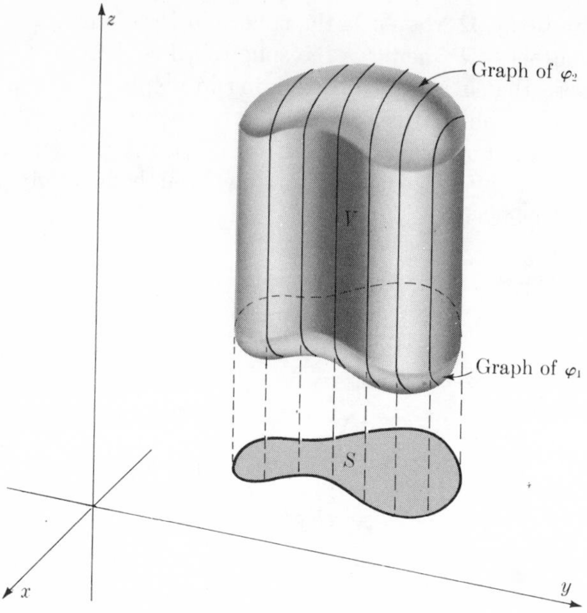

FIGURE 5.24

V is determined in (1) by functions φ_1 and φ_2 of x and y. If this same set V can also be determined by functions of x and z,

$$V = \{(x,y,z) : (x,z) \text{ in } S', \psi_1(x,z) \leq y \leq \psi_2(x,z)\},$$

or by functions of y and z,

$$V = \{(x,y,z) : (y,z) \text{ in } S'', \eta_1(y,z) \leq x \leq \eta_2(y,z)\},$$

then it can be proved that the corresponding integrals all give the same result,

$$\iint_S \left[\int_{\varphi_1}^{\varphi_2} f\,dz\right] dx\,dy = \iint_{S'} \left[\int_{\psi_1}^{\psi_2} f\,dy\right] dx\,dz = \iint_{S''} \left[\int_{\eta_1}^{\eta_2} f\,dx\right] dy\,dz.$$

For example, if V is the rectangular solid

$$V = \{(x,y,z) : x_1 \leq x \leq x_2,\ y_1 \leq y \leq y_2,\ z_1 \leq z \leq z_2\},$$

then the integral over V can be evaluated in numerous ways:

$$\iiint_V f = \int_{z_1}^{z_2}\left[\int_{y_1}^{y_2}\left[\int_{x_1}^{x_2} f\,dx\right] dy\right] dz = \int_{x_1}^{x_2}\left[\int_{y_1}^{y_2}\left[\int_{z_1}^{z_2} f\,dz\right] dy\right] dx$$

$$= \int_{y_1}^{y_2}\left[\int_{x_1}^{x_2}\left[\int_{z_1}^{z_2} f\,dz\right] dx\right] dy = \cdots.$$

The square brackets show how the integral is to be computed, i.e. as three successive single integrals, beginning with the "inner" one. In practice, these brackets are left out.

Example 1. Evaluate $\int_0^1 \int_0^x \int_0^y x\,dz\,dy\,dx$. *Solution.* Since x and y are held constant in taking the integral with respect to z,

$$\int_0^y x\,dz = x\int_0^y dz = xy.$$

Thus

$$\int_0^x \int_0^y x\,dz\,dy = \int_0^x xy\,dy = \frac{1}{2}xy^2\Big|_{y=0}^{y=x} = \frac{1}{2}x^3$$

and

$$\int_0^1 \int_0^x \int_0^y x\,dz\,dy\,dx = \int_0^1 \frac{1}{2}x^3\,dx = \frac{1}{8}x^4\Big|_0^1 = \frac{1}{8}.$$

Example 2. Sketch the region of integration in Example 1, and rewrite the integral in the order $\iiint \cdots dx\,dy\,dz$. *Solution.* The two "outer limits" $\int_0^1 \int_0^x \cdots dy\,dx$ indicate an integral over the triangle S in Fig. 25(a); thus V lies somewhere in the prism-shaped region in Fig. 25(a) generated by lines parallel to the z axis and passing through S. (This region is called the *cylinder* parallel to the z axis with S as cross section.) Next, the "inner limits" $\int_0^y \cdots dz$ show that for each (x,y) in S, z varies from 0 to y, so V lies above the plane defined by $z = 0$ and below the plane defined by $z = y$; thus V is the tetrahedron in Fig. 25(b).

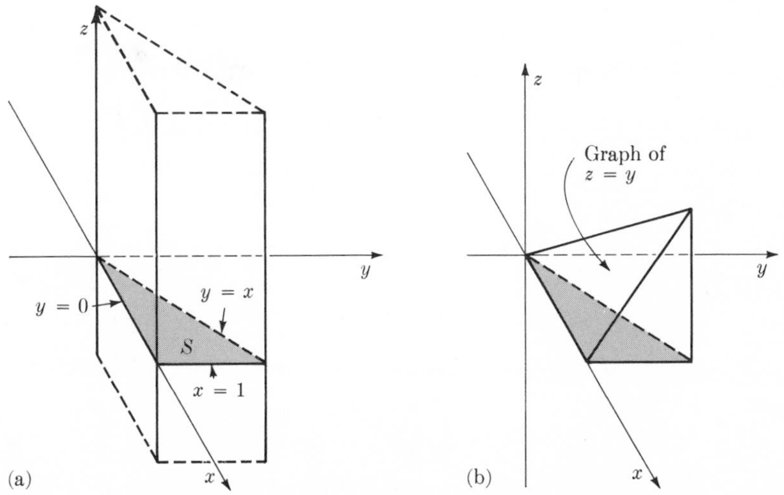

FIGURE 5.25

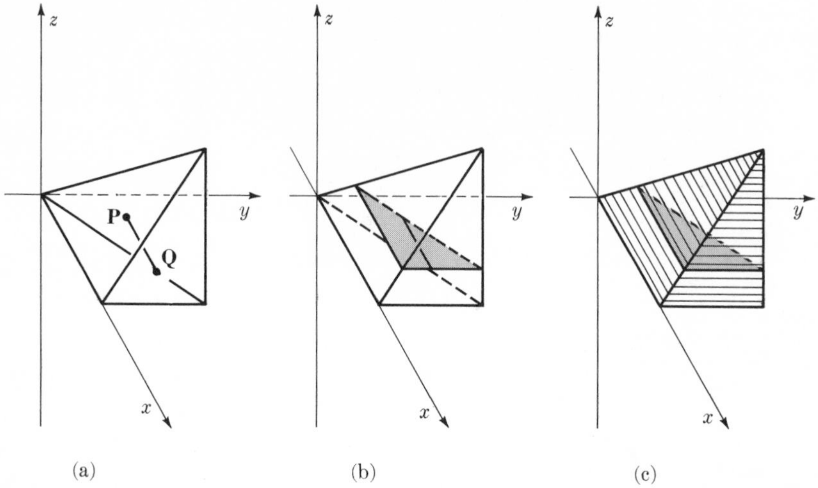

FIGURE 5.26

To write the integral in the order $\int\int\int \cdots dx\, dy\, dz$, begin with the inner limits. For each fixed y and z, x varies along the heavy segment in Fig. 26(a), from the point **P** lying in the plane in back (whose equation is $y = x$) to the point **Q** lying in the plane in front (whose equation is $x = 1$). Thus, for each fixed y and z, x varies from y to 1, generating a line segment representing a typical "linear section" of V. Next, for each fixed z, y varies from z to 1, and the corresponding segments in Fig. 26(a) sweep out the planar cross section of V shown in Fig. 26(b). Finally, as z varies from 0 to 1 these plane cross sections sweep out all of V (Fig. 26(c)). Thus the integral is $\int_0^1 \int_z^1 \int_y^1 x\, dx\, dy\, dz$. As a check, we evaluate the integral in this order:

$$\int_0^1 \int_z^1 \int_y^1 x\, dx\, dy\, dz = \int_0^1 \int_z^1 \frac{x^2}{2}\bigg|_{x=y}^{x=1} dy\, dz$$

$$= \int_0^1 \int_z^1 \frac{1 - y^2}{2}\, dy\, dz = \int_0^1 \left(\frac{y}{2} - \frac{y^3}{6}\right)\bigg|_{y=z}^{y=1} dz$$

$$= \int_0^1 \left(\frac{1}{3} - \frac{z}{2} + \frac{z^3}{6}\right) dz = \left(\frac{z}{3} - \frac{z^2}{4} + \frac{z^4}{24}\right)\bigg|_0^1 = \frac{1}{8},$$

which agrees with the answer in Example 1.

Example 3. Evaluate $\iiint_V f$ when $f(x,y,z) = x^2 + y^2 + z^2$ and V is the unit ball $\{(x,y,z): x^2 + y^2 + z^2 \leq 1\}$.
Solution.

$$\iiint_V f = \int_{-1}^{1}\int_{-\sqrt{1-y^2}}^{\sqrt{1-y^2}}\int_{-\sqrt{1-x^2-y^2}}^{\sqrt{1-x^2-y^2}} (x^2 + y^2 + z^2)\,dz\,dx\,dy$$

$$= \int_{-1}^{1}\int_{-\sqrt{1-y^2}}^{\sqrt{1-y^2}} \left[x^2z + y^2z + \frac{z^3}{3}\right]_{-\sqrt{1-x^2-y^2}}^{\sqrt{1-x^2-y^2}} dx\,dy$$

$$= \int_{-1}^{1}\int_{-\sqrt{1-y^2}}^{\sqrt{1-y^2}} \frac{2}{3}(1 + 2x^2 + 2y^2)\sqrt{1 - x^2 - y^2}\,dx\,dy.$$

This last integral is an obvious candidate for polar coordinates; it becomes

$$\int_0^{2\pi}\int_0^1 \frac{2}{3}(1 + 2r^2)\sqrt{1 - r^2}\,r\,dr\,d\theta$$

$$= \frac{4\pi}{3}\int_0^1 (1 + 2r^2)\sqrt{1 - r^2}\,r\,dr$$

$$= \frac{4\pi}{3}\int_0^1 [1 + 2(1 - u^2)]u^2du \qquad (\sqrt{1 - r^2} = u;\, r\,dr = -u\,du)$$

$$= \frac{4\pi}{3}\left[u^3 - \frac{2}{5}u^5\right]_0^1 = \frac{4\pi}{5},$$

and $\iiint_V f$ is evaluated.

The various interpretations of triple integrals are natural extensions of the one- and two-dimensional cases. When $f \equiv 1$, then $\iiint_V f$ is the *volume* of V. When V is occupied by a substance of variable density f, then $\iiint_V f$ is the *total mass* of the substance in V. When $T(P)$ is the temperature at the point P in V, and $S(P)$ the specific heat of the substance at the point P, then TS is the "heat density," and $\iiint_V TS$ is the total heat in V.

PROBLEMS

1. Evaluate the following integrals, and sketch the region over which the integral is taken.

(a) $\displaystyle\int_2^3\int_1^2\int_0^1 x\,dx\,dy\,dz$

(b) $\displaystyle\int_{-1}^{0}\int_x^0\int_0^{\sqrt{3-x^2-2y^2}} z\,dz\,dy\,dx$

(c) $\displaystyle\int_1^5\int_0^4\int_1^{y+z} y\,dx\,dz\,dy$

(d) $\displaystyle\int_{\pi/2}^{\pi}\int_1^{2x}\int_0^{\cos(x+z)} 1\,dy\,dz\,dx$

2. Evaluate $\iiint_V f$ in the following cases.

(a) $f(x,y,z) = xy, \quad V = \{(x,y,z): 0 \le z \le x + 2,\ x^2 + 4y^2 \le 4\}$

(b) $f(x,y,z) \equiv 1, \quad V = \{(x,y,z): x^2 + y^2 \le a^2,\ y^2 + z^2 \le a^2\}$

(c) $f \equiv 1, \quad V = \{(x,y,z): x \ge 0,\ y \ge 0,\ z \ge 0,\ x + y + z \le 1\}$

(d) $f \equiv 1, \quad V = \{(x,y,z): x^2 + y^2 + z^2 \le R^2,\ x^2 + y^2 \ge r^2\}$, where $0 < r < R$. (This is the volume of a "cored apple.")

(e) $f \equiv 1, \quad V = \{(x,y,z): x^2 + y^2 + z^2 \le R^2,\ (x - r)^2 + y^2 \ge r^2\}$, where $2r = R$. (This is the volume of an "eccentrically cored apple.")

3. Let V be the cylinder $\{(x,y,z): (x - a)^2 + y^2 \le a^2,\ 0 \le z \le b\}$, and suppose V is occupied by material of constant density ρ. Compute

(a) $\iiint_V \rho$ (the mass of V).

(b) $\iiint_V \rho x\, dx\, dy\, dz$ (the *first moment of V with respect to the yz plane*, denoted M_{yz}.)

(c) $\iiint_V \rho y\, dx\, dy\, dz$ (the *first moment of V with respect to the xz plane*, denoted M_{xz}.)

(d) $\iiint_V \rho z\, dx\, dy\, dz$ (the *first moment of V with respect to the xy plane*, denoted M_{xy}.)

(e) The *center of gravity* of V, the point $(\bar{x},\bar{y},\bar{z})$ where

$$\bar{x} = \frac{M_{yz}}{\text{mass}}, \qquad \bar{y} = \frac{M_{xz}}{\text{mass}}, \qquad \bar{z} = \frac{M_{xy}}{\text{mass}}.$$

(You should find $(\bar{x},\bar{y},\bar{z}) = (a,0,\tfrac{1}{2}b) =$ center of the cylinder.)

4. Let V be the slice of the sphere $\{\mathbf{P}: |\mathbf{P}| \le b\}$ lying above the plane defined by $z = a$, where $0 < a < b$ (Fig. 27). Let S be the disk $\{(x,y): x^2 + y^2 \le b^2 - a^2\}$. Assume V is occupied by material of constant density 1. Find the center of gravity by computing

(a) the volume of V,

$$\iiint_V 1 = \iint_S \int_a^{\sqrt{b^2 - x^2 - y^2}} dz\, dx\, dy.$$

(Use polar coordinates.)

(b) M_{xy}, M_{yz}, M_{xz} (See Problem 3. You should find $M_{xz} = 0$ and $M_{yz} = 0$ with very little work; use polar coordinates on M_{xy}.)

(c) Show that the center of gravity is

$$\left(0, 0, \frac{3(b - a)(b + a)^2}{4(2b^2 - ab - a^2)}\right).$$

(d) As an interesting exercise in calculus of one variable, you can show that if $a < b$, then

$$a < \frac{3(b - a)(b + a)^2}{4(2b^2 - ab - a^2)} < b, \tag{*}$$

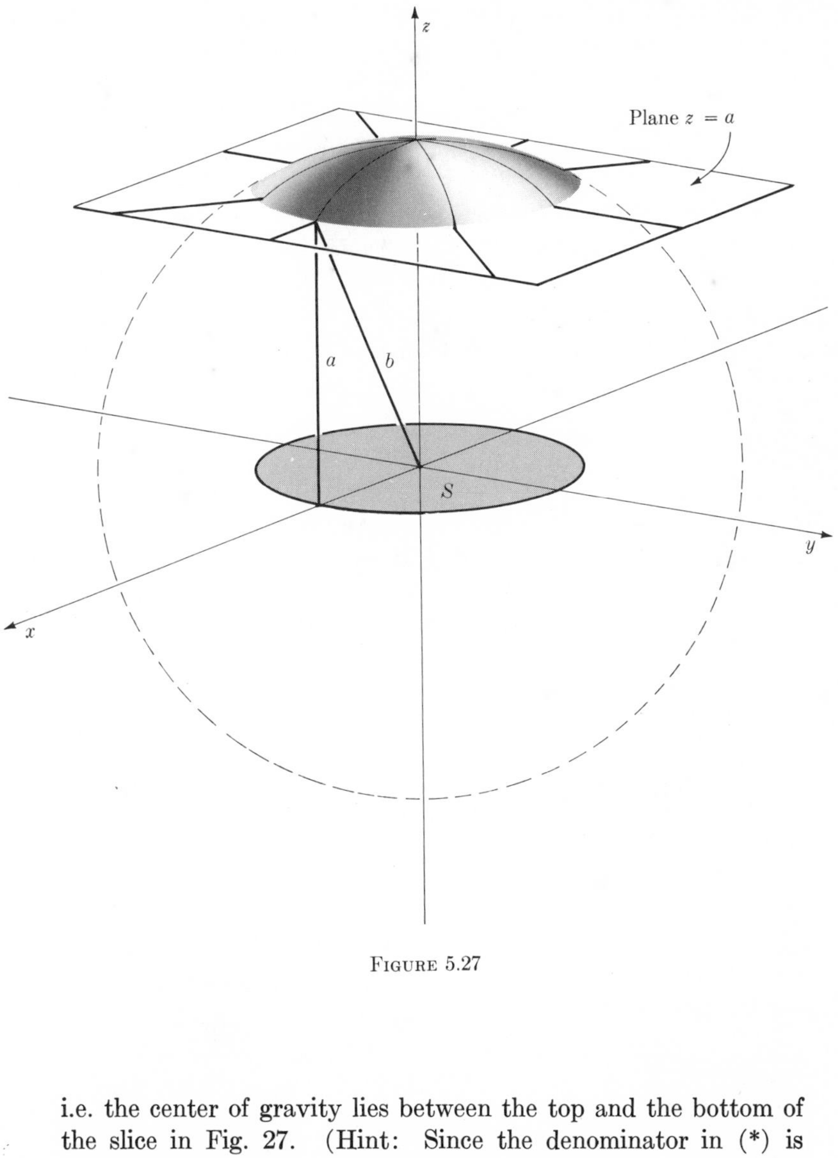

FIGURE 5.27

i.e. the center of gravity lies between the top and the bottom of the slice in Fig. 27. (Hint: Since the denominator in (*) is positive for $a < b$, you can multiply through by it. Then divide through by b^3, set $x = a/b$, and study the resulting functions on the interval $0 \leq x \leq 1$.)

5. Evaluate $\iiint_V f$ when $f \equiv 1$ and

$$V = \{(x,y,z) : 0 \leq x \leq 4 - y^2, 0 \leq z \leq y\}.$$

(Hint: Sketch V, and set up the integral in the order $dz\, dx\, dy$.)

6. Let $V = \{(x,y,z) : 8 - x^2 - y^2 \leq z \leq x^2 + y^2\}$.

(a) Evaluate $\iiint_V (x^2 + y^2)\,dx\,dy\,dz$. (This is the *moment of inertia* of V about the z axis. Set up the integral in the order $dz\,dx\,dy$. It helps if you can sketch, or at least visualize, the boundary surfaces $z = x^2 + y^2$ and $z = 8 - x^2 - y^2$. The first is a paraboloid of revolution opening upward, and the second is a similar paraboloid opening downward. The region for the $dx\,dy$ integration is determined by the intersection of these two surfaces.)

(b) Evaluate $\iiint (x^2 + z^2)\,dx\,dy\,dz$ (the moment of inertia about the y axis).

7. Let $V = \{(x,y,z): a \le x \le b,\ \varphi_1(x) \le y \le \varphi_2(z),\ \psi_1(x,y) \le z \le \psi_2(x,y)\}$. Suppose that $f(x,y,z,t)$ and its first derivative $f_t(x,y,z,t)$ are continuous for (x,y,z) in V and $c < t < d$. Prove that

$$\frac{d}{dt}\iiint_V f(x,y,z,t)\,dx\,dy\,dz = \iiint_V f_t(x,y,z,t)\,dx\,dy\,dz$$

for $c < t < d$. (Hint: Begin with the right-hand side, supply the limits of integration, and apply Leibniz' rule for single integrals (Theorem 3, §4.1) three times.)

8. Take V as in Problem 7, and let f be continuous on V. Prove that the function

$$g(x,y,z,t) =$$

$$t^{-3/2}\iiint_V \exp\left(\frac{(x-\xi)^2 + (y-\eta)^2 + (z-\zeta)^2}{-4t}\right) f(\xi,\eta,\zeta)\,d\xi\,d\eta\,d\zeta$$

satisfies the equation for (non-steady state) heat conduction,

$$g_t = g_{xx} + g_{yy} + g_{zz}\,.$$

9. (a) Take V as in Problem 7. Suppose that f and g are continuous in V, and $f \le g$. Prove that $\iiint_V f \le \iiint_V g$. (Hint: By a known result for single integrals,

$$\int_{\psi_1(x,y)}^{\psi_2(x,y)} f(x,y,z)\,dz \le \int_{\psi_1(x,y)}^{\psi_2(x,y)} g(x,y,z)\,dz;$$

obtain from this a similar inequality for $\int_{\varphi_1(x)}^{\varphi_2(x)} \cdots dx$, and finally obtain the desired inequality for $\iiint_V$.)

(b) Suppose that f is continuous and $m \le f \le M$ in V. Prove that $m\,|V| \le \iiint_V f \le M\,|V|$, where $|V|$ denotes the volume of V.

10. (a) Suppose that f is continuous in an open set V, and that $\iiint_B f = 0$ for every ball B contained in V. Prove that $f \equiv 0$ in V. (Hint: If $f(\mathbf{P}_0) > 0$, there is a ball B of radius δ contained in V, such that $f(\mathbf{P}) > \frac{1}{2}f(\mathbf{P}_0)$ at every point $\mathbf{P}$ in B.)

(b) Suppose that V and V' are sets of the form in Problem 7, and that V contains V', i.e. if V is described by functions φ_j and ψ_j, and V' by φ_j' and ψ_j', then $\varphi_1 \leq \varphi_1' \leq \varphi_2' \leq \varphi_2$ and $\psi_1 \leq \psi_1' \leq \psi_2' \leq \psi_2$. Prove that if $f \geq 0$ in V, then $\int\int\int_{V'} f \leq \int\int\int_V f$.

(c) Suppose that f is continuous and $f \geq 0$ in a set V of the form in Problem 7, and that $\int\int\int_V f = 0$. Let U be any open set contained in V. Prove that $f \equiv 0$ in U. (Hint: If B is any ball contained in U, then B is in V, so $0 \leq \int\int\int_B f \leq \int\int\int_V f = 0$.)

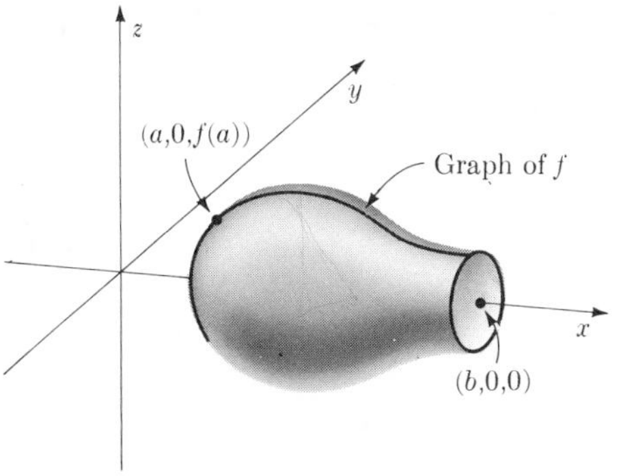

FIGURE 5.28

11. Let V be the solid of revolution in Fig. 28, where $f(x) \geq 0$ for $a \leq x \leq b$.

(a) Show that the volume of V is

$$\int_a^b \int_{-f(x)}^{f(x)} \int_{-\sqrt{f(x)^2-y^2}}^{\sqrt{f(x)^2-y^2}} dz\, dy\, dx.$$

(b) Show that

$$\int_{-f(x)}^{f(x)} \int_{-\sqrt{f(x)^2-y^2}}^{\sqrt{f(x)^2-y^2}} dz\, dy = \pi f(x)^2.$$

(c) Deduce that the volume of V is $\int_a^b \pi f(x)^2\, dx$.

5.7 THE DIVERGENCE THEOREM

Green's theorem in R^2, relating line integrals to double integrals, has an analog in R^3, called *Gauss' theorem* or the *divergence theorem*, relating surface integrals to triple integrals. The *divergence* of a vector field $\mathbf{F} = (f_1, f_2, f_3)$ is defined to be

$$\nabla \cdot \mathbf{F} = D_1 f_1 + D_2 f_2 + D_3 f_3 = \frac{\partial f_1}{\partial x} + \frac{\partial f_2}{\partial y} + \frac{\partial f_3}{\partial z}.$$

The divergence theorem says that if $\mathbf{F}$ has continuous derivatives in V, then

$$\iiint_V \nabla \cdot \mathbf{F} = \iint_\sigma \mathbf{F}, \tag{1}$$

where the surface $\boldsymbol{\sigma}$ forms the positively oriented boundary of V. In this case, "positively oriented" means "with the normal vector pointing out of V," as in Fig. 29. Thus if $\mathbf{F}$ is a flow, then the right-hand side of (1) is the rate of flow through the surface from inside to outside, in other words, the rate of flow out of V. The divergence theorem (1) says that this is the same as the integral of $\nabla \cdot \mathbf{F}$ over all of V. Thus, for any point $\mathbf{P}$ in V, we interpret the divergence $(\nabla \cdot \mathbf{F})(\mathbf{P})$ as the rate at which fluid leaves $\mathbf{P}$; hence the name "divergence."

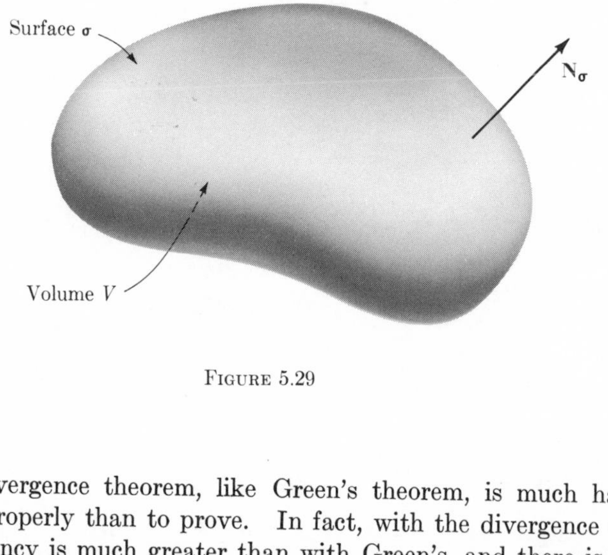

FIGURE 5.29

The divergence theorem, like Green's theorem, is much harder to formulate properly than to prove. In fact, with the divergence theorem the discrepancy is much greater than with Green's, and there is no half-decent elementary formulation. The jig is up; we leave it to you to interpret formula (1) and Fig. 29 in the examples and problems below. (However, Problems 3 and 4 below prove the two most important special cases, where V is either a rectangle or a ball.)

If you want to see a real proof of (1), you should study *differentiable manifolds* and *differential forms*. The next section gives a very brief introduction to differential forms in R^3, and shows how they unify the theorems named for Green, Stokes, and Gauss. The references in §4.1 develop the theory rather thoroughly. Another good reference is J. Woll, *Functions of Several Variables* (Harcourt, Brace, 1966).

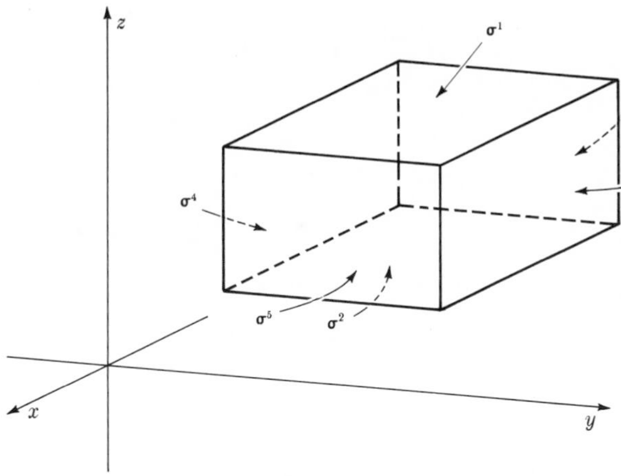

FIGURE 5.30

Example 1. Let $\mathbf{F}(x,y,z) = (0,0,z)$, and let

$$V = \{(x,y,z): a \leq x \leq b, c \leq y \leq d, e \leq z \leq f\}.$$

The oriented boundary of V consists of the six rectangles $\boldsymbol{\sigma}^1, \ldots, \boldsymbol{\sigma}^6$ in Fig. 30. Since $\mathbf{N}_{\sigma^j} \cdot \mathbf{F} = 0$ for each surface except $\boldsymbol{\sigma}^1$ and $\boldsymbol{\sigma}^2$, the integral over the boundary of V is $\iint_{\sigma^1}\mathbf{F} + \iint_{\sigma^2}\mathbf{F}$. Along $\boldsymbol{\sigma}^2$ we have $z = e$, so $\mathbf{F}$ has the constant value $(0,0,e)$ on $\boldsymbol{\sigma}^2$. Further, the unit normal on $\boldsymbol{\sigma}^2$ is $\mathbf{N} = (0,0,-1)$; hence (see Problem 4, §5.5) $\iint_{\sigma^2}\mathbf{F} = \mathbf{N}\cdot(0,0,e) \times (\text{area of } \boldsymbol{\sigma}^2)$. Evaluating $\displaystyle\iint_{\sigma^1}$ analogously, we find

$$\iint_{\sigma^1}\mathbf{F} + \int_{\sigma^2}\mathbf{F} = f\cdot(\text{area of } \boldsymbol{\sigma}^1) - e\cdot(\text{area of } \boldsymbol{\sigma}^2)$$

$$= -e(b-a)(d-c) + f(b-a)(d-c)$$

$$= (f-e)(b-a)(d-c) = \text{volume of } V.$$

On the other hand, the divergence of $\mathbf{F}$ is $\nabla \cdot \mathbf{F} = 1$, so

$$\iiint_V \nabla \cdot \mathbf{F} = \text{volume of } V.$$

Thus the divergence theorem checks in this case.

Figure 31 (a) shows the situation when $a = c = e = -1$ and $b = d = f = 1$, or

$$V = \{ (x,y,z) \colon |x| \leq 1, |y| \leq 1, |z| \leq 1 \}.$$

There is a flow out of the top of V, and a flow out of the bottom of V; thus it is obvious that there is a net outward flow, and $\mathbf{F}$ has positive divergence in V. In Fig. 31 (b) this is only a little less obvious; there is a flow in through the bottom and out through the top, but the outward flow is greater, so once again there is a net outward flow, and the divergence is positive.

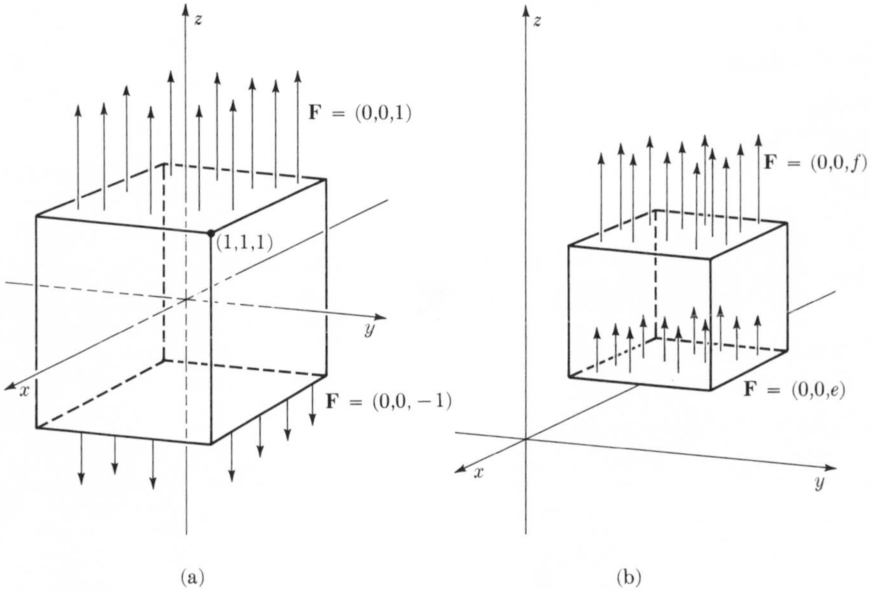

FIGURE 5.31

Example 2. We derive the so-called *equation of continuity* for fluid flows. Let $\mathbf{F}(x,y,z,t)$ denote the velocity of a fluid at the point (x,y,z) and time t, and let $\rho(x,y,z,t)$ denote the *density* of the fluid at the point (x,y,z) and time t. If the fluid is incompressible (as water is, very nearly) then ρ is constant; but if the fluid is compressible (as air is) then ρ can vary with time and position.

Consider a ball B with boundary $\boldsymbol{\sigma}$. The total mass of fluid in B at time t is $\iiint_B \rho(x,y,z,t) dx\, dy\, dz$. By Leibniz' rule (Problem 7, §5.6), the rate of increase of mass in B is

$$\frac{d}{dt} \iiint_B \rho(x,y,z,t) dx\, dy\, dz = \iiint_B \frac{\partial \rho}{\partial t}. \tag{2}$$

On the other hand, unless mass is being produced in B by some mysterious process, then the change of mass in B is due solely to the flow in and out through the boundary $\boldsymbol{\sigma}$. The integral $\iint_\sigma \mathbf{F}$ gives the volume rate of flow out of B; the rate of flow of *mass*, on the other hand, is given by $\iint_\sigma \rho\mathbf{F}$. (You can simply accept this as a proper definition from the point of view of physics, or you can explain it by modifying the discussion based on Fig. 19 in §5.5 so as to take the density into account.) Since the rate of flow of mass *out* of B is $\iint_\sigma \rho\mathbf{F}$, the rate of *increase* of mass must be $-\iint_\sigma \rho\mathbf{F}$. By the divergence theorem, then, the rate of increase of mass in B is given by

$$-\iint_\sigma \rho\mathbf{F} = -\iiint_B \nabla\cdot(\rho\mathbf{F}).$$

Comparing this to (2), we get

$$\iiint_B \frac{\partial\rho}{\partial t} = -\iiint_B \nabla\cdot(\rho\mathbf{F}).$$

Since this equation must hold for *every* ball B, it follows (see Problem 10(a), §5.6) that

$$\frac{\partial\rho}{\partial t} = -\nabla\cdot(\rho\mathbf{F}).$$

This is the equation of continuity. In particular, if the fluid is incompressible (i.e. if ρ is constant) we get $\partial\rho/\partial t = 0$ and $\nabla\cdot(\rho\mathbf{F}) = \rho(\nabla\cdot\mathbf{F})$; hence $\nabla\cdot\mathbf{F} = 0$. Thus, for an incompressible fluid, the divergence is always zero.

PROBLEMS

1. Compute the divergence of the following vector fields in R^3. Try to visualize the flow, and reconcile your answers physically.
(a) $\mathbf{F}(x,y,z) \equiv (1,0,0)$
(b) $\mathbf{F}(x,y,z) = (x,0,0)$
(c) $\mathbf{F}(x,y,z) = (0,x,0)$
(d) $\mathbf{F}(\mathbf{P}) = \mathbf{P}$
(e) $\mathbf{F}(\mathbf{P}) = \dfrac{1}{|\mathbf{P}|^2}\mathbf{P}$
(f) $\mathbf{F}(\mathbf{P}) = |\mathbf{P}|^r\mathbf{P}$, r a real number. For which value of r is $\nabla\cdot\mathbf{F} \equiv 0$?

2. Let V be the ball of radius r, $V = \{\mathbf{P}: |\mathbf{P}| \le r\}$, and

$$\boldsymbol{\sigma}(u,v) = (r\sin u\cos v, r\sin u\sin v, r\cos u), \quad 0 \le u \le \pi, 0 \le v \le 2\pi.$$

For each of the following vector fields, compute $\iiint_V \nabla\cdot\mathbf{F}$ and $\iint_\sigma \mathbf{F}$, and compare the results. Try to visualize the flow, and reconcile the value of $\iint_\sigma \mathbf{F}$ physically.
(a) $\mathbf{F}(x,y,z) \equiv (1,0,0)$
(b) $\mathbf{F}(x,y,z) = (x,0,0)$
(c) $\mathbf{F}(x,y,z) = (0,x,0)$
(d) $\mathbf{F}(\mathbf{P}) = \mathbf{P}$

3. In this problem you prove the divergence theorem for the rectangular solid

$$V = \{(x,y,z): x_1 \le x \le x_2\,,\ y_1 \le y \le y_2\,,\ z_1 \le z \le z_2\},$$

where x_1, x_2, etc. are constants. The *positively oriented* boundary of V consists of the following six faces $\boldsymbol{\sigma}^1, \ldots, \boldsymbol{\sigma}^6$ (Fig. 30):

$$\begin{aligned}
\boldsymbol{\sigma}^1(u,v) &= (u,v,z_2), & x_1 \le u \le x_2\,,\ y_1 \le v \le y_2\\
\boldsymbol{\sigma}^2(u,v) &= (v,u,z_1), & y_1 \le u \le y_2\,,\ x_1 \le v \le x_2\\
\boldsymbol{\sigma}^3(u,v) &= (v,y_2,u), & z_1 \le u \le z_2\,,\ x_1 \le v \le x_2\\
\boldsymbol{\sigma}^4(u,v) &= (u,y_1,v), & x_1 \le u \le x_2\,,\ z_1 \le v \le z_2\\
\boldsymbol{\sigma}^5(u,v) &= (x_2,u,v), & y_1 \le u \le y_2\,,\ z_1 \le v \le z_2\\
\boldsymbol{\sigma}^6(u,v) &= (x_1,v,u), & z_1 \le u \le z_2\,,\ y_1 \le v \le y_2\,.
\end{aligned}$$

(a) Check that the "standard normal" on $\boldsymbol{\sigma}^1$ points up, and on $\boldsymbol{\sigma}^2$ points down; on $\boldsymbol{\sigma}^3$ points toward positive y, and on $\boldsymbol{\sigma}^4$ toward negative y; on $\boldsymbol{\sigma}^5$ toward positive x, and on $\boldsymbol{\sigma}^6$ toward negative x. In other words, all the normals point out of V. (Hint: Sketch the cube, and on each face sketch $\boldsymbol{\sigma}_u$ and $\boldsymbol{\sigma}_v$.)

(b) Check that

$$\iiint_V \frac{\partial f_1}{\partial x}\,dx\,dy\,dz = \iint_{\sigma^5} (f_1,0,0) + \iint_{\sigma^6} (f_1,0,0)$$

$$= \sum_{j=1}^{6} \iint_{\sigma^j} (f_1,0,0).$$

(In the last step you have to show that $\iint_{\sigma^j} (f_1,0,0) = 0$ for $j = 1, 2, 3, 4$.)

(c) Check that

$$\iiint_V \frac{\partial f_2}{dy}\,dx\,dy\,dz = \sum_{j=1}^{6} \iint_{\sigma^j} (0, f_2,0).$$

(d) Check that

$$\iiint_V \frac{\partial f_3}{\partial z}\,dx\,dy\,dz = \sum_{j=1}^{6} \iint_{\sigma^j} (0,0, f_3).$$

(Adding up the results in (b)–(d) gives

$$\iiint_V \nabla\cdot\mathbf{F} = \sum_{j=1}^{6} \iint_{\sigma^j} \mathbf{F}.)$$

4. This problem proves the divergence theorem for a ball

$$V = \{\mathbf{P}: |\mathbf{P} - \mathbf{P}_0| \le r\}.$$

The positively oriented boundary of V can be given parametrically by

$$\boldsymbol{\sigma}(u,v) = (x_0 + r \sin u \cos v,\ y_0 + r \sin u \sin v,\ z_0 + r \cos u),$$
$$0 \leq u \leq \pi,\ 0 \leq v \leq 2\pi,$$

where $\mathbf{P}_0 = (x_0,y_0,z_0)$.

(a) Check that $(\boldsymbol{\sigma}_u \times \boldsymbol{\sigma}_v)\cdot(\boldsymbol{\sigma} - \mathbf{P}_0) \geq 0$, in other words, the standard normal points out of V.

(b) Check that

$$\iiint_V \frac{\partial f_3}{\partial z}\, dz\, dy\, dx = \iint_S f_3(x,y,\sqrt{r^2 - x^2 - y^2}\,)\, dy\, dx$$
$$- \iint_S f_3(x,y,-\sqrt{r^2 - x^2 - y^2}\,)\, dy\, dx$$
$$= \iint_{\sigma^1} (0,0,f_3) + \iint_{\sigma^2} (0,0,f_3)$$
$$= \iint_{\sigma} (0,0,f_3),$$

where S is the disk $\{(x,y): (x - x_0)^2 + (y - y_0)^2 \leq r^2\}$, and $\boldsymbol{\sigma}^1$ is the part of the surface $\boldsymbol{\sigma}$ where u is restricted to $0 \leq u \leq \pi/2$, and $\boldsymbol{\sigma}^2$ the part where $\pi/2 \leq u \leq \pi$. (Use formula (9), §4.5.)

(c) Check that $\displaystyle\iiint_V \frac{\partial f_1}{\partial x}\, dx\, dy\, dz = \iint_{\sigma} (f_1,0,0)$.

(d) Check that $\displaystyle\iiint_V \frac{\partial f_2}{\partial y}\, dy\, dz\, dx = \iint_{\sigma} (0,f_2,0)$.

(Adding up parts (b)–(d) gives $\displaystyle\iiint_V \nabla\cdot\mathbf{F} = \iint_{\sigma} \mathbf{F}$.)

(*Remark:* The preceding two problems show that for an explicitly given V, it is often possible to say explicitly what we mean by the positively oriented boundary of V, and then to prove the divergence theorem. In fact, if we allow "proof by picture," then it is possible to "prove" the divergence theorem for a general class of regions V, following the lines of the preceding two problems. These proofs generally rely on a picture to show you what the boundary of V is.)

5. Suppose that $\iint_{\sigma} \mathbf{F} = 0$ for every sphere $\boldsymbol{\sigma}$ as in Problem 4. Prove that $\nabla\cdot\mathbf{F} \equiv 0$.

6. (a) Suppose that the components of $\mathbf{F}$ have continuous first derivatives, and that ρ has continuous first derivatives. Prove that $\nabla\cdot(\rho\mathbf{F}) = (\nabla\rho)\cdot\mathbf{F} + \rho(\nabla\cdot\mathbf{F})$.

(b) Suppose that f has continuous second derivatives, and g has continuous first derivatives. Prove that $\nabla\cdot(g\nabla f) = \nabla g\cdot\nabla f + g\Delta f$, where $\Delta f = f_{xx} + f_{yy} + f_{zz}$ is the *Laplacian* of f.

(c) Let $\boldsymbol{\sigma}$ be the oriented boundary of V, and prove *Green's formula* $\iiint_V (g\Delta f + \nabla g\cdot\nabla f) = \iint_\sigma g\nabla f$. (Assume the divergence theorem for V.)

(d) Let S be the parameter domain of a surface $\boldsymbol{\sigma}$, and show that

$$\iint_\sigma g\nabla f = \iint_S g\frac{\partial f}{\partial n}|\mathbf{N}_\sigma|,$$

where $\partial f/\partial n$ is the *outer normal derivative* of f, the directional derivative of f in the direction of the unit outer normal

$$\frac{1}{|\mathbf{N}_\sigma|}\mathbf{N}_\sigma .$$

(e) Suppose that $\Delta f \equiv 0$ in V, and $f \equiv 0$ on $\boldsymbol{\sigma}$. Prove that $\nabla f \equiv 0$ in V, f is constant in V, and in fact $f \equiv 0$ in V. (Assume V connected.)

(f) Suppose that $\Delta f \equiv 0$ in V, and the normal derivative $\partial f/\partial n \equiv 0$ on $\boldsymbol{\sigma}$. Prove that f is constant in V. (Assume V connected.)

(g) Assuming that f and g have continuous second derivatives, prove that

$$\iiint_V (g\Delta f - f\Delta g) = \iint_\sigma (g\nabla f - f\nabla g)$$

$$= \iint_S \left(g\frac{\partial f}{\partial n} - f\frac{\partial g}{\partial n}\right)|\mathbf{N}_\sigma|.$$

7. (a) Suppose that the components of $\mathbf{F}$ have continuous second derivatives. Prove that $\nabla\cdot(\nabla\times\mathbf{F}) = 0$.

(b) Show that there is *no* vector field $\mathbf{F}$ such that $(\nabla\times\mathbf{F})(x,y,z) = (x,0,0)$.

(c) Find, if you can, a vector field $\mathbf{F}$ such that

$$(\nabla\times\mathbf{F})(x,y,z) = (y,0,0).$$

8. Suppose that $\nabla\cdot\mathbf{G} = 0$ in an open rectangle R containing the origin $\mathbf{0}$. This problem shows that there is a vector field $\mathbf{F}$ defined in R such that $\nabla\times\mathbf{F} = \mathbf{G}$.

(a) Show that $\nabla\times\mathbf{F} = \mathbf{G}$ is equivalent to the system of equations

$$-D_3f_2 + D_2f_3 = g_1 \qquad (3_1)$$

$$D_3f_1 - D_1f_3 = g_2 \qquad (3_2)$$

$$-D_2f_1 + D_1f_2 = g_3 . \qquad (3_3)$$

(b) Set $f_3 = 0$, and show that equations (3_1) and (3_2) are equivalent to

$$\begin{aligned} f_1(x,y,z) &= \int_0^z g_2(x,y,t)\,dt + \varphi_1(x,y) \\ f_2(x,y,z) &= -\int_0^z g_1(x,y,t)\,dt + \varphi_2(x,y) \end{aligned} \tag{4}$$

for some functions φ_1 and φ_2 having continuous partial derivatives.

(c) Let f_1 and f_2 be defined by (4), and show that

$$-D_2 f_1(x,y,z) + D_1 f_2(x,y,z) = g_3(x,y,z) - g_3(x,y,0) + D_1\varphi_2(x,y) - D_2\varphi_1(x,y).$$

(Recall that $\nabla \cdot \mathbf{G} = 0$.)

(d) Show that the functions φ_1 and φ_2 in (4) can be chosen so that $D_1\varphi_2(x,y) - D_2\varphi_1(x,y) = g_3(x,y,0)$. (Actually, you can take $\varphi_1 = 0$.)

(e) Conclude that there is a vector field $\mathbf{F}$ such that $\nabla \times \mathbf{F} = \mathbf{G}$.

5.8 A VERY BRIEF INTRODUCTION TO DIFFERENTIAL FORMS

Differential forms are the ultimate in Leibniz notation; they reduce to a single formula the theorems of Green, Stokes, and Gauss, as well as the fact that $\int_\gamma \nabla f = f(\boldsymbol{\gamma}(b)) - f(\boldsymbol{\gamma}(a))$; and they make the formula for change of variable look as "obvious" in n dimensions as in 1.

A *differential* 1-*form* looks like

$$f_1\,dx + f_2\,dy + f_3\,dz,$$

where f_1, f_2, f_3 are continuous real-valued functions on R^3. A differential 1-form can be integrated over a differentiable curve $\boldsymbol{\gamma}$, by the formula

$$\int_\gamma (f_1\,dx + f_2\,dy + f_3\,dz) = \int_a^b \left(f_1 \frac{d\gamma_1}{dt} + f_2 \frac{d\gamma_2}{dt} + f_3 \frac{d\gamma_3}{dt} \right) dt.$$

(This is the same as the line integral $\int_\gamma \mathbf{F}$ of the vector field $\mathbf{F} = (f_1, f_2, f_3)$.)

A *differential* 2-*form* looks like

$$f_1\,dy\,dz + f_2\,dz\,dx + f_3\,dx\,dy;$$

it can be integrated over a differentiable surface $\boldsymbol{\sigma}$ with standard normal vector $\mathbf{N}_\sigma$, by the formula

$$\iint_\sigma f_1\,dy\,dz + f_2\,dz\,dx + f_3\,dx\,dy = \iint_S \mathbf{F}\cdot\mathbf{N}_\sigma = \int_\sigma \mathbf{F}$$

where S is the parameter domain of $\boldsymbol{\sigma}$, and $\mathbf{F} = (f_1, f_2, f_3)$. A *differential 3-form* looks like $f\,dx\,dy\,dz$, where f is a function on R^3. If f is continuous, the 3-form can be integrated over a set V in R^3, simply as $\int\int\int_V f\,dx\,dy\,dz$. Finally, a 0-form is just a function; it is not to be integrated at all.

In other words, if a vector field $\mathbf{F} = (f_1, f_2, f_3)$ is destined to be integrated over a curve, we write it in the form $f_1\,dx + f_2\,dy + f_3\,dz$ and call it a 1-form. Similarly, if $\mathbf{F}$ is destined to be integrated over a surface, we write it $f_1\,dy\,dz + f_2\,dz\,dx + f_3\,dx\,dy$ and call it a 2-form. This alone is not a very exciting advance beyond the older notation, but now the fun begins. We define a *multiplication* of the symbols dx, dy, and dz, satisfying the strange rules

$$\left.\begin{aligned} dx\,dy &= -dy\,dx \\ dx\,dz &= -dz\,dx \\ dy\,dz &= -dz\,dy \end{aligned}\right\} \tag{1}$$

$$dx\,dx = dy\,dy = dz\,dz = 0. \tag{2}$$

(Notice the similarity with cross products.) We then extend this multiplication to differential forms by decreeing that the usual associative and distributive laws shall hold, and that *functions* commute with the symbols dx, dy, and dz, i.e. $f\,dx = (dx)f$. Thus for example, we multiply the 1-form $f_1\,dx + f_2\,dy + f_3\,dz$ by the 2-form $g\,dx\,dy$ by applying (1) and (2) as follows:

$$\begin{aligned}(f_1\,dx + f_2\,dy + f_3\,dz)\cdot(g\,dx\,dy) \\ &= f_1g\,dx\,dx\,dy + f_2g\,dy\,dx\,dy + f_3g\,dz\,dx\,dy \\ &= 0 - f_2g\,dx\,dy\,dy - f_3g\,dx\,dz\,dy \\ &= 0 + 0 + f_3g\,dx\,dy\,dz.\end{aligned}$$

Further, we define *exterior differentiation* d, beginning with the exterior derivative of a function:

$$df = \frac{\partial f}{\partial x}\,dx + \frac{\partial f}{\partial y}\,dy + \frac{\partial f}{\partial z}\,dz. \tag{3}$$

The exterior derivative of a 1-form

$$f_1\,dx + f_2\,dy + f_3\,dz$$

is taken by applying d to each of the components f_1, f_2, f_3, then combining the terms by using the rules (1) and (2):

$$
\begin{aligned}
d(f_1\,dx + f_2\,dy + f_3\,dz) &= d(f_1\,dx) + d(f_2\,dy) + d(f_3\,dz) \\
&= \left(\frac{\partial f_1}{\partial x}\,dx + \frac{\partial f_1}{\partial y}\,dy + \frac{\partial f_1}{\partial z}\,dz\right) dx \\
&\quad + \left(\frac{\partial f_2}{\partial x}\,dx + \frac{\partial f_2}{\partial y}\,dy + \frac{\partial f_2}{\partial z}\,dz\right) dy \\
&\quad + \left(\frac{\partial f_3}{\partial x}\,dx + \frac{\partial f_3}{\partial y}\,dy + \frac{\partial f_3}{\partial z}\,dz\right) dz \\
&= 0 - \frac{\partial f_1}{\partial y}\,dx\,dy + \frac{\partial f_1}{\partial z}\,dz\,dx \\
&\quad + \frac{\partial f_2}{\partial x}\,dx\,dy + 0 - \frac{\partial f_2}{\partial z}\,dy\,dz \\
&\quad - \frac{\partial f_3}{\partial x}\,dz\,dx + \frac{\partial f_3}{\partial y}\,dy\,dz + 0.
\end{aligned}
$$

Hence $d(f_1\,dx + f_2\,dy + f_3\,dz)$

$$
= \left(\frac{\partial f_3}{\partial y} - \frac{\partial f_2}{\partial z}\right) dy\,dz + \left(\frac{\partial f_1}{\partial z} - \frac{\partial f_3}{\partial x}\right) dz\,dx + \left(\frac{\partial f_2}{\partial x} - \frac{\partial f_1}{\partial y}\right) dx\,dy. \tag{4}
$$

Working in the same way, we get the exterior derivative of a 2-form,

$$
\begin{aligned}
&d(f_1\,dy\,dz + f_2\,dz\,dx + f_3\,dx\,dy) \\
&\qquad = \left(\frac{\partial f_1}{\partial x}\,dx + \frac{\partial f_1}{\partial y}\,dy + \frac{\partial f_1}{\partial z}\,dz\right) dy\,dz + \cdots \\
&\qquad = \frac{\partial f_1}{\partial x}\,dx\,dy\,dz + 0 + 0 \\
&\qquad\quad + 0 + \frac{\partial f_2}{\partial y}\,dy\,dz\,dx + 0 \\
&\qquad\quad + 0 + 0 + \frac{\partial f_3}{\partial z}\,dz\,dx\,dy.
\end{aligned}
$$

By applying the rules (1) twice to each of the last two terms, this reduces to

$$
d(f_1\,dy\,dz + f_2\,dz\,dx + f_3\,dx\,dy) = \left(\frac{\partial f_1}{\partial x} + \frac{\partial f_2}{\partial y} + \frac{\partial f_3}{\partial z}\right) dx\,dy\,dz. \tag{5}
$$

Now the expressions on the right in (3), (4), and (5) are quite familiar; (3) gives the components of ∇f, (4) gives the components of $\nabla \times \mathbf{F}$, and (5) gives $\nabla \cdot \mathbf{F}$. Thus the various formulas we developed take the form:

$$\int_\gamma df = f(\boldsymbol{\gamma}(b)) - f(\boldsymbol{\gamma}(a))$$

$$\iint_\sigma d\boldsymbol{\omega}^1 = \int_\gamma \boldsymbol{\omega}^1$$ (Stokes' theorem; $\boldsymbol{\omega}^1 = f_1\,dx + f_2\,dy + f_3\,dz$ is a 1-form, and $\boldsymbol{\gamma}$ is the oriented boundary of $\boldsymbol{\sigma}$.)

$$\iiint_V d\boldsymbol{\omega}^2 = \iint_\sigma \boldsymbol{\omega}^2$$ (Divergence theorem; $\boldsymbol{\omega}^2 = f_1\,dy\,dz + f_2\,dz\,dx + f_3\,dx\,dy$ is a 2-form, and $\boldsymbol{\sigma}$ is the oriented boundary of V.)

These formulas can be further unified by letting $\boldsymbol{\sigma}^k$ stand for an oriented k-dimensional "surface," and dropping the notational distinction between $\int$, $\iint$, and $\iiint$. Then everything is given in the single equation

$$\int_{\sigma^k} d\boldsymbol{\omega}^{k-1} = \int_{\sigma^{k-1}} \boldsymbol{\omega}^{k-1},$$

where $\boldsymbol{\sigma}^{k-1}$ forms the oriented boundary of $\boldsymbol{\sigma}$. In the case $k = 1$, the 0-form $\boldsymbol{\omega}^{k-1}$ is a function f, $\boldsymbol{\sigma}^k$ is a curve $\boldsymbol{\gamma}$, the oriented boundary $\boldsymbol{\sigma}^{k-1}$ consists of the two points $\boldsymbol{\gamma}(b)$ taken as "+" and $\boldsymbol{\gamma}(a)$ taken as "−", and the integral

$$\int_{\sigma^{k-1}} \boldsymbol{\omega}^{k-1} \qquad \text{stands for} \qquad f(\boldsymbol{\gamma}(b)) - f(\boldsymbol{\gamma}(a)).$$

We hope that this sketchy outline, together with the problems below, will suggest the great value of differential forms in unifying old results and suggesting new ones. A real understanding, however, requires a thorough development of the subject. This is given, for example, in the references mentioned at the bottom of page 282.

PROBLEMS

1. This problem shows how the rules for multiplying differentials lead directly to the formulas for change of variable in double and triple integrals.
   (a) Let $x = \varphi(u,v)$, $y = \psi(u,v)$, and use (1), (2), and (3) to show that $dx\,dy = (\varphi_u\psi_v - \varphi_v\psi_u)\,du\,dv$.
   (b) Let $x = \varphi(u,v,w)$, $y = \psi(u,v,w)$, $z = \eta(u,v,w)$, and show that $dx\,dy\,dz = \dfrac{\partial(\varphi,\psi,\eta)}{\partial(u,v,w)}\,du\,dv\,dw$, where $\partial(\varphi,\psi,\eta)/\partial(u,v,w)$ is the *Jacobian determinant*

$$\begin{vmatrix} \varphi_u & \varphi_v & \varphi_w \\ \psi_u & \psi_v & \psi_w \\ \eta_u & \eta_v & \eta_w \end{vmatrix}.$$

(*Caution:* The rules for differentials involve a certain orientation of R^3, which can be reversed by changing the order of the variables; for example, by the rules for multiplying differentials, $dy\,dx\,dz = -dx\,dy\,dz$. Hence, in problems where the orientation is not involved (e.g. computing a volume or a moment of inertia) the change of variable formula uses the *absolute value* of the Jacobian determinant.)

(c) Let $x = \rho \sin \varphi \cos \theta$, $y = \rho \sin \varphi \sin \theta$, $z = \rho \cos \varphi$; here, ρ, φ, and θ are *spherical coördinates* of (x,y,z). Show that $dx\,dy\,dz = \rho^2 \sin \varphi \, d\rho \, d\varphi \, d\theta$.

(d) Let V be a sphere of radius R about the origin, and let $f(\mathbf{P}) = |\mathbf{P}|^2$. Evaluate $\iiint_V f$ by using spnerical coordinates. (Compare this to the calculation of $\iiint_V (x^2 + y^2 + z^2)\, dx\,dy\,dz$ in §5.6.)

2. (a) Suppose that f has continuous second derivatives. Show that $d(df) = 0$.

(b) Suppose that f_1, f_2, f_3 have continuous second derivatives. Show that $d(d(f_1\,dx + f_2\,dy + f_3\,dz)) = 0$.

(These formulas are equivalent to

$$\nabla \times (\nabla f) = \mathbf{0} \text{ and } \nabla \cdot (\nabla \times \mathbf{F}) = 0.$$

3. This problem shows how the notation $\iint f_1\,dy\,dz + f_2\,dz\,dx + f_3\,dx\,dy$ for a surface integral, together with the rules for multiplying differentials and the formula

$$df(u,v) = \frac{\partial f}{\partial u}\,du + \frac{\partial f}{\partial v}\,dv,$$

leads to the expression $\iint_S (\mathbf{F} \circ \boldsymbol{\sigma}) \cdot (\boldsymbol{\sigma}_u \times \boldsymbol{\sigma}_v)$ for surface integrals.

(a) Suppose $\boldsymbol{\sigma} = (\sigma_1, \sigma_2, \sigma_3)$ has parameter domain S. Then the surface is given by the parametric equations

$$x = \sigma_1(u,v), \qquad y = \sigma_2(u,v), \qquad z = \sigma_3(u,v),$$

so

$$dx = \frac{\partial \sigma_1}{\partial u}\,du + \frac{\partial \sigma_1}{\partial v}\,dv.$$

Find analogous expressions for dy and dz.

(b) Multiply the expressions for dx, dy, and dz, using the rules

$$dv\,du = -du\,dv, \qquad du\,du = 0, \qquad dv\,dv = 0,$$

and thus obtain $f_1\,dy\,dz + f_2\,dz\,dx + f_3\,dx\,dy$ as $\mathbf{F} \cdot (\boldsymbol{\sigma}_u \times \boldsymbol{\sigma}_v)\,du\,dv$.

Index

2 3 4 5 6 7 8 9 10 11 12 13 14 15 16 17 18 19 20 21 22 23 24 25 78 77 76 75 74 73 72 71